MEDICAL ETHICS

MEDICAL ETHICS

CHARLES J. MCFADDEN, O.S.A., PH.D.

FACULTY OF VILLANOVA COLLEGE, VILLANOVA, PA.

FOREWORD BY

FULTON J. SHEEN, PH.D., D.D.

1955

THIRD EDITION

F. A. DAVIS COMPANY, PUBLISHERS

PHILADELPHIA

Nihil Obstat:

ROBERT E. REGAN, O.S.A., S.T.D.
Censor Deputatus

Imprimi Potest:

JOSEPH M. DOUGHERTY, O.S.A.
Prior Provincialis

Nihil Obstat:

JOSEPH A. M. QUIGLEY
Censor Deputatus

Imprimatur:

JOHN F. O'HARA, C.S.C.
Archiepiscopus Philadelphiensis
January 22, 1953

The "nihil obstat" and "imprimatur" are official declarations that a book or pamphlet is free from doctrinal or moral error. No implication is contained therein that those who have granted the "nihil obstat" and "imprimatur" agree with the contents, opinions, or statements expressed.

Affectionately Dedicated

to

The Creamer Family

FOREWORD

Every doctor and nurse ought to have two things: A sense of humor, and an incision. A sense of humor in order that they might spread joy and gladness; an incision in order that they might have an experimental understanding and appreciation of pain.

By a sense of humor is not meant wit, nor the ability to "wise-crack," nor the capacity to make others laugh. The sense of humor here referred to is Divine rather than human. We say a person has a sense of humor when he can "see through things," and that a person lacks a sense of humor when he cannot "see through things"; then he is "too thick." Now God made the world with a sense of humor in that He intended we should be seeing Him through things. In the original plan, nothing was ever to be taken seriously, except the salvation of a soul. A mountain was not just a mountain; if we saw through it, we would perceive the power of God; a sunset was not just a sunset; it was a revelation of the beauty of God. A snowflake was not just a snowflake; thanks to the gift of transparency, it was a telltale of the purity of God. In this respect we may say that God made the world with a Divine Sense of Humor in that through the visible we were to discern the Invisible, through the temporal the Eternal, through the fleeting the Abiding and Everlasting.

When Our Lord came to this earth, He never took anything seriously, except the salvation of a soul. A wedding garment to Him was only a symbol of charity; salt, goats, camels and wheat, patches on old clothing, bottles and eyes of needles, grapes and figs—all were the external symbols of Eternal Truths concerning the Father's house.

Poets have a highly developed Divine Sense of Humor, for they can look at a common phenomenon of nature, such as a sunset, as Francis Thompson did, and see the sun as a Host, the day as a priest. Each morning the priest goes to the Orient tabernacle, lifts the Host from it, raises It in benediction over the world and at night sets It in the flaming monstrance of the West. Saints above all people have a Divine Sense of Humor in

vii

a highly developed way. *For those in the medical profession to have it means that they must not see just the sick, but Christ in the sick.* The patient in Room 258 is not just a patient, but Christ. To the doctor and nurse who has a sense of the invisible every wounded hand has been pierced with a nail; every aching brow has been crowned with thorns; every bruised and feverish body is hanging on a Cross. But is Christ seen in these disguises? Our Blessed Lord has forewarned us that most doctors and nurses lead opaque lives and never see the Vision of Christ in their profession. We know this from the words He will address to them on the last day: "For I was hungry and you gave me food, thirsty and you gave me drink . . . sick and you cared for me." And those who are saved—will say: "When was it that we saw Thee hungry and fed Thee, or thirsty and gave Thee drink? When was it that we saw Thee sick and came to Thee?" And the King will answer them: "Believe Me, when you did it to one of the least of My brethren here, you did it unto Me."

And His healing servants will be surprised that in the operating rooms, wards, clinics, and in the midst of charts, needles and icepacks, food trays and hypos, they were moving, seeing, touching Christ. But only those with a sense of humor will know it.

But a man or woman of medicine also needs an incision. The incision need not be physical, though perhaps it would be better if it were, but it must be at least spiritual and mystical. By incision is here meant the appreciation and understanding of the meaning of pain. Most people do not know its meaning until they have walked down its long corridors; for them a mystical incision is needed and the deeper the better, for they learn only by experience. In others this want of a physical cut can be compensated for spiritually by schooling oneself in sympathy and by understanding the purpose of pain.

Pain of itself does not make us better; it is very likely to make us worse. No man was ever better simply because he had an earache. Unspiritualized suffering does not improve man; it degenerates him. The thief at the left is no better for his crucifixion; it sears him, burns him, and tarnishes his soul.

Refusing to think of pain as related to anything else, he ends by thinking only of himself and who would take him down from the cross. So it is with those who have lost their faith in God. To them Our Lord on a cross is only an event in the history of the Roman Empire; He is not a message of hope nor a proof of love.

They would not have a tool in their hands five minutes without discovering its purpose, but they live their lives without ever having inquired into the meaning of suffering. Having no reason for living, suffering embitters them, poisons them, and finally, the great door of life's opportunity is closed in their faces, and like the thief on the left they go out into the night unblessed.

It is not so much what people suffer that makes the world mysterious; it is rather how much they miss when they suffer. They seem to forget that even as children they made obstacles in their games in order to have something to overcome.

Why, then, when they grow into man's estate, should there not be prizes won by effort and struggle? Cannot the spirit of man rise with adversity as the bird rises against the resistance of the wind? Do not the game fish swim upstream? Must not the alabaster box be broken to fill the house with ointment? Must not the chisel cut away the marble to bring out the form? Must not the seed falling to the ground die before it can spring forth into life? Must not the little streams speed into the ocean to escape their stagnant self-content? Must not grapes be crushed that there may be wine to drink, and wheat ground that there may be bread to eat?

Why, then, cannot pain be made redemption? Why, under the alchemy of Divine Love, cannot crosses be turned into crucifixes? Why cannot chastisements be regarded as penances? Why cannot we use a cross to become God-like? We cannot become like Him in His power; we cannot become like Him in His knowledge. *But we can become like Him in His sufferings.*

It is the duty of the nurse and doctor to explain, when the occasion arises, how suffering fits into the universe. In the face of the undeserved suffering of the just, the unmerited prosperity of the wicked, the misery of the merciful, the pleasures of the sinful, many are wont to ask this question: "Is this a planned universe, or is it the plaything of chance?"

This question would have been unanswerable in this life had not Goodness itself descended into the level of the world's woe, deliberately and wilfully. But once the Best freely goes down to the worst, and fits it into His plan and purpose, then no man can ever be without hope.

If God, Who could have foregone the trials and sorrows of man, and yet by a free act descends to man, assumes his nature, and unites it with His Own Divine Nature, and then with eyes open and with full knowledge of the world's iniquity, walks into it and even embraces it, it must be because it fits into His Divine pattern.

Our Blessed Lord did not walk blindly into a world capable of crucifying virtue, as you and I might walk into an unknown forest. He came into it as a doctor into his hospital with full knowledge of how to deal with pain. His whole course was charted beforehand; nothing took Him by surprise. At any given moment He had the power to overcome, but He would not use the power regardless of how much He was challenged until He *willed* it. It is this Divine Knowledge which explains His rejoinder to Mary and Joseph in the temple, when He was only twelve years of age: "Did you not know that I must be about my Father's business?" Already He talks of a plan, and in particular of a plan that is made in Heaven. It also explains His many prophecies concerning His death, its time, its place, and its circumstances, and in almost impatient urge He had to realize it. "I have a baptism wherewith I am to be baptized; and how I am straitened until it be accomplished!"

Death then would not be a stumbling block to Him as it was to Socrates for whom it was but an unwanted interruption of his teaching. For Our Lord, death was the goal He was seeking, the supreme objective of His mission on earth. Everyone else who ever came into the world, came into it *to live*. Our Lord came into it *to die*. But that death with its scourgings and tears would not come to Him in an unguarded moment. Bodily suffering, mental anguish, bitter disappointment, the false judgment of justice, the betrayal of true friendship, the court's perversion of honesty, and the violent separation from a mother's love—all these He took upon Himself knowingly, freely, deliberately, and purposely.

Then after three hours of crucifixion, surveying all the prophecies made about Him in Old Testament days, and the prophecies He had made of Himself, and seeing them all fulfilled and the last stitch drawn on the tapestry of His Life and the pattern completed, He uttered His sixth word—a word of triumph: "It is finished." That cry meant: This is a planned universe. Suffering fits into it, otherwise He would have refused it. The cross fits into it, otherwise He would not have embraced it. The crown of thorns fits into it, otherwise He would not have worn it.

Nothing was accidental; everything was ordered. His Father's business was completed. The plan was finished.

The full significance of the plan was not revealed until three days later, when the Seed which fell to the ground arose into the newness of Life. It was this plan Our Lord gave to the disciple at Emmaus: "Ought not Christ to have suffered these things and so to enter into his glory?"

In other words, unless there is a Good Friday in our lives, there will never be an Easter Sunday; unless we die in this world, we shall not live in the next; unless there is the crown of thorns, there will never be the halo of light; unless there is the cross, there will never be an empty tomb; unless we lose our life, we shall not find it; unless we are crucified with Christ, we shall never rise with Christ.

Such is the plan, and on our choice depends eternal issues. Our attitude toward the inescapable cross immortalizes us, either for gain or loss.

And though the plan seems hard, it is not blind, for Our Lord has not merely told us to follow Him; He has led the way. We can follow His footsteps out of the dark forest of our sufferings, but we can never say, "He does not know what it means to suffer."

He suffered first to teach us how to bear it. He did not say: "Go to the Cross," but He did say: "Come, follow Me."

Because He was God He knew that men would not go just because they were told, but that they would follow if an example were given.

Though doctors and nurses need a sense of humor and an incision they must use both in the pattern of a moral universe. Without an understanding of what is right in the field of medicine they would be devoid of a sense of humor, for sin is seriousness, the using of means as ends. And what doth it profit doctors and nurses to have an incision if they lose the moral sense of oughtness which comes from God. The rest of this book is dedicated to the application of moral principles to medicine and done so well that each member of the medical profession with a holy impatience should proceed to the mastering of it.

FULTON J. SHEEN

PREFACE TO THIRD EDITION

Several notable changes and additions have been made in the third edition of this work.

First, the entire text has been adapted to suit the needs of pre-medical students, medical students, doctors, and nurses. The earlier editions were directed *solely* to the nurse, and it was only with some measure of hardship that the text was used in regular college courses on Medical Ethics. This difficulty has now been overcome. With a firm determination that the work must not sacrifice *anything* in the way of direct application and value to the nursing profession—for whom the first edition was exclusively written and of whom the author is a devoted admirer—this edition was rendered equally suitable as a text for the pre-medical and medical students in our Catholic colleges and universities.

Second, earlier editions made frequent reference to the moral obligations which rest on the *"Catholic"* doctor and nurse. Unfortunately, emphasis on the fact that the "Catholic" possessed this or that moral obligation created the false impression among many that no such obligation rested on those who are not members of the Church. Non-Catholic students often interpreted the text as meaning that the Church had imposed these obligations on its members, but that—since they were not members of the Church—they had no such obligation. Actually, of course, almost all of the moral principles treated in the book are principles of Natural Law or Divine Positive Law which bind *all* men. The use of the word 'Catholic' in those references has therefore been omitted; and it is hoped that *all,* regardless of the faith which they profess, will realize their duty to abide by the Natural Law (as known by reason) and Divine Positive Law (as known by revelation).

Many notable additions and changes have been made in the text: the Holy Father's addresses on the Safe Period Method and Artificial Insemination are treated at length; the new law on the Eucharistic Fast is explained; much new matter on euthanasia has been added to the chapter on *The Christian Philosophy of Suffering;* significant new contributions to the chapter

xiii

on *Sterilization* include treatment of elective appendectomy
and ovarian graft. Many other changes and revisions will be
encountered throughout this new edition and it is hoped that
they will prove to be of interest and value to members of the
medical profession.

Pre-medical students on the college level will find the present
text most suitable for their course on Medical Ethics. A full
semester course of forty-five hours on Medical Ethics, along the
lines of this text, should adequately prepare the student for
the future. These students will already have had a course in
General Ethics. If there is need of a brief review of that material, the first two chapters *(The Nature and Value of Ethics*
and *The Foundations of Morality)* will serve that purpose.
Otherwise these chapters may be omitted in a college course
on Medical Ethics.

These students will usually enter secular medical schools in
which they will receive no formal training in morals as applied
to their future profession. In fact, they will be taught a great
deal which is morally objectionable on therapeutic abortion,
sterilization, contraception, artificial insemination, sterility
tests, and on countless other topics. It is the definite duty of
the Catholic College to give its pre-medical students a sound
and comprehensive course on Medical Ethics, in order to prepare them both for the teaching which they will encounter in
medical school and for the proper conduct of their future professional life.

An adequate course on Medical Ethics for the pre-medical
student cannot legitimately confine itself to the level of natural
philosophy. The moral problems of the medical student and
the future doctor will often revolve around the Sacraments
(particularly Baptism, Marriage, Holy Viaticum, and Extreme
Unction), and he must be prepared to handle these matters
properly for his own peace of conscience and in the interest of
the spiritual welfare of his patient. Ordinary college religion
courses cannot be expected to concern themselves with the
numerous specifically medical problems allied to the sacraments. Hence, an adequate course in Medical Ethics must not
be bounded by the arbitrary limitations of natural ethics. Such

a course must be a preparation for life and it must face reality
by showing the student how he is to solve the moral problems
which he will soon encounter on the level of both ethics and
religion.

*   *   *

The author would like to offer a word of counsel or suggestion to those who are responsible for the moral training of the
nurse. It is a simple and clear fact that the nurse of today requires a much more extensive training in medical ethics than
did her sister of a generation ago. The advance of medical
science has multiplied the medical, surgical, and obstetrical
procedures in which she is asked to participate and whose
moral nature she must be able to evaluate. In addition, each
year sees more and more responsibility placed on the shoulders
of the nurse in hospital practice, and she must be trained to
carry this responsibility with a due regard for the moral laws
which bind all men.

In the home, at church, and in grade and high school, the
girl received her education in fundamental morality and religion. The Nursing School cannot allow its courses on religion
and ethics to be mere reviews of those fundamentals. It must
give the nurse such courses on religion and morality as are
specifically designed to train her to handle the problems of her
newly-chosen profession.

No one appreciates the fact better than the author that all
of the matter in this text cannot be adequately covered in a
typical Nursing School thirty hour course on Medical Ethics.
If no greater amount of time can be devoted to the moral and
religious training of the nurse, it is most unfortunate and the
teacher must simply select the main points of the principal
topics for class-room work. In this way, the teacher can feel
confident that at least the foundation has been laid and the
nurse has her text at hand as a ready reference for the solution
of the more complex moral problems which will inevitably
arise.

In his own teaching of nurses, however, the author has
adopted a method which has worked most successfully at Fitzgerald-Mercy Hospital. At this hospital, in their first year, the

nurses receive a thirty hour course on religion and in their second year a thirty hour course on medical ethics. The author uses *Medical Ethics* as the text book for both courses.

The first year *Religion* course is on *The Sacraments*—and is specifically designed for nurses. After an introductory lecture on the general nature of the sacraments, the text of *Medical Ethics* is followed on Baptism, Penance and the Holy Eucharist for the sick and dying, Extreme Unction for the dying, and the spiritual care of the dying non-Catholic patient. This constitutes the first half of the course. The second half of the course aims at giving the nurse the proper ideals of Christian Marriage both as a means of assuring her own happy marriage and for guidance in much of her nursing work. In this second half of the course, the text book is followed in the chapters on *Christian Marriage, Contraception,* and the *Safe Period Method.* A supplementary lecture on mixed marriage is also given.

The second year course on *Ethics* first offers an introduction to basic principles of morality. This matter is adequately covered in the first two chapters of the text *(The Nature and Value of Ethics* and *The Foundations of Morality).* The next part of the course concerns man's duties to life and to preservation of integrity of the body. In this section the text is followed rigidly on the chapters dealing with *Direct Abortion, Therapeutic Abortion, Indirect Abortion, Ectopic Gestation,* and *Sterilization.* The final part of the Ethics course treats of man's duties to others. This section is based upon the chapters on *Assistance at Immoral Operations, Truthfulness* and *Professional Secrecy,* and *Property Rights.*

In the above manner the author has been successful in giving the nurse the training in both religion and morality which she truly needs; and he has found her both interested in the matter and capable of assimilating it. Needless to say, the fact that one book serves for both courses has been a tremendous asset: the nurse becomes very familiar with the book; cross reference from one course to the other is facilitated; and it obviously represents a saving in money for the nurse or the school.

Finally, the author would like once again to express his gratitude to the medical and nursing profession for their constant appreciation of this work; to those writers in this field whose contributions merit special praise, such as Father Francis Connell, C.Ss.R. and Father Gerald Kelly, S.J., and to all those who have helped or guided him, especially Doctor John A. Sharkey whose knowledge of medical science is surpassed only by the admirable Catholicity of his thought, Father Robert E. Regan, O.S.A., and Joseph A. M. Quigley.

CHARLES J. McFADDEN, O.S.A.

PREFACE TO FIRST EDITION

The primary purpose of a Catholic Training School is to produce a truly Catholic nurse. A Catholic Training School which would confine its teaching to the purely secular aspects of nursing would be forgetful of the very reason for its existence. Such an education could be obtained by a girl in any community hospital. It is precisely because the choice of the nursing profession is such an important step in her life and because it is so full of complex moral problems that the conscientious Catholic girl is strenuously urged to train in a Catholic hospital. She *needs* a moral education in the duties of her newly-chosen state of life and she rightfully *expects* to receive it in a Catholic hospital.

Due to a lack of proper home environment and the failure to receive a Catholic elementary or high school education, student nurses frequently lack an adequate knowledge of their religion. Hospital authorities are rightfully concerned about this matter and often place courses in religion in the nurse's curriculum. When possible, it is certainly commendable for a hospital to supply courses which will make up for a girl's defective religious education in early life. *But the moral education required by a Catholic nurse is not supplied by ordinary courses in religion. The first obligation of the Catholic Nursing School is to train the nurse in the moral obligations of her profession.* After it has fulfilled its own specific obligations as a Training School for Nurses, it should, when possible, fill up the gaps in general religious education which have resulted from the negligence of others or lack of opportunity. After all, many of the girls will have had a Catholic elementary or high school education, and most will have had some basic religious education. Attentive attendance at religious services and sermons, as well as membership in parish study clubs in postgraduate days, will provide them with a fundamental knowledge of their Faith. *But if the Catholic Nursing School does not give its student nurses a thorough course in Medical Ethics, it is unlikely that they will ever acquire such a knowledge in later life.* It is for this reason that Monsignor Sheen, in the Foreword, says that the professional work of a nurse is spiritually profitless "if she lose the moral sense of oughtness which comes from God."

It is the hope of the author that this work will provide the basis for the proper moral education of the Catholic nurse. It is the experience of the author that the matter is neither too abstract nor too comprehensive for the nurse to master. It appears that the nurse's constant practical contact with the problems involved facilitates a grasp of the pertinent moral principles. When both teacher and pupil do their part, priceless results can be achieved.

A great deal of consideration was given to the advisability of footnotes in the work. For the most part, references, if made, would be to the classical works on Moral Theology. These works would usually be in Latin and would neither be available to the average nurse nor within her intellectual grasp. Furthermore, the academic schedule of a nurse, coupled with her practical work on the hospital floor, seldom gives her time to go beyond the matter contained in her own textbook. Teachers who would be interested in consulting the standard works on Moral Theology are, for the most part, already familiar with them. For these reasons, it was thought best not to burden the text with footnotes but to add a list of appropriate reading references at the end of each chapter. These references cover the material treated in the chapter, and it is hoped that they will prove adequate for interested students and helpful to teachers.

The author wishes to acknowledge a debt of gratitude to many friends who helped him in the preparation of this work, first, to my fellow Augustinian, Fr. Robert E. Regan, O.S.A., who acted as censor, who suggested much that was helpful in the way of Moral Theology, and whose scholarly dissertation on "Professional Secrecy" was most valuable in preparing the chapter on that topic; to Doctor John A. Sharkey, who carefully read the manuscript and who so frequently and so willingly placed his excellent knowledge of obstetrics at my disposal; to the Sisters of Mercy, for the experience gained while teaching in Misericordia and Fitzgerald-Mercy Hospitals; to Fr. Joseph

Quigley, Sr. M. Elaine, O.S.F., Sr. M. Dolores, C.S.J., and in a special manner to Mary Elizabeth Creamer Reedy who assisted in various capacities; to my sister, Mrs. Albert Haas, for typing the entire manuscript; and, finally, to Monsignor Fulton J. Sheen, for writing the Foreword.

CHARLES J. McFADDEN, O.S.A., PH.D.

CONTENTS

CHAPTER 1

The Nature and Value of Ethics

It is customary to begin a study of the science of Ethics with a careful consideration of its definition. In this way, a clear understanding of the nature and scope of the science is best obtained.

Definition of Ethics

Before presenting a strict definition, it is well to recall the etymological meaning of the word "ethics." The word *ethics* is derived from the Greek *ethos,* which means "custom or practice, a characteristic manner of acting, a more or less constant mode of behaviour in the deliberate actions of men."

More technically, Ethics is defined as that science which studies the morality of human acts through the medium of natural reason. It is that science which is directive of the moral acts of man's will according to basic rational principles. In a word, Ethics teaches us how to judge accurately the moral goodness or badness of any human action.

The Nature of Ethics

A clear grasp of the many implications of this concept of Ethics necessitates a deeper analysis of the above definition.

First, it has been said that Ethics is a *science.* A science is systematized knowledge; it is a body of coördinated conclusions clearly established and based upon proven principles. A science is by its very nature focused upon a specific field of knowledge. Its objective is to discover the origin, nature, and purpose of those things which fall within its sphere. Ethics

1

is focused on the field of moral truth, and it presents, in an orderly manner, a sound rational basis for the moral goodness or badness of all human actions. It is, therefore, unquestionably a science.

Second, Ethics is a *natural* science. This statement is made with particular reference to the means which are used by this science to establish its conclusions.

Biology, chemistry, and most of the other sciences with which we are familiar are "natural" sciences in a twofold sense. They utilize purely natural or human means to arrive at their conclusions and, for the most part, they are concerned in certain specific ways with the world of physical nature.

In contrast, Theology is a supernatural science. Its conclusions have particular reference to the supernatural life of man and its conclusions are based primarily on the revealed word of God.

Ethics, however, is a natural science in the sense that it uses a purely natural means, the power of human reason, to arrive at its conclusions. It is based neither on the revealed word of God nor on the traditional teachings of Christ's infallible Church. Ethics is a branch of philosophy, a science which derives its truths from the accurate use of unaided human reason.

It is admittedly true that the infallible teaching of Christ's Church is of indirect value to the student of Ethics. Such teachings serve as an excellent guide and constant "check-up" on the accuracy of our reasoning processes. But, in itself, Ethics depends solely upon the natural power of human reason to discover the morality of any specific action. For this reason, Ethics is properly called a purely natural science.

Third, Ethics is a *practical* and *directive* science. These qualities belong to a certain extent to almost all sciences. Ethics, however, is "practical and directive" in a unique sense.

Some sciences are primarily speculative in character and not particularly intended for practical application. Other sciences, such as physics, chemistry, and biology, are obviously intended for practical use.

Ethics is a practical science in the truest sense. For one may learn such sciences as physics, chemistry, or biology, and then proceed to neglect them for the rest of his life. One may turn one's activities into other equally worthwhile fields of endeavor and never put into practice the truths of these sciences. *But this may not be done with the truths learned in the science of Ethics.* Unlike other sciences, Ethics does not bring us truths which we may learn and then legitimately 'pigeon-hole' for the rest of our lives. Ethics does not merely teach us that certain moral ideals are highest and most deserving of acceptance. The truths of Ethics, when once known, morally bind man to accept and apply them. He must mold and direct his life according to those moral ideals which he has learned in the science of Ethics. In a word, many other sciences are practical in the sense that man *may* apply them, whereas Ethics is practical in the sense that man *must* apply its principles in his life.

It should be clear from the preceding that the science of Ethics is concerned with moral action.

A cursory glance at many books on "Medical Ethics" or "Nursing Ethics" reveals, however, that these works are not primarily concerned with moral principles. For the most part, they treat of what one might call the "etiquette" of the medical profession. Such subjects as good manners, tact, development of personality, civil law's regulation of various professional activities—and comparable topics form their major part. Both doctor and nurse must certainly receive education along these lines. But far more necessary and fundamental are proper ethical standards for guidance in the very difficult and very real moral problems which they constantly encounter.

The Division of Ethics

The field of Ethics is ordinarily divided into General Ethics and Special Ethics.

General Ethics is the basic course of the science of Ethics. Just as General Physics, General Chemistry and General Biology present the fundamental principles upon which all specialized branches of these sciences are based, so does General Ethics establish the basic principles of the moral science.

Special Ethics is devoted to an application of general ethical principles to the solution of the moral problems of particular institutions or professions. Thus, Ethics of the State, Ethics of the Family, and Medical Ethics are specialized branches of this science. In these particular branches of the science of Ethics, general moral principles are applied to the problems of the State, the family, and the medical profession.

Medical Ethics is, therefore, a form of Special Ethics. It is concerned with the application of general principles to the moral problems of the medical profession.

Truths Assumed in Ethics

A course in Ethics admittedly proceeds upon the assumption that certain basic truths are accepted by the student entering upon the study of this science of morals. In no sense does this procedure imply that these basic truths are incapable of proof. Rather, the science of Ethics accepts these truths from other sciences wherein they are adequately established. In its acceptance of truths proven in other sciences, Ethics is pursuing a course which all sciences must follow. No science could possibly attempt to prove all the truths which it must utilize in its own investigations.

The science of physics, for example, legitimately accepts as valid innumerable truths proven in the science of mathematics. The science of medicine rightfully accepts countless truths established by the sciences of biology and chemistry. Each science has its own proper field of endeavor. Each science unhesitatingly uses the truths established by other sciences in the pursuit of knowledge. To refuse any science the right to utilize truths established by other sciences would obviously be destructive of progress in all realms of knowledge.

The science of Ethics, therefore, frankly assumes that its students accept certain basic truths from various sciences. The more fundamental branches of philosophy, such as Epistemology, Natural Theology and Rational Psychology, are the principal sources from which Ethics derives these vital truths.

The science of *Epistemology* establishes the reliability of human reason as an instrument for the acquisition of knowledge. All sciences necessarily proceed upon the assumption that the proper use of the intellect will lead man to truth. Refusal to accept this truth established by Epistemology would make impossible all science. Such an attitude would be one of rigid scepticism and would render impossible the certainty of any human knowledge. In common with all other sciences, Ethics, therefore, accepts from Epistemology the truth that human reason, when properly used, is capable of discovering truth.

The science of *Natural Theology* establishes the existence of an all-perfect Supreme Being who is the Creator of the entire universe. This just and merciful God is to be the final Judge of man's life. A good life shall merit an eternal reward; an evil life, an eternal punishment. These truths are adequately and convincingly established in the science of Natural Theology. Ethics proceeds upon the assumption that its students accept these vital truths from this more fundamental branch of philosophy.

The science of *Rational Psychology* is primarily concerned with the existence, nature and destiny of the human soul. From this science it is learned that man's soul is immortal and endowed with the spiritual faculties of intellect and will. Through the medium of his intellect, man is capable of knowing that which is true and good; through the medium of his free will, he is capable of choosing either moral good or moral evil. Ethics accepts these vital truths from Rational Psychology and then proceeds to show that they constitute the very groundwork of the science of morals.

Similarly, most sciences hold certain truths to be self-evident; that is, there are some truths which are so obvious that they require no proof. Thus the science of geometry accepts as self-evident the truth that the whole is greater than any of its parts and equal to their sum total. In a comparable manner, the science of Ethics regards it as self-evident that "good must be done and evil avoided."

We know from the previously mentioned sciences that God has created man for a specific destiny, and we call certain acts "good" because they lead man to that Final End and other acts "evil" because they prevent him from attaining it. Since man is a creature of God, he must certainly endeavor to achieve the purpose for which he was created. And, since certain acts are called "good" because they help man to achieve that purpose and other acts "evil" because they hinder him, it should be perfectly clear that man must "do good and avoid evil."

It is, then, the task of Ethics to establish the moral goodness or badness of specific actions. The point to be remembered is that when Ethics does prove the moral goodness of certain acts, man must perform such of these as are required for the achievement of his final destiny. And, when Ethics shows the moral evil of certain other actions, man must abstain from them. For only by doing good and avoiding evil can man fulfill his moral obligation to strive for the Eternal Destiny set up for him by his Creator.

The foregoing explanation of the nature of Ethics should be understood, *but it must not be allowed to create a false impression. There is no intention to restrict the treatment of the various topics in this book to the purely ethical and natural level. The nature of Ethics has been explained in detail because our approach is to be primarily, but by no means exclusively, a rational one.*

God has raised man to a level higher than the natural by bestowing upon him a supernatural end, by giving him abundant graces to achieve that end, and by revealing countless vital truths to him.

The moral ideals of the Christian doctor and nurse should certainly be molded on the revealed word of God and the teachings of Christ's Church, as well as on the dictates of reason. Both reason and revelation will, therefore, be utilized in this work. But no doctor or nurse, regardless of his or her religious background, may ever forget that *all* men are bound by the Natural Law—*and practically all of the moral conclusions in this work, save those that are expressly related to the sacraments,* are simply expressions of Natural Law.

The Value of Ethics

Those who are familiar with the social problems of the present time are thoroughly convinced that revitalized ethical principles are sorely needed by our age. The relationship between these social problems and ethical principles is twofold. On the one hand, the widespread violation of moral principles is a common cause of many social problems. On the other, the very presence of social problems creates in man an increased tendency to flout numerous moral ideals.

Every doctor and nurse should certainly feel it to be a duty to do all in their power to remedy this lamentable situation. As servants of humanity, they profess that they have at heart the welfare of man. Certainly their concern is not only with the physical welfare of the patient but also with that which is highest, noblest and most important in man, namely, his immortal soul. Doctors and nurses, therefore, can never regard their profession in a purely material way. The Catholic doctor and nurse, in particular, must never forget they are members of Christ's Church and the fortunate recipients of knowledge and graces which are not possessed by those who lack the gift of Faith. These blessings aid them immeasurably in their noble work and help to draw them close to their patient, in whom they see the image of our common Saviour.

The Value of Ethics to the Doctor and Nurse

In several respects, Ethics is the most important subject in the curriculum. Sound ethical principles are absolutely essential to good character, and good character is of such importance that nothing can take its place. Right conduct in the innumerable situations of daily life can be expected only from one who has developed a sound moral character. Obviously enough, such a character can be born only of an adequate understanding and habitual application of proper moral standards.

For the doctor and nurse, therefore, the science of Ethics cannot be a mere speculative study. It is intensely practical; so practical and necessary, indeed, that the lack of Ethics will seriously lessen, if not totally destroy, the value of their work.

Of all the professions which students may enter, it can truthfully be said that none even approaches the medical profession as a source of difficult moral problems. The care of life itself is constantly in the hands of the doctor and nurse. In some cases, they usher life into the world amidst many dangers; in other cases, they preserve life threatened by innumerable evils. And they see life depart from this world in the supreme moment of the patient's existence, when death is upon him.

One who is so continually close to the most sacred and most important realities in life must expect to face serious moral problems.

It will be of great help to medical personnel to be prudent enough and humble enough to seek counsel in their greatest difficulties. But there will be countless times when immediate action is essential. It is then that they will have to rely on their own ethical principles and ideals. The realization that they possess a clear understanding of these vital principles and the practical ability to apply them will not only increase the value and efficiency of their work but will also give them a conscience at peace with God and man.

For doctors and nurses, service to man becomes much more than merely another job. No longer is it simply a profession through which they may earn their livelihood. For doctors and nurses who are constantly striving to guide their daily work according to noble ethical ideals, the profession of medicine becomes Christ-like in its objective. Instead of being merely other job-holders, they become in no small way true missionaries of Christ. Instead of accomplishing mere routine duties, their daily life is devoted to the corporal and spiritual works of mercy. Instead of being interested merely in the physical health of the patient for reasons of expediency, they are interested in both his physical and spiritual welfare for the purest of motives.

Needless to say, noble idealism will characterize the social work of the doctor and nurse only if it be first realized in their own personal lives.

The Value of Ethics to the Patient

Many patients of the doctor and nurse have never had the opportunity of receiving a proper moral education. Many others have had that opportunity and have since strayed from the ideals of moral living. During long periods of sickness, man has much time to think over eternal truths. Long and lonely hours give him an opportunity to ponder over much that has received no attention in the rush of a busy life. No time is more opportune for the presentation of moral ideals.

By no means is it meant that doctors and nurses are to set out determinedly on the moral reformation of all of their patients. Such conduct would antagonize innumerable patients, displease hospital authorities and be out of keeping with their position. But doctors and nurses who possess a deeply spiritual character and imbue their work with Christian love cannot fail to be a good moral influence on all whom they attend. Noble example remains one of the best teachers of men. At least, in this respect, the true doctor and nurse can influence all patients for the better.

In countless instances, however, doctors and nurses will be explicitly questioned by their patients on moral matters. In these cases they can be of invaluable help. If they possess the proper knowledge of moral ideals, and the zeal to impart them, they will be able to guide many lives back to the path of good living.

A clear grasp of ethical principles will also enable doctors and nurses to present a sound Christian philosophy of pain to their patients. Those unfortunates who are incurable or maimed for life will especially derive untold courage from such an inspiring outlook on life. There is frequently a decided tendency toward despair on the part of such patients. The amount of physical and spiritual good that can be done for them is truly incalculable. It is no small achievement to give a despairing man a reason for wanting to live.

The Value of Ethics to the Profession

Doctors and nurses are members of one of the most noble of all professions. But the value of its contribution to mankind simply reflects the self-sacrificing work of its individual members, and the respect with which this great profession is held in society is dependent upon the conduct of its individual members.

It is obvious that the medical profession has an obligation to conduct its activities according to sound ethical ideals. But we may go further and state that failure to live up to these ideals would be ruinous to the profession. Disregard of moral standards has often eaten into the very heart of the most powerful nations, and these nations have collapsed. The strongest social organization loses both its efficiency and the respect of men when it flouts moral ideals.

The medical profession is no exception to this rule. It must never run the risk of losing either its efficiency or the profound respect of men. The moral standards which characterize this profession in any community merely reflect the ethical character of its members. In any community the profession is no better than a cross-section of its doctors and nurses. The youngest nurse, as well as the oldest doctor, has a personal responsibility in this matter toward the profession. They elevate and preserve the moral standards of their profession by applying them in their own personal careers, as well as by the example and inspiration which they thereby give to their co-workers.

The estimation which innumerable people will have of the medical profession will frequently depend upon the ideals they encounter in the relatively few doctors and nurses who attend them during their illnesses. Doctors and nurses who always act according to the highest ethical ideals will necessarily create in all with whom they come in contact a deep respect for the medical profession.

The effect of this good influence will be far-reaching. Society will have confidence in, and respect for, the medical profession. Such confidence and respect will enable this great profession to bring to mankind in the fullest degree all of its invaluable services.

In conclusion, any person's career is successful in proportion to his achievement of the highest ideals possible in that career. The Christian moral ideals are certainly the highest ideals possible in the medical profession, for this profession, above almost all others, is Christ-like in its objective. Love of mankind is its very soul. The corporal and spiritual works of mercy are its principal work. Both doctor and nurse may therefore regard themselves as successful in their medical careers precisely to the extent that their labors are molded on proper ethical standards.

Problems for Discussion

1. The primary motive prompting some students to select medicine or nursing as a career is that it will provide them with an adequate livelihood. What do you think of this motive as a basis for a career in medicine or nursing? What influence, if any, will this motive have on the efficiency and value of their work? What motive or motives prompted you to choose this profession? What motives for entering this field provide the soundest assurance of being happy and successful in the work of your profession? Do you think students ever enter this profession because of the glamour attached to it, because of the admiration which most people have for a doctor or nurse, or for the social contacts which may follow? Do you know of any instances in which students failed because of wrong motives which prompted them to enter this field?

2. Glance through the chapter headings of several of the widely used secular texts in Medical or Nursing Ethics. You will seldom encounter the treatment of a moral subject. Tact, hygiene, courtesy, use of recreational time, personal appearance, and comparable topics form the bulk of these works. How do you account for so many books being confined to etiquette for nurses, rather than providing the nurse with a comprehensive moral code?

3. Compare *reason* and *revelation* as sources of moral principles. What should be the relationship of reason and revelation to each other? What is the relationship between revelation and the teaching authority of the Church? Can reason provide man with any moral truths which are not formally and explicitly found in revelation? Does revelation provide man with any moral truths which are not clearly, easily, and readily discoverable by reason?

4. Nurses sometimes refer to their course in *Ethics* as a course in "religion." Is this accurate?

5. How is the reputation of a hospital affected by its ethical standards?

6. What influence, if any, do the ethical standards of the medical and nursing professions have on the welfare of the community?

7. Would you say that *moral laws* and *moral ideals* are synonymous?

References for Reading

AIKENS, C.: *Studies in Ethics for Nurses,* Phila., 1938.

BROGAN, J.: *The Character of a Nurse,* Milwaukee, 1924.

DIETZ, L.: *Professional Adjustments,* Vol. I, Phila., 1942.

FINK, L.: "Catholic Ethical Nursing" in *Graduate Nurses,* pp. 272-284, N. Y. 1939.

FITZGERALD, SR. M. ISABEL: *The Philosophy of Saint Thomas in Relation to the Spiritual Aspects of Nursing,* Catholic University, Washington, D. C., 1938.

GARESCHE, E.: *Ethics and the Art of Conduct for Nurses,* pp. 17-28; 157-305, Phila., 1937.

MOORE, T.: *Principles of Ethics,* pp. 3-11; 333-371, Phila., 1935.

MORRISON, B.: "The Moral Education of a Nurse," *Hospital Progress,* June, 1948; "How to Pray," *Hospital Progress,* July, 1948; "But We Don't Need More Religion," *Hospital Progress,* March, 1948.

VAUGHAN, SR. ROSE HELEN: *The Actual Incidence of Moral Problems in Nursing,* Catholic University, Washington, D. C., 1935.

WALSH, J.: "Faith and Science in Nursing" in *Graduate Nurses,* pp. 1-13, N. Y., 1938.

Proceedings of the Symposium on the Curriculum of a School of Nursing, pp. 1-75, Catholic University, Washington, D. C., 1940.

CHAPTER 2

The Foundations of Morality

Even the beginner in science knows that every reality in the universe has a purpose and is governed and directed by law. In fact, the various sciences devote their time and resources to the discovery of the hidden laws of nature. Once discovered, these laws are systematized and integrated with each other and then presented to mankind for further study and practical application. The thought that each reality in the universe has a purpose and is governed by law is of deep significance and will furnish us with the true basis of all morality.

Purpose in Nature

Few individuals have as splendid an opportunity as the doctor and nurse to appreciate the design and purpose which prevails throughout all nature. From both their science courses and their medical work, they learn that purpose is everywhere evident.

On the *inanimate* level of creation, they know that the sun and the moon, the massive planets and the countless stars speed unerringly through space in their well-regulated orbits. The purpose of this vast and intricate system is clear: the Creator has so ordered the movement of these bodies as to manifest His glory, intelligence, and power; to make the earth habitable for man; and to create with perfect regularity the succession of day and night, as well as the change of our seasons.

On the *vegetative* level of creation, each seed has, from the first moment of its existence, a definite purpose to achieve. It is inherent in the very nature of the seed to seek one sole objective, namely, to become a fully-grown and healthy member of its species. Each plant, moreover, is composed of many parts, and the scientist is able to point out the specific purpose of each of these parts in relationship to the growth of the organism.

On the *animal* level of creation, purpose is likewise everywhere visible. Each embryo has but one objective of its existence, to become a mature member of its species. Each organ in the animal body serves a purpose; and the qualities with which each animal is endowed indicate a marvelous Divine Plan for even the smallest creature; strength, swiftness, cunning, and a myriad of other special endowments are given to animals for the purpose of self-preservation.

Almost all of the work of doctor and nurse is devoted to caring for the injured and the sick. It is their constant hope that their tireless efforts will restore integrity and health of body. And though they may never have thought of it in such terms, their work is intimately concerned with *purpose in nature*. An internal organ is attacked by disease, and health vanishes because the organ is no longer serving its purpose. An eye is injured, and it no longer serves its purpose of providing adequate vision. A limb is crushed or broken, and it is incapable of serving its purpose in the body. Disease and accidents injure these and innumerable other parts of the human organism and render them incapable of serving their normal purposes.

Turning momentarily from the physical creation to the soul of man, one cannot fail to understand that it, too, must have a specific destiny. Certainly, the God of infinite wisdom who set a goal for even the lowest being in the universe did not create the highest being in our visible world without a purpose. For the moment, we shall not ask the purpose of man's existence. We wish only that it be understood that the infinitely wise Creator must have given man's nature a destiny toward which it should progress.

Law in Nature

We have seen that the Creator has given each reality in the universe a definite goal or objective of its existence. We wish now to show that *each created being reaches its established goal by the observance of law.*

The nature of the orange seed, for example, demands that certain requirements be realized in order that it may grow and become a healthy tree. It requires a specific amount of moisture, a definite type of soil, and especially the extensive sunlight and warmth of a southern climate. The growth and development of this seed depends upon its obtaining these needs of its nature. In a word, the sum total of these requirements constitutes what we might call "the law of its nature," the law which this seed must observe in order to reach the goal of its existence.

What is true of the orange seed is likewise true of every other species of vegetative life. Each species has a nature peculiar to itself, a nature different from that of all other plants. Each of these different natures has, therefore, a different set of requirements upon which its growth and development depends. The sum total of the requirements of each of these vegetative natures might be called "the law which must be observed in order that it may reach the objective or goal of its existence."

Similarly, on the animal level of creation we find, not only that each species has a different nature, but also that each species has requirements peculiar to itself. Upon the obtaining of these necessities of its nature, the growth of the animal depends. One animal nature will require but little food, another will require much. One will be able to live in subzero temperature, while the nature of another will require a tropical climate. The varying necessities of their natures are as innumerable as the species themselves. The sum total of the requirements which each species must obtain in order to grow and develop is simply the law which it must observe in order to progress toward its perfection and the goal of its existence.

In reference to the body of man, everyone realizes that health is the desired objective. Throughout the entire life of man, laws of health are urged upon him by medical science, and violations of these laws take their toll in the form of sickness, disease, and death. In a word, certain laws must be observed in order to secure the desired goal of health.

Turning our attention momentarily to man, and thinking particularly of his spiritual soul, we can readily understand that just as the infinitely wise God has given a law to each being in lower creation to guide it toward its goal and its perfection, so must there be a law which man must observe in order to so perfect his nature that it will thereby progress toward, and finally reach, its divinely-appointed destiny.

Law in Harmony with Nature

Further reflection reveals that every reality in the universe is governed by a law in harmony with its nature. In this regard, we know that all creation below man has at least one thing in common: *all created reality below man is wholly material.* Quite consistently, then, do we find that the laws which govern lower creation are physical laws and, as such, are, of course, absolutely determining laws. The sun, moon, and stars are *determined* by physical laws to move at definite velocities in their respective spheres. The various vegetative natures grow and develop *necessarily* when the proper soil, sunlight, and moisture are present. When these requisite conditions of growth are not present, the plants *necessarily* die. Similarly, the animal nature is driven by *determining* laws, such as instinct, to seek its needs; when these requirements of its nature are secured, the animal lives and develops; when these needs are not obtained, the animal necessarily dies. In a word, the material beings of all lower creation are guided by forces over which they have no control. They are purely material beings and, as such, are governed by laws in keeping with the type of nature they possess, that is, by rigid physical laws.

The same general principle applies also to man. He, too, must be governed and directed *by a law in harmony with his nature.* Man, however, possesses a nature composed of matter and spirit. In so far as his nature is material, it is, of course, subject to physical laws. Such laws do not directly concern us in this chapter. But we know that man also possesses a spiritual soul which can progress toward its eternal destiny only through the observance of a law suited to itself. In other words, the development of man's spiritual nature hinges upon his observance of what we may call a *spiritual or moral law.*

The law which governs the development of man's spiritual nature cannot possibly be a law imposed on him in any physically determining manner. Such a law would be destructive of the nature of man, especially of his free will. If man is to remain man, an intellectual and free being, the law imposed on him will have to be a law which preserves his freedom of will. It cannot possibly be a physical and determining law. It will have to be a spiritual or moral law which man *knows* through the use of his intellect and *obeys or disobeys* by an act of his free will. Only such a law would be in harmony with the nature of man. Any other kind of law would be destructive of his nature, particularly of the endowments of intellect and free will.

Brief consideration of these vital truths reveals that, unlike all lower creation, man alone is truly the molder of his destiny. He alone decides whether he shall observe that law which, when observed, results in the perfecting of his spiritual nature and ultimately in the attainment of his eternal destiny.

We have said that man can come into the possession of the moral law through the medium of his intellect. It requires little explanation to show the general way in which this is accomplished.

At the very outset, the intelligence of a normal man leads him to the acceptance of the existence of a Supreme Being. His intellect tells him that this is the only reasonable and adequate explanation of the existence of the universe, as well as the marvelous order and design which characterizes it.

Similarly, the intellect of man soon tells him that his nature and destiny differ from that of the beast. Abstract and difficult as is the reasoning process on such a matter, even the most uneducated and uncivilized peoples have arrived at a concept of immortality.

Once man recognizes the fact of God's existence, he realizes immediately that he owes this Supreme Being a fitting love, honor, and worship. Once man recognizes the fact that he is endowed with a spiritual soul and an immortal destiny, he knows that he must subject the desires of his lower nature to the interests of his higher spiritual nature. Once man recognizes that his fellowmen are endowed with a nature and destiny similar to his own, he understands that they possess certain rights which he is morally obliged to respect. Once man recognizes that he was created by God with a social nature and destined to live in society with fellowman, he realizes that the State is therefore indirectly of divine origin and that its just laws should be respected and obeyed.

It is in this way that the intellect of man can build up a body of moral ideals. This moral code is commonly called the *Natural Law* and has been defined as "the participation in the eternal law (Divine Wisdom guiding *all* creatures to their proper ends) by a rational creature inclining the rational creature toward the end and actions proper to its nature."

The Natural Law is *universal* because, being based on human nature, it binds all men. It is *immutable,* because it is not subject to change, abrogation, or dispensation. It is *absolute* because man must observe it at all costs.

There are, however, some moral truths which are so abstract and complex that it is most difficult for even the best intellects to arrive at complete accuracy regarding them. Many men, moreover, are not blessed with fine intellects; and few men would have the opportunity to devote much time to the rational investigation of difficult moral truths.

All men should have at their disposal from the beginning of their rational life all those truths which will help them develop themselves spiritually and make constant progress toward their final spiritual destiny. It is for these good reasons that God in His Mercy and Wisdom has seen fit to reveal to man in a complete and accurate manner all of the moral truths which he must observe. The Moral Law possessed by the Christian is therefore most perfect. It is to be found in tradition, in Sacred Scripture, and in the teaching of Christ's infallible Church. It is this law known both by reason and Divine Revelation which should be cherished by doctor and nurse alike as the source and basis of their moral ideals.

Conscience

Through the use of reason and revelation, man can arrive at an adequate body of moral ideals. But the question immediately arises: *how are these universal and abstract moral principles applied to the concrete situations in human life? Very briefly, it is conscience which is the subjective authoritative guide of man's moral conduct.*

From our earliest years we are aware of the presence of conscience within us. It has invariably given its approval or disapproval, both to the actions we have done and those we have contemplated. For the most part, however, even those who have had the advantages of an early religious and moral education rarely understand the real nature of conscience. Some people regard it as an obscure "feeling" which is sensitive to the moral character of actions, while others believe that it is a moral instinct with which human nature is endowed.

The truth of the matter is quite simple. *Conscience is a dictate of man's practical reason deciding that a particular act is morally right or wrong.*

The process by which man arrives at this judgment of practical reason involves only the formation of a simple syllogism. As previously mentioned, man possesses a vast body of universal and abstract moral principles. In his daily life he then encounters some particular action which has an obvious relationship to some one of these moral laws or principles. It is the task of the intellect to compare the contemplated action with the pertinent universal law. If the proposed action is in harmony with this moral law, reason draws the practical conclusion that the action is morally permissible and may therefore be done. On the contrary, if such a comparison indicates that the particular action would involve a violation of the moral law, reason classifies the act as morally wrong and forbidden.

An example or two will clarify the manner in which we arrive at these moral conclusions which we call *dictates of conscience.*

A doctor knows that, when it is possible to do so, charity obliges him to help those who are in grave need. This is just one of many universal and abstract principles in his moral code. Then, while on vacation, he witnesses a serious accident. His intellect goes immediately to work. In an instant, he reasons that when it is possible to do so, charity obliges him to help those who are in grave need; and these accident victims are in grave need of aid that he can render; therefore, *charity obliges him to assist them.*

On the other hand, a nurse knows that stealing is immoral. This is a universal moral principle which she accepts. Then, on a certain case, there is an opportunity to take some personal property from a patient without being discovered. Immediately, her intellect arrives at its dictate of conscience through the most simple form of a reasoning process: stealing is immoral; to take this property would be stealing; therefore, *to take this property would be immoral.*

Man stands alone in our visible universe as the only being with an immortal destiny. His incomparable endowments of intellect and free will raise him far above lower creation. The attainment of his immortal destiny is, however, dependent upon his willingness to perfect his spiritual nature. This spiritual development is impossible without man's observance of the moral obligations which rest upon him and which are embodied in what we have called the *Moral Law.* This *Moral Law* is made known to man through the medium of reason and Divine Revelation, and it is applied to the concrete situations in human life by practical reason or conscience.

Kinds of Conscience

Many divisions of conscience are given by moralists. Our interest is only in those types which are of most practical value in solving the moral problems of the medical profession.

A true or correct conscience is one whose judgment of the morality of an act is in conformity with the real moral character of the action. It judges those acts to be sinful which are objectively opposed to Moral Law; it judges those acts to be permissible or praiseworthy which are objectively in conformity with Moral Law. Thus, contraception is in its nature an immoral act; while, on the other hand, the act of ministering to the sick, out of a spiritual motive, is in its nature a good act. A true conscience is one which arrives at these conclusions.

A true conscience must always be obeyed when it commands or forbids an action. It is an accurate guide to the morality of actions which have a vital relationship to the achievement of man's final end. To oppose a true conscience would constitute a deliberate choice of evil.

A false or erroneous conscience is one which judges to be good and lawful an action which is opposed to *Moral Law.* Thus, the direct and deliberate destruction of the life of an infant born with a damaged brain is murder. A conscience which would judge such an act to be morally permissible would be false and erroneous.

Very frequently, persons have erroneous consciences through their own fault; that is, a normally diligent investigation of the matter would have brought them an accurate knowledge of the morality of a contemplated action. A doctor or nurse, for example, who has ample opportunity to learn the morality of various operations, and who fails to take advantage of these opportunities, is morally responsible for the violations of Moral Law which result from the lack of required knowledge. Such a conscience is called *vincibly* erroneous, because the error of judgment could have been overcome or prevented by reasonable effort; it is called *culpably* erroneous because the doctor or nurse is morally at fault for his or her negligence in this regard.

A vincibly erroneous conscience may not be followed. It is not an accurate guide to moral truth, and personal negligence is the cause of this deficiency. A person with a vincibly erroneous conscience must make the required "reasonable diligent effort" to overcome his or her ignorance of moral matters. The person will then be in a position to direct his or her life according to proper standards.

In other instances, an erroneous conscience is in no way the product of a person's negligence. It sometimes happens that lack of time, absence of a capable spiritual adviser, immaturity of years, deficient moral education or bad home environment make it practically impossible for some individuals to possess accurate moral knowledge. Whenever reasonable effort on the part of the person is incapable of supplying requisite knowl-

edge, the conscience is called *invincibly and inculpably erroneous*. It is called invincibly erroneous because the ignorance
could not have been overcome by normally diligent effort. It
is called inculpably erroneous because there is no moral guilt
attached to actions done from such a conscience.

An invincibly erroneous conscience may be either a certain
or a doubtful conscience. The course of action to be followed
in such cases will be explained presently under each of those
types of conscience.

A certain conscience is one which holds its conclusion with
conviction and assurance that it is right. It may be either a
true or a false conscience. A nurse, for example, who firmly
believes that one should baptize a dying infant has a certain
and true conscience. A doctor who is thoroughly convinced
that therapeutic abortion is sometimes morally permissible has
a certain but false conscience.

*A certain conscience must always be obeyed when it com-
mands or forbids an action*. To choose a course of action condemned by a certain conscience would constitute a deliberate
choice of what one believed to be evil. Such a choice would
always be sinful.

A probable conscience is one which lacks speculative certitude as to the morality of an action but has formed an opinion
which rests on good and solid grounds, such as a man of
prudence and judgment would be inclined to accept. This
probability is sufficient to provide the individual with the
practical certitude required for moral action.

It is not always possible to obtain certitude in our moral
conclusions. And, since we may not act on a doubtful conscience, some guide to action must be available to man. Briefly,
when it is impossible to attain certitude, *and when it is a question merely of the sinfulness of an act,* it is morally permissible
to follow a solidly probable opinion, even though another
opinion on the matter may possess somewhat stronger weight.
As the above phrasing indicates, the use of this principle is
restricted to cases in which the only question is whether a given
course of action is sinful. This principle will be ordinarily
applicable, though frequently it would be more virtuous to

follow the more probable opinion. By way of example, it is a solidly probable opinion that the excision of a fallopian tube containing a living inviable fetus is, under certain conditions, morally permissible. On the basis of this probable opinion, it would be allowable for a surgeon to perform or for a nurse to assist at such an operation.

There are, however, three types of cases in which one may not follow any opinion which is genuinely probable but in which one must take the safer course. These are cases in which it is of vital importance that one definite result be achieved and the surest possible method of attaining the result must, therefore, be used.

First, it is morally compulsory to follow the safer course when there is a question of means to be taken to save a soul. Thus, an infant which was baptized in the uterus may be born in a dying condition. It is only probable that the uterine baptism fulfilled the requirements for the valid reception of the sacrament. The infant *must,* therefore, be baptized again conditionally.

Second, it is morally compulsory to follow the safer course when there is a question of the validity of the sacraments. A nurse, for example, comes across an unbaptized infant who is obviously dying. An emergency baptism is an immediate necessity. At hand is a vessel which contains what appears to be water, and *probably is,* but the nurse is not certain that it is not some solution used for medical purposes. She realizes that she can get what is certainly water by going down the corridor, and she is morally obliged to do so.

Finally, it is morally compulsory to follow the safer course when there is a question as to the means required to preserve that to which someone has an absolute right. Thus, a patient's life could be seriously endangered by a certain disease, and a doctor might know that one treatment would *certainly* result in recovery, while a second treatment would *probably* produce restoration of health. Even though the doctor might have a scientific interest in the effectiveness of the second method, he is morally obliged to adopt the first treatment which is certain to return the patient to health.

A doubtful conscience is one which suspends judgment on the morality of an action or, if it does form a judgment, is in fear of error.

Doubt, as affecting conscience, is said to be either *speculative* or *practical*. Doubt is *speculative* when the mind is not certain that a particular law exists or that it refers to a contemplated action. Doubt is *practical* whenever the mind is incapable of arriving at a *certain* conclusion regarding the morality of a proposed act.

In reference to speculative doubt, persons are morally obliged to make a reasonably diligent effort to discover and understand the laws which bind them. If the existence or interpretation of the law is not clear after such an effort, a person is free to act. The reason for this freedom is that a lawgiver must make a law known to its subject before it is binding. If, after a normally diligent effort to learn of the existence or interpretation of a law, no such knowledge is available, the subject's freedom to act is reasonably presumed. Such a person is not acting on a doubtful conscience; rather, there is now present practical certitude that no obligation exists which would curtail freedom. This principle is usually stated in these words: *a doubtful law has no binding force.*

In contrast, one may never act with a conscience which is in a state of practical doubt. To realize that a contemplated action may be morally wrong, and nevertheless to do the act, is indicative of malice of will. In such cases, one may refrain from acting at all, if the matter permits; or one may choose the safer side, that is, follow a course of action which would result in the fulfillment of the obligation in question; or one may take steps to remove the practical doubt. It will almost always be possible to resolve such doubts by a more careful examination into the matter, by consulting trustworthy reference books, or by making an inquiry from a competent spiritual adviser.

A *perplexed conscience* is one which is torn between two duties and believes that sin will be committed by either course of action. Needless to say, the perplexed conscience is both an erroneous and doubtful conscience. *Normally, a person with a perplexed conscience must postpone action and seek proper guidance.* Should it be impossible to delay acting or to obtain helpful advice, the person should choose what appears to be the lesser of the two evils.

A nurse, for example, who has never received a course on moral principles as applied to her nursing duties will often have a perplexed conscience. Thus, she might be caring for a patient who is sick at home. On Sunday, she realizes that the Church has imposed the obligation on its members to attend Mass, and she knows also that the patient is truly in need of her care. She fears that she will be committing sin if she misses Mass, and she feels that it would be sinful to desert the needy patient. If it is possible to resolve her doubt and obtain a certain knowledge of her moral duty, she must do so. This may often be done by consulting a trustworthy book or a reliable spiritual guide. If it is impossible to resolve her doubt, and she must naturally follow some course in this case, she does not commit any sin if she chooses whichever course of action seems to her to involve the lesser of the two evils.

A scrupulous conscience is one which finds sin where it does not actually exist or magnifies it where it does. Scrupulosity is not so much an error in judgment as it is a state of anxiety arising from physical or psychological causes. A doctor, for example, has a scrupulous conscience who carries out his duties with reasonable care and diligence and yet constantly worries about harmful effects which he thinks may have resulted from insufficient effort on his part.

A scrupulous conscience is erroneous and, as such, it may not be followed. The scrupulous person must realize that the mind can become impaired in its ability to evaluate the precise morality of actions. A proper humility and an obedient following of the advice of a capable spiritual adviser is an absolute necessity for the scrupulous person.

A lax conscience is one which regards questionable acts as morally permissible for very trivial reasons. It grasps at the slightest reason which would classify a gravely sinful act as only slightly immoral. It unhesitatingly regards venially sinful acts as possessing no moral character at all. A nurse, for instance, might possess a professional secret which would make a choice bit of gossip in the community; if she were to reveal this matter without feeling at all concerned about the possible grave harm that might be inflicted on the patient and on the reputation of her profession, she has a lax conscience.

A lax conscience is erroneous and, as such, it may not be followed. A person with a lax conscience is morally obliged to acquire a proper appreciation of spiritual and moral values. The means through which this can be done are both numerous and effective. Any spiritual adviser will be glad to assist a person who needs help of this nature.

The Moral Act

Though it is true that man is a rational being, it does not follow that every act done by man is under the control of his reason. Doctors and nurses are familiar with countless cases of this type. Patients who are under the influence of ether or who are delirious sometimes reveal information which is injurious to others. Patients who are addicted to sleep-walking or who are mentally unbalanced sometimes commit actions which inflict serious losses upon innocent persons.

Man differs from the beast in that he possesses a spiritual nature which is endowed with an intellect capable of accurate knowledge and a will capable of free choice. Any act, therefore, which is done by man but without at least some knowledge and some freedom is not truly a human act. Such an act does not proceed from man's complete human nature, and is technically known as *an act of man.*

We must realize that there can be a question of morality only when an action is done with some degree of knowledge and freedom. God is an All-Just Judge and will not condemn a man for an action which is wholly beyond his control. Any act, therefore, which involves a complete absence of knowledge, or a complete absence of freedom, or both, is called an act of man and contains no morality.

In contrast, *a human action* is one which proceeds from man's rational nature. It is an action which is done with at least some knowledge and some free choice. Most of our actions are of this type. It is with both knowledge and freedom that we perform a high percentage of the countless actions in our daily life.

A human action which involves some principle of Moral Law is known as *a moral act*. More strictly, a moral act is one which is freely done by man with an awareness of its relationship to Moral Law and his own final end. Whenever such an action is in conformity with Moral Law, it is called *good;* if opposed to Moral Law, it is called *bad*. Some of these actions involve most serious obligations, while others are concerned with matters of lesser weight. But whether they be concerned with grave or slight obligations, moral acts are most important. Unlike all other acts, they help or hinder man in the pursuit of his final end, and this one fact alone places them in a class by themselves.

Knowledge and freedom, it has been said, are essential constituents of a moral act. Any evaluation of the merit of good actions or of the guilt attached to bad actions must, therefore, hinge upon the amount of knowledge and freedom possessed by the person who performs the act.

It is true that knowledge and freedom are often fully and obviously present in an action. Sometimes, however, these essential elements are present in imperfect and rather obscure ways. For this reason, a precise understanding of the various types of moral acts is most helpful and important.

Types of Moral Acts

A perfect moral act is one which is done with full knowledge and full freedom of choice. Such an act may be either good or bad. It is called "perfect" simply because the essential constituents of a human act, knowledge and freedom, are not impaired in any way.

Whenever a perfect act is morally good, there is no lessening of merit due to ignorance or constraint. A doctor, for example, might know that a certain patient could be greatly helped by services which he was not obliged to give. If, out of Christian charity, he should make certain sacrifices in order to render these services, his action is wholly good.

Whenever a perfect act is morally bad, the malice of will and the consequent guilt are not lessened in any way. A nurse, for instance, might know that a certain professional secret could, if revealed, seriously injure a patient. If she should then deliberately reveal it for the sake of gossip, her moral guilt would be full and complete.

An imperfect moral act is one in which either the knowledge or freedom, or both, are deficient. At least some knowledge and some freedom are present in the act, but not in a perfect way.

Whenever a morally good action is done with only a partial realization of its goodness, or under some form of constraint, it is lessened in its spiritual value. Thus, a doctor might perform his duties partially out of Christian charity and partially because of some unworthy motive. His medical work would lose spiritual value in proportion to the weight of his unworthy motive. Should the partial unworthy motive be gravely sinful, the entire spiritual value of the act would be destroyed and mortal sin would be committed.

Whenever a morally bad action is performed by one who, through no fault of his own, does not fully understand the evil character of his action, or who is to some extent forced to perform the action, his guilt is partially lessened. Thus, a nurse might be ordered to instruct a patient in the practice of contraception and be told that refusal would involve the loss of her position. Normally, such a threat would not notably lessen freedom of choice in the matter, and thus grave culpability would not be removed. But it is always true that guilt is lessened in proportion to the impairment of freedom of choice.

A positive moral act is one which involves the performance of a deed. Needless to say, such actions may be either good or bad. Doctors and nurses, for example, perform *positive* moral acts when, out of spiritual motives, they faithfully fulfill any of their many important duties.

A negative moral act is one which involves an omission. It is an offense committed by neglect of duty. Thus, a nurse who would deliberately go to sleep while on night duty would be guilty of many moral offenses of this type.

A directly voluntary act is present whenever an objective is sought for its own sake or as a means to a further end. Thus, a nurse who would deliberately lie in order to escape responsibility for some act of negligence directly wills to lie in the hope that it will serve as a means of avoiding a reprimand or punishment.

An indirectly voluntary act is present whenever a directly voluntary act is also productive of a secondary effect which could and should be foreseen as at least a probable consequence of the directly-willed act.

In the indirectly voluntary act, the secondary effect is not sought for its own sake nor as a means toward the achievement of a further end. Furthermore, it must be possible for the person to foresee, at least obscurely, that the evil effect may follow from the act which is being directly willed. Since knowledge is an essential constituent of a moral act, responsibility for the evil effect can be present only if there be at least a vague realization that the evil may result from what is being done.

In reference to foreseeing the evil effect, this foresight will sometimes be present because it is known that the direct action will, by its very nature, produce the evil effect. In other instances, a person may know from past experience that the direct action will either certainly or probably bring about the evil effect. In order, however, that an evil effect be called indirectly voluntary, there must be a moral obligation to avoid bringing it about. This condition will usually be verified, for the simple reason that we have many sources of obligation which compel us to avoid injuring fellowman, society, and even ourselves. It must always be kept in mind that in the indirectly voluntary act, the motive attracting the will is admittedly *not* a desire to procure the evil effect. This effect is not sought for its own sake nor as a means which will be useful in the procuring of a further end. It is simply an evil effect which one is obliged to avert and which one foresees will at least probably result from a contemplated action.

A precise knowledge of the nature of the indirectly willed act is very important to the doctor and nurse. Their responsibilities to others are both serious and numerous, and they must exercise constant care to avoid actions which might be detrimental to their patients.

An example should serve to clarify the nature of an indi-

rectly willed action. It might easily happen that a nurse would
have a patient to whom she is indebted or in whom she has a
special personal interest. The patient might be restricted to a
liquid or soft diet but might plead with the nurse to obtain
additional food. Should the nurse, out of mistaken sympathy
or a distorted concept of friendship, consent to procure such
food for the patient, she is morally responsible for whatever
harmful effects he may suffer. In the light of her training, she
should and undoubtedly would foresee, at least vaguely, that
the patient may suffer some harm, possibly a very serious setback, from her action.

An habitually voluntary act is one which occurs here and
now as the result of an intention formerly made, not presently
adverted to, but never retracted. An habitually voluntary act
on one's part always presupposes the activity of some other
person who knows of one's original intention, knows that it
was never retracted, and now performs the act in accordance
with the unretracted intention. Even though the person to
whom the habitually voluntary act is attributed is not conscious or is not aware that another is acting for him, the deed
is morally imputable to him because it is done in conformity
with the unretracted desire of his will.

As an example of an habitually voluntary act, we might mention the case of a person who has had the firm desire to receive
the sacrament of baptism, but who has been prevented by unfortunate circumstances from carrying out his plans. While in
this condition, the person becomes the victim of an accident, is
rendered unconscious and in danger of death. A doctor or
nurse who has knowledge of this person's expressed and unretracted desire for baptism should, in the absence of a priest,
administer the sacrament.

A virtually voluntary act is one which takes place here and
now, without present knowledge and present choice, but as the
physical result of an intention once made and never retracted.
It happens frequently that a person knowingly and freely
allows certain actions to become deeply imbedded physical
habits. Such tendencies can become so strong that the victim
of the habit will sometimes perform these acts without even
realizing it.

Doctors and nurses must always be on guard to avoid the formation of dangerous habits. There is, for example, the constant temptation to take "short cuts" in doing their work, as well as the inclination to develop habits of carelessness in the handling of instruments, in the waste of materials, and in the manner of caring for their patients. As soon as a person realizes that he or she is developing a bad habit, and does not take adequate steps to eradicate it, he or she becomes morally responsible for the harmful effects which flow from it.

An interpretatively voluntary act is one which is performed by a second person when, according to a prudent and unprejudiced judgment, a deliberate and free act would here and now be done by a person if he or she had the ability and opportunity to make such a choice.

An illustration of the interpretatively voluntary act is had in the case of an accident victim whose identity is unknown and who is brought into the hospital in an unconscious condition. The doctors realize that an immediate operation is necessary to save the victim's life, but it is impossible to obtain consent to the operation from the unconscious patient or from unknown relatives. Nevertheless, the surgeons are morally justified in performing any required operation. They judge rightly that if the victim had the opportunity to realize his grave need of the operation and had the ability to make a choice, he would certainly request the operation.

One must not be too ready "to interpret" the mind of an unconscious person and to presume his consent to certain actions on our part. It is only too clear that abuses could readily arise. But whenever a common-sense and unprejudiced judgment tells us that the good of a helpless person is at stake, we should not hesitate to presume his consent to any reasonable action which may aid him.

The Twofold Effect Principle

We have already discussed the *indirectly voluntary act*. In this type of act, it will be recalled, an act is done which one could and should foresee will produce a further effect. The "second" effect of the action is not directly willed; it is not the primary objective of the action. But the person should have been able to foresee, at last obscurely, that this secondary effect would follow from the directly-willed action.

The example given to illustrate the indirectly voluntary act was that of a nurse who, out of a distorted concept of sympathy, deliberately gives solid food to a liquid-diet patient. With her training, she could and should foresee the grave effects which her action is likely to produce.

Morally, she is responsible for whatever ill effects the patient may suffer because such harm is *indirectly willed* by her.

The soundness of the moral conclusion in cases of the above type is not very difficult to understand. But there are cases of a somewhat similar character which very often become extremely complex. These are cases in which the performance of an action will produce *both a good effect and a bad effect.*

With full justification, doctors and nurses will often hesitate when faced with cases of this type. On one hand, they perceive that the proposed action will bring about a good result and this is something which they earnestly desire. On the other hand, they know that a bad effect will also necessarily follow from their action. In the face of this difficulty they hesitate and ask: "May I perform an action of this type?" "May I assist at such an operation?"

Before presenting the moral principles which must guide them in the solution of these problems, let us present a sample case of this type.

> A woman who is three months pregnant is brought into the hospital with a cancerous uterus. Removal of the uterus is *immediately* necessary if the woman's life is to be preserved. Removal of the cancerous uterus will produce a good effect, namely, the preservation of the woman's life. Removal of the cancerous uterus will produce an evil effect, namely, the loss of life to the unborn child. May a doctor perform this operation? May a nurse assist at this operation?

The answer to the case, as stated above, is definitely in the affirmative. A surgeon may perform this operation and a nurse may assist him. But let us apply the moral principles which govern such cases to this particular problem.

In order that one may do an action from which two effects, one good and one bad, will necessarily follow, four conditions must be simultaneously verified. If the four conditions are fulfilled, the action may be done. If any one of these four conditions is violated, the proposed action may not be done.

1. *The action must be in itself a morally good action, or at least a morally indifferent action.*
2. *The good effect of the action must precede the evil effect or at least be simultaneous with it.*
3. *The motive prompting the action must be directed to the achievement of the good effect, never in any way to the evil effect.*
4. *The good effect must be at least equivalent in importance to the evil effect.*

A thorough understanding of these four conditions will bring about a clear knowledge of the application of the twofold effect principle.

1. *The action must be in itself a morally good action, or at least a morally indifferent action.* It must not be an act which is in itself morally wrong; if it were, one would be doing evil to achieve good, and one may never do evil to bring about good. *A good objective does not justify the use of an evil means.*

Let us apply the first principle to our sample case. The *act* from which the two effects will follow is the removal of a cancerous uterus. The *good effect* which will follow from this removal is the preservation of the woman's life. The *bad effect* is the loss of life to the unborn child.

Is this proposed action—the excision of a cancerous uterus— a morally good or at least a morally indifferent act? Certainly, it is. Considered in itself, the removal of a cancerous section from a patient's body is at least a morally indifferent act. Quite rightly, one might even consider it a morally good act in so far as it is fulfilling the obligation to preserve one's health and life. The first principle is therefore verified in our sample case.

2. *The good effect must precede the evil effect or at least be simultaneous with it.* Under no consideration may the evil

effect be the cause of the good effect; this would be doing evil in order to attain good.

One should not get the impression that this second principle is concerned primarily with the time sequence of the good and bad effects. It is principally concerned with *causality*. It demands that the good effect result immediately from the good or indifferent action. It will not tolerate the achievement of the good effect through the medium of the evil effect. Rather, the action in question should produce immediately both the good and bad effects.

The second principle is clearly fulfilled in our sample case. The good effect (the preservation of the woman's life) results directly from the action of removing the cancerous uterus. The evil effect (the loss of life to the unborn child) also results directly from the excision of the cancerous section. The good effect is clearly *not* a result of the evil effect: the woman's life is not safeguarded because her child has died. Her life is preserved as a result of the removal of a cancerous uterus. Clearly, then, the indifferent action of removing a cancerous section is the immediate cause of the good effect. The good objective is not attained through the medium of the evil effect, and the second principle is therefore fully verified in the sample case.

3. *The motive prompting the action must be directed to the achievement of the good effect, never to the evil effect.* Although the person doing the action certainly foresees the evil effect, he must in no way desire it. If the evil effect were to stand alone, it must be that the person would not seek it. If the good effect were to stand alone, it must be that the person would certainly endeavor to achieve it. Under no consideration may the action be prompted, even partially, by the desire for the evil effect.

The third principle is clearly fulfilled in the normal case of the type under consideration. The surgeon foresees that if an operation does not take place, both mother and child will die. He performs the operation out of a desire to save the woman's life. The motive prompting his action is obviously *not* a desire to kill the unborn child. True, he foresees the death of the fetus and regrets it, but he certainly does not operate out of a desire to kill the unborn child. The motive prompting the surgeon's action is pure and noble, namely, the desire to preserve the woman's life.

4. *The good effect must be at least equivalent in importance to the evil effect.* In other words, even though the three preceding conditions are fulfilled in a given case, if the evil effect outweighs the good effect, the action may not be done. One could not permit a grave evil to result simply to bring about a comparatively slight good. If the act is to be morally permissible, there must be a proportionately grave cause for allowing the evil effect to take place.

In our sample case there is a perfect proportion between the good and bad effects which will follow from the removal of the cancerous uterus; the life of the mother is equivalent in value to the life of the child.

It should now be clear that the four conditions are simultaneously verified in the sample case. The ethical basis for the performance of the operation in this case is thereby established beyond any reasonable doubt. The surgeon is therefore morally justified in performing the operation, and a nurse is morally justified in rendering him all necessary assistance.

Another type of case will, however, present a different picture.

Cases of uterine fibroids during pregnancy present a moral problem which is similar in many respects to that created by cancer of the pregnant uterus. There is, however, one important difference between the two conditions; delay in operating, without consequent risk to life, will be frequently possible in case of fibroids, whereas this is seldom, if ever, true in the case of cancer.

> A pregnant woman is operated on for appendicitis. Her child is not yet viable but will reach viability within three weeks. In the course of the operation it is discovered that an unusually serious and complicated case of uterine fibroids is present. In contrast to ordinary cases of fibroids, the sincere judgment of the surgeons is that the uterus will have to be removed in order to safeguard the woman's life. Due to the predictability of the rate of progress of the con-

dition and the fact that it has accidentally been discovered
before it reached its most serious stage, the judgment of the
doctors is that a three weeks' delay in excising the uterus
will not gravely risk the woman's life. May the surgeon
immediately excise the uterus? May the nurse assist in the
immediate removal of the uterus?

The answer to this case is definitely in the negative. The
surgeon may not perform this operation and the nurse may
not assist.

In this second sample case, one can easily verify the first
three conditions of the twofold effect principle. First, the
action which produces the good and bad effects is in itself a
morally indifferent act, namely, the removal of a diseased
uterus. Second, the good effect results directly from the indifferent act; it does not come through the medium of the evil
effect. The removal of the uterus attacked by fibroids preserves
the woman's life. Her life is not safeguarded because death
comes to her child. Third, the surgeon performing the operation is prompted by a desire to bring about the good effect.
He performs the operation in order to preserve the woman's
life; his action is in no way motivated by a desire to kill the
unborn child.

But is the fourth condition verified in this case? Is there a
proportion between the good and bad effects? *The answer must
be in the negative.* The evil effect which will result from
immediate operation is the death of the unborn child. But in
this case, there is no good effect proportionate to the death of
the unborn child. There is no notable good which an immediate operation will produce which a delayed operation will
not effect. As the case is stated, the expectant mother can delay
the operation for three weeks without endangering her life,
and this delay will enable the fetus to reach viability. A premature delivery will then offer the child a chance to live and
an operation at that time will safeguard the woman's life.

The only good which an immediate operation would produce which will not be attained by a delayed operation is
possibly the freedom from three weeks' pain, expense and
worry. In contrast, immediate operation would result in the

loss of life for the inviable fetus. Obviously, the good effect of immediate operation does not begin to compare with the evil result which would follow from it. To undertake an immediate operation in this case would be to bring about a grave evil without any necessity. Immediate operation in the case as stated would be an immoral action.

When the operation for fibroids can safely be delayed until a premature delivery is possible, there is, then, the moral obligation to postpone the operation until that time.

When the operation for fibroids cannot be postponed until the viability of the fetus without seriously endangering the mother's life, the operation may be performed. The four conditions requisite for the doing of such an action are fulfilled in such a case. The application of the four principles to the case is made in exactly the same manner as in the first sample case of the pregnant cancerous uterus.

A slightly different type of case will provide another example of the application of the twofold effect principle.

> A woman who is two months pregnant has a slight attack of malaria. She is not desirous of having a child. Knowing that large doses of quinine may occasionally effect abortion, she requests excessive doses of quinine. Would a doctor or nurse be morally justified in acceding to her request?

The answer to this case is probably very clear. A doctor or nurse would not be morally justified in granting this request, because any intelligent person would perceive the motive behind the woman's unusual request. In a case of this type, the third condition would not be fulfilled, because there would be present a desire to bring about the evil effect of abortion. The fourth condition would likewise not be verified: the good effect of restoring health could be achieved by lesser doses of the drug, or the use of some other drug (atabrine), without a loss of fetal life. There is, therefore, no reason present to justify the administering of excessive doses which may result in a loss of life to the unborn child.

A final case will provide sufficient illustration of the manner in which the twofold effect principle must be applied.

A woman is subject to frequent, severe colds. She finds
that large doses of quinine remedy her colds more readily
than any other medicine. After becoming pregnant she
wonders whether she may continue to take large doses
of quinine for her colds. Her doubt arises from the fact
that she has heard that the quinine may produce an abortion. May she take the quinine?

The answer to this question depends on whether the doses
of quinine are likely to narcotize the unborn child or even to
produce abortion. If the doses may have either of these effects,
it is not morally permissible to take them.

First, there are many remedies for colds and there is no justification for the selection of the one remedy which may be so
harmful to the unborn child.

Second, there is no proportion between the good and bad
effects; the cure of a cold is in no sense proportionate to the
loss of a child's life.

Such a person should consult a skilled physician. If the
doctor felt certain that she could use small doses of quinine
without any danger to the health or life of the fetus, he would
be normally justified in prescribing them. But under no consideration could quinine be used in such cases if it appeared
likely to harm the unborn child.

The practical cases used in this section to illustrate the application of the twofold effect principle have been of the most
simple type. Throughout later chapters, we shall have to have
frequent recourse to this principle for the solution of very
difficult moral problems. Both doctor and nurse will do well to
understand thoroughly this key principle of ethics.

Hindrances to Accountability

Since it is only our free human actions for which we can be
held responsible, it is evident that any factor which lessens
knowledge or freedom also decreases the moral guilt attached
to an action. These "hindrances to accountability" are many
and varied; the most important, however, are *ignorance, emotion, violence,* and *habit.*

(a) *Ignorance* has been defined as "the absence of intellectual knowledge in a subject capable of knowing."

Moralists make reference to various types of ignorance, and a brief consideration of some of its more important forms will be most helpful.

A first division of this topic is into *ignorance of law* and *ignorance of fact*.

The former is present when a person either does not know that a certain law exists or, if the existence of the law is known, its interpretation is not understood. Thus, a nurse who did not know that State Law prohibited her from practicing medicine would be in *ignorance of law*.

In contrast, *ignorance of fact* is present when a person does not know that a contemplated action is prohibited by a law which is known to exist. A nurse, for example, might be on regular call in an industrial plant. In the absence of the doctor who visited at specified hours, the nurse might fall into the habit of diagnosing certain conditions and prescribing for them without realizing that she was engaging in the illegal practice of medicine.

A second division of ignorance is into *negative* and *privative*.

Negative ignorance is the absence of knowledge which one is *not* obliged to possess. All persons are bound to have a knowledge of both fundamental moral obligations and of those duties which are proper to their state in life. Specialized knowledge, however, which does not pertain to one's state in life need not be possessed. Thus, a nurse would frequently have little or no knowledge of the treatment that should be given for certain types of injuries. While driving a car she might encounter an accident and find that the knowledge and skill required to save one of the victims was such as would be possessed by a doctor, but not by a nurse. Even though the accident victim should die, there is no moral guilt on the part of the nurse. Her lack of knowledge is *negative* ignorance, and one is never morally at fault for harmful effects which result from a lack of knowledge of this type.

Privative ignorance, on the contrary, is the absence of knowledge which one is obliged to have.

Usually this knowledge must be possessed because it involves either the fundamental moral obligations which bind all men or those which are proper to an individual's state in life. Thus, some technique might be explained to a group of interns. A member of the class might fall asleep or fail to pay attention. The matter is important, and the interns are expected to use the technique in their actual hospital work. Rather than undergo the embarrassment and inconvenience of having an instructor repeat the explanation, the intern decides to attempt it on a patient. He does so, and grave injury results. This young doctor has committed a grave moral offense because he was obliged to possess the knowledge of this technique and he knew both of his obligation and of the grave harm which might be inflicted upon a patient by improper treatment. His ignorance is privative, and the resulting serious injury to his patient is attributable to him.

A third helpful division of ignorance is into *vincible* and *invincible*.

As the term more or less implies, *vincible* ignorance is that which could be overcome by a reasonably diligent effort. Whenever the knowledge should be possessed and is not had (*privative* ignorance), the person is said to be in a state of *culpable* ignorance. A nurse, for example, is taught that some postoperative patients must be kept in certain positions and not allowed to rise or walk. Should she decide that such matters were undoubtedly overemphasized in their importance and in the harm that could result from a violation of these recommendations, she would be in a state of vincible (privative and culpable) ignorance. It is true that her guilt is not as great as if she maliciously willed to inflict such injuries upon her patient. But she would nevertheless be morally responsible for whatever ill effects her patient might suffer as a result of her unconcern or negligence in this regard.

Invincible ignorance, on the other hand, is that which could not have been overcome by a moderately serious investigation of the matter. Persons are only obliged to make a reasonably diligent and sincere effort to acquire knowledge of moral duties. Many factors, such as a lack of time and a deficient moral background, may produce invincible ignorance. A person is, therefore, morally responsible only for knowledge which should and could be possessed. Hence there is no moral guilt atached to harmful acts which are done through invincible ignorance. Through accident or negligence, for example, a drug might be mislabeled. A doctor or nurse who would receive this bottle through proper channels would often have no way of knowing of the previous error. If he or she were to administer this drug to a patient, believing it to be the one charted to be given, there would be no moral responsibility for any harmful effects suffered by the patient. The ignorance would be both invincible and inculpable.

(b) *Emotion* is defined as "a movement of the sensory appetite, following upon conscious recognition of some stimulus, and characterized by definite modifications in the regulated activities of the body."

The emotions are reducible to the following: love and hatred, desire and aversion, joy and grief, hope and despair, courage and fear, and rage.

As the above definition indicates, there are three steps involved in the origin of emotion. First, there is the *cognitive* aspect of emotion since it always originates from some kind of knowledge. Second, there is the *appetitive* phase of the emotion which takes the form of an impulse or tendency to project consciousness in an outward direction and attach itself, by a positive or negative attitute, to some external object or situation. Third, there are *organic changes* which naturally follow upon the apprehension, as part of the orectic tendency. Hence, when an orectic inclination is accompanied by marked physiological changes (in glandular secretion, peristalsis, respiration, a pulse beat, etc.) we call it *emotion*.

A detailed study of the nature and types of emotion properly belongs in a course on Psychology. From the moral viewpoint, there are only two general forms of emotion which need be considered.

Antecedent emotion is that which precedes the act of the will and at least partially causes it.

From all that has preceded, it will be understood that as soon as some factor other than knowledge and freedom is a cause of a moral action, responsibility is decreased.

From personal experience, everyone knows that emotions can impair our ability to think clearly, to deliberate sufficiently, and to choose freely.

When emotion is not deliberately fostered but does arise and at least partially causes an act of the will, it is antecedent emotion. In so far as deliberation and free choice are impaired by such emotion, responsibility for the act is lessened. Should *all* deliberation or *all* freedom of choice be destroyed, no moral guilt whatever remains in the act. An insane, drugged, or incurable patient, for example, might be determined to take his own life. A nurse who attempts to intervene is seriously threatened and she flees in terror. The moral guilt attached to her abandonment of duty is lessened in proportion to the impairment of her deliberation and free choice.

Consequent emotion, on the contrary, is that which the will itself stirs up, or to which the will gives consent and encouragement once it arises. Since consequent emotion is in no way even a partial cause of the act of the will but only an accompaniment of it, moral guilt is not lessened. By way of illustration, a nurse may have a patient to whom she has taken a strong dislike. While off duty she ponders over the many disagreeable words and acts of this patient. She realizes that such reflections are arousing and intensifying her dislike and that, if she goes on duty in this condition, she may say and do things which she should not. Yet, realizing these probabilities, she deliberately continues to think about the patient. When she goes on duty in an excitable and disagreeable condition, she may injure the patient through detraction, calumny, neglect, or in some other way. Her guilt is not at all lessened by the fact that she is in an emotional condition when she commits the offense.

(c) *Violence* is defined as "physical constraint placed upon a free person." Violence is physical force from a source outside a person which compels the person to act contrary to his will.

Violence is said to be *perfect* whenever it destroys *all* freedom of action. If a person resists such physical compulsion to the full extent of his or her powers and is yet forced to perform an action, *perfect* violence has been committed. Perfect violence, therefore, is physically irresistible and the victim is in no way responsible, if the will refuses to consent. One must not forget the fact that since violence remains outside, it cannot coerce the will. If, however, a person is compelled to perform some action by violence, yet at the same time gives a real consent of the will, the person is morally at fault, but not to the same extent as would be the case if there had been no violence. By way of example, it may be said that there are times when ruthless individuals desire the death of a sick person. It could happen that such individuals would secretly place some drug, such as sleeping powders, in the nurse's coffee, so as to deprive the patient of her protective custody, and thus obtain an opportunity to attain their ends. The nurse would be the victim of perfect violence in such a case and would be in no way morally responsible for any harm which might come to her patient.

Violence is said to be *imperfect* whenever it partially destroys freedom. If a person resists physical coercion to some degree but not to the full extent of his or her powers, the violence is called imperfect. Such violence involves some lessening of moral guilt, since the partial resistance which has been made is evidence of a lack of full consent. But, on the other hand, all moral guilt is not destroyed, because the deliberate refusal to resist fully is indicative of a partial consent of the will to the action. A nurse, for instance, might have care of an invalid in his private home. Some of her friends, desirous of having her join them in an automobile ride, might exercise imperfect violence on her. She honestly resists to some extent and sincerely pleads that she is not supposed to leave the patient alone, but she certainly does not resist to the full extent of her powers nor does she evidence bitter resentment at their actions. The moral guilt attached to the neglect of her patient is lessened somewhat by virtue of the imperfect violence; but the decrease is probably very slight because the impairment of her freedom is not notable.

(d) *Habit* is a lasting readiness and facility, born of frequently repeated acts, for acting in a certain manner. It is also defined as a quality, difficult to change, whereby a person whose nature it is to act one way or another at will is disposed to act easily and readily in one particular way.

Habit does not destroy the voluntary character of an action, and acts done under the influence of habit are always at least indirectly voluntary, as long as the habit is allowed to endure. A person is therefore morally responsible for acts done under the force of habit. Even if such acts are done without present knowledge or present choice, the habit itself, so long as adequate steps to overcome it are not taken, is willed in itself and its effects are indirectly voluntary.

A nurse might gradually develop the habit of cutting short the time prescribed for the sterilization of instruments. Particularly at the outset, she would realize that she is not acting in the proper manner and that some patient may suffer an infection as the result of her unwarrantable haste. When she realizes this danger and does not disown the habit by taking reasonably diligent steps to overcome it, she becomes morally responsible for the evil effects which it may produce. Her guilt is not as great as if she maliciously willed to inflict such an injury upon the patient; but neither is the lessening of her guilt very appreciable, since she fully realizes the grave harm which may result from her negligence and takes no steps whatever to prevent it.

In contrast, if a habit is disowned, and diligent and constant effort is made to eradicate it from one's character, any act which spontaneously results from it is an "act of man" and contains no moral guilt.

A doctor, for example, might develop the habit of using profane language. He realizes that this habit is both immoral and completely out of keeping with his position as a gentleman and a doctor. He works strenuously to overcome the habit and is making notable progress. On a certain occasion, however, he breaks a needle while giving an injection. Without any deliberation or choice of will, the underlying habit comes to the fore and he spontaneously uses some profane language. Since there is no deliberation or choice in his act, either directly or indirectly, there is no moral guilt whatever involved.

The present chapter should impress upon both the doctor and the nurse the importance of acquiring a sound body of moral ideals. Such a foundation is indispensable for anyone, but particularly for those who are engaged in a field in which there are so many complex moral problems. Only this knowledge will enable them to carry out their countless tasks in a manner which is both helpful to man and pleasing to God.

Problems for Discussion

1. A nurse turns in a set of instruments for an abdominal operation. She is not certain whether these instruments have been sterilized. Evaluate the morality of her action.

2. A nurse falls asleep on night duty and, as a result, a patient does not receive a medicine at a prescribed time. To avoid detection, she charts the medicine as given and mentions the matter to no one. Over and above the deceit involved in her action, what other moral matter is present?

3. A nurse is convinced that the quantity of drug which a doctor has ordered her to give will be harmful to the patient. She checks the matter with the doctor and he insists on his original order. The nurse firmly believes that the doctor realizes that he has made a mistake but that he is too proud and strong-willed to admit it. What should the nurse do?

4. A nurse believes that a doctor has forgotten to order the discontinuation of a medication for a patient. She finds it impossible to contact the doctor, so she discontinues the administration of the drug. What do you think of her act?

5. A young nurse is told that her patient has suicidal tendencies and is instructed as to the precautions which she must take. Through lack of experience, she minimizes the importance of the instructions given to her. Due to negligence on her part, the patient succeeds in taking his own life. To what extent do you think the nurse is guilty?

6. Do you think that constant contact with suffering and death ever hardens a nurse's conscience to the point that she minimizes the importance of actions which may produce injury or even death to a patient?

7. A nurse accidentally contaminates an instrument just before she is expected to hand it to a surgeon in the course of an

operation. Infection in this case could cause the death of the patient. Rather than delay the operation and risk the wrath of the surgeon, the nurse hands the instrument to him. Evaluate the morality of the nurse's act.

8. A nurse has been assigned the task of sterilizing some instruments. She is fearful of missing a train connection if she carries out the sterilization for the fully prescribed time. She decides that the assigned time of sterilization is probably more than is actually required, so she cuts short the time of sterilization. What do you think of the morality of her act?

9. Mention some of the matters in which nurses tend to develop a lax conscience.

10. Mention some of the matters in which a nurse might develop a scrupulous conscience.

11. Mention some habits of carelessness which nurses acquire which may result in injury to patients. Are the harmful effects of these habits indirectly willed? Could you say that these harmful effects are virtually voluntary?

12. What relationship should exist between State Law and the regulations set up by the Medical and Nursing professions for their own governance? What relationship should exist between the Natural Law and all laws or regulations of human origin?

References for Reading

BONNAR, A.: *The Catholic Doctor* (*2nd ed.*), pp. 17-33; 40-42; 153-156; N. Y., 1939.

BRITT, R.: "Moral Limitations in Mental Disease," *The Linacre Quarterly*, Oct., 1947, pp. 16-25.

GARESCHE, E.: *Ethics and the Art of Conduct for Nurses*, pp. 17-156, Phila., 1937.

McALLISTER, J.: *Ethics: with Special Application to the Nursing Profession*, Phila., 1947.

MOORE, T.: *Principles of Ethics*, pp. 12-73, Phila., 1935.

ROCHELLE-FINK: *Handbook of Medical Ethics*, pp. 27-58, Westminster, Md., 1943.

SIMONART, P.: "The Imputability of the Mental Patient," *The Linacre Quarterly*, Oct., 1947, pp. 8-15.

Christian Marriage

Many of the ethical problems confronting the doctor and nurse have a definite relationship to the married state. For this reason it is necessary for them to have a clear and accurate appreciation of the true nature of marriage. Such knowledge will furnish them with the proper background and basis for the solution of many of their difficult moral problems.

The Divine Authorship of Marriage

Marriage was instituted by God soon after the creation of man, when He joined our first parents in a sacred union. From that moment on, matrimony was the divinely-appointed means for the propagation and conservation of the human race. As established by God, marriage has a physical, spiritual, and moral basis.

The physical basis of marriage is the bodily adaptation and attraction of each sex to union with the other. The Creator has so fashioned the bodies of man and woman that one is the complement of the other; and in each sex there has been implanted dynamic urges, both intellectual and instinctive, which have for their objective the intimate union of the sexes.

The spiritual basis of marriage is the pure and mutual love of a man and woman. It has its finest and firmest foundation in the love of the other person as a child of God; it involves a glowing admiration for the other's character and ideals, and an intense interest in the other's hopes and aspirations. It is not the love of another person simply for wealth, talent, or beauty. Rather, it is the unselfish love of the other for what he or she truly is as a person.

The moral basis of marriage is the fundamental ethical principle that sexual intercourse is permissible only to those who have been wed to each other by some type of formal and mutual agreement sanctioned by proper public authority.

The Natural Contract

From the union of our first parents until the coming of Christ, marriage was a natural contract. It was unquestionably most sacred, since it came directly from the hands of God; it was certainly most dignified, since it had for its objective the conservation of the human race by bringing children into the world who were destined for eternal happiness.

The essence of the natural contract of marriage is the formal, mutual and externally expressed agreement between a man and woman to bestow upon each other the right to sexual relationship and to all the other commonly understood features of married life, such as cohabitation and mutual support in both the mental and physical hardships of life.

Since marriage is a true contract, it follows that only those who are capable of fulfilling the essence of the contract can validly enter this institution of nature. Obviously, it would be a purely fictional act if someone professed to give the right to sexual relationship when some physical deficiency made this impossible. For this reason, a person who is permanently incapable of performing the marital act is barred from marriage by the very law of nature. By *permanent inability* to perform the marital act is *not* meant the inability to have children, whether because of sterility or any other similar reason. Rather, by permanent inability is here meant the physical impossibility of having sexual intercourse in the manner ordained by nature. It should be emphasized that whenever such physical incapacity prevails, the person is barred by the *law of nature* from entering marriage. This thought should be kept in mind, lest anyone think that the Church, solely on its own authority, forbids such persons to attempt marriage.

Impotence and the Marriage of Paraplegics

This problem is now frequently encountered, as the result of the ever-increasing number of paraplegics in society. Most of these are war casualties. It is evident from what has been said above that anyone who is *permanently impotent prior to marriage* is incapable by the law of nature of making the contract (Canon 1068, #1). Impotence is said to be "relative" if the person is incapable of normal sex relations with only a specific person or certain persons of the opposite sex. Impotence is called "absolute" if the person is incapable of normal sex relations with any member of the opposite sex. In the case of paraplegics, the problem usually concerns "absolute" impotence.

There seems to be a widespread belief that men afflicted with paraplegia are completely and permanently impotent. Medical facts do not, however, justify taking such an unqualified stand on the matter. A recent study of this problem was made by Dr. Herbert Talbot and it is his conclusion that a considerable number of paraplegics retain their physical capacity for sex relationship and are therefore wholly capable of contracting a valid marriage (*Journal of Urology,* Feb. 1949, pp. 265-270). Approximately ten per cent of those who came under his observation actually participated in complete sex relationship, and he firmly believes that the number capable of doing so is much greater. More abundant evidence was not available because three-fourths of the paraplegics were hospitalized and a high percentage were unmarried. It is at least clear from these facts that paraplegics should not be summarily classified as permanently impotent; nor should anyone, without further knowledge in the particular case, inform a person that he could not marry simply because he is a paraplegic. The rule of the Church is: "If the impediment of impotence is doubtful, whether by doubt of law or by doubt of fact, a marriage is not to be prevented" (Canon 1068, #2). Evidently, *a doubt of fact must be presumed in the case of every paraplegic.* When such a person seeks permission to marry, competent medical authority should be sought, with the hope that the doubt can be resolved. If the judgment of one specialist is unfavorable, it would appear prudent to substantiate the verdict with the opinion of a second capable doctor. Needless to say, no immoral means may be used to arrive at these conclusions. If, after investigation, the doubt still exists, the paraplegic should be allowed to marry. It is only when the impotence is *certain* that person must be refused entrance into marriage.

Since marriage is a binding contact, only those persons who have the *use of reason* can validly enter it. This use of reason implies both *knowledge* and *freedom*. These qualities belong to the nature of every contract and must certainly be present in a valid marriage.

For the contracting of a valid marriage, it is necessary that persons have a fundamental *knowledge* of the nature of married life. This basic concept must include at least the idea that marriage is a permanent union between man and woman for the primary purpose of bringing children into the world and properly rearing them. Various factors, such as temporary insanity, mental deficiency, drugged condition, and immaturity of years, can result in knowledge being so imperfect that a valid marital contract is not possible.

Since *freedom* of choice is also an essential element of every valid contract, the free consent of the parties to be married is absolutely required. Personal freedom is so necessary for the validity of marriage that no human power, whether it be parental, ecclesiastical, or civil, can supply for its absence. A marriage is, therefore, invalid if contracted under the influence of a threat or physical coercion which notably and substantially impairs the freedom of either party.

Since marriage is an institution of natural law, only those persons validly enter it who have the intention of giving and receiving the rights and obligations with which the Author of Nature has endowed it. In a word, unless both parties give each other the permanent right to marital intercourse in the manner ordained by nature, they have not contracted a valid marriage.

Thus, if one or both parties simply pronounce the words of the marriage ceremony *but have the intention either not to give or not to receive the right to natural marital intercourse,* these persons are not married. Of course, if such a person later attempted to claim that his marriage was invalid because of lack of proper intention, he would have to bring forward good proof of the fact, over and above his own testimony. In this matter, as well as in reference to sufficient knowledge and freedom, the Church presumes that a marriage performed in conformity with all of the external requirements of law is valid until the contrary has been established. If this procedure were not followed, unscrupulous persons would have an easy method of freeing themselves from the bonds of marriage.

The precise character of marriage, with all of its inherent rights and duties, is specified by the Creator. Man is free to enter this contract, or to refrain from it, but he has no power to alter its nature.

Anyone who would go through a marriage ceremony without intending to give and to receive the permanent right to natural marital relationship would not be entering into the state of marriage established by God. Needless, to say, such a person would be guilty of grave sin for abusing so sacred an institution.

Similarly, if it were the intention of the parties to bestow on each other only *the right to contraceptive intercourse,* their attempted marriage would not be valid. It is of the very essence of marriage that the contracting parties grant each other *the right to natural sexual relationship.* Where such rights are not mutually given, there is no true marriage.

In contrast, should both parties actually bestow on each other the right to proper marital intercourse *but mutually agree to have only contraceptive relationships with each other,* their marriage is valid but gravely sinful. Their marriage is valid because they have mutually granted true marital rights, even though they intend to violate these rights. Their marriage is sinful because they have professed a determined intention to engage in an immoral act throughout their married life.

The foregoing thoughts are of great importance in an age in which the unnatural vice of contraception has become so widespread.

The Sacrament of Marriage

The Christian doctor and nurse understands well that Christ instituted certain external signs, known as *sacraments,* which

are capable of conferring grace upon the members of the
Church. One of the sacraments instituted by Christ is that of
matrimony.

From the beginning of time until the coming of Christ, all
marriages were purely natural contracts. Since the time of
Christ, the marriage of non-baptized persons has continued to
remain merely a natural and indissoluble contract.

It is understood, of course, that no one can partake of the
other sacraments of the Church until baptism has been received. It is for this reason that baptism is called "the gate of
the Church." Hence, when non-baptized persons get married,
they enter a valid and binding contract, but they do not receive
the Christian sacrament of matrimony.

Through the bestowal of a sacramental character upon
matrimony, Christ made this institution the source of married
sanctity and domestic happiness. When Christians marry, they
not only enter a valid contract, but also receive an increase in
sanctifying grace, and an abundance of special sacramental
graces which help them to lead a holy married life, and to
fulfill the new duties which are incumbent upon them.

The *sacrament* of matrimony is not something superadded
to the natural contract of marriage. In Christian marriage,
the sacrament and the natural contract are identical; that is,
the marriage contract between two Christians is in itself sacramental in character. In accordance with the designs of Christ,
the very act of marital consent whereby the Christian man and
woman take each other as husband and wife bestows sacramental grace upon them.

Through the reception of the sacrament, husband and wife
receive in abundance, both at the actual time of marriage and
during the entire course of their married life, all those supernatural aids which they will need to overcome the many serious
hardships of conjugal life. In the first place, this sacrament
imparts sanctifying grace, that beautiful supernatural quality
which renders the soul pleasing to God. Secondly, it confers a
special sacramental grace which carries with it a claim to all
those supernatural helps which the couple will need throughout their lives in order to be faithful to their duties of married

life. It is important to remember that the sacramental effects of matrimony are not restricted to the time at which the contract is made but are continually bestowed on husband and wife until death separates them. Needless to say, these supernatural aids can be received only by one who is at the time in the state of grace.

Since Christian marriage is a sacrament, only the Church of Christ possesses supreme and absolute authority over it. The State dare not infringe upon this inviolable right of the Church. To the Church alone belongs the right and power to determine what shall or shall not constitute a valid sacramental marriage. Under ordinary circumstances, the Church, therefore, demands that her children contract marriage before an authorized priest and two witnesses.

There are, moreover, certain impediments to marriage. A detailed consideration of the many impediments to marriage properly belongs in a course on Religion. It is sufficient to note here that some impediments are based upon Natural Law or Divine Positive Law, while others are of ecclesiastical origin.

Impediments that are solely and certainly based upon ecclesiastical law may be dispensed by the Church, since a legislator always possesses the authority to make exceptions to his own law. Naturally, the Church will demand the presence of a sufficient reason before it will grant such dispensations, and it alone possesses the right to evaluate the sufficiency of reason in any particular case.

The Church does not have the power to grant a dispensation from impediments based upon Natural Law or absolute Divine Positive Law. Such impediments are of direct Divine origin and even the Church cannot set them aside.

Protestant Marriages

In considering the marriage of two baptized non-Catholics, it is important to remember that there is only one true Church of Christ and that through baptism one becomes a member of that Church. In a word, each and every person who receives a valid baptism becomes subject to the ruling authority of the Roman Catholic Church.

Recognizing the sincerity of countless baptized non-Catholics and desiring to avoid unnecessary complications, the Church does not bind these people to the Catholic form of marriage. Naturally, the Church cannot exempt anyone from any part of Natural Law or absolute Divine Positive Law. All baptized persons are affected directly by ecclesiastical impediments, and it is certain that baptized non-Catholics are bound by the Church's impediments except in so far as they are clearly exempt in special cases. Thus, the Church exempts the baptized non-Catholic from the solemn form of marriage (canon 1099) and from the impediment of disparity of cult when they marry unbaptized persons (canon 1070).

The Church, therefore, recognizes a Protestant marriage as valid, provided it is contracted in conformity with the requirements of Natural Law, Divine Positive Law, and is free from the ecclesiastical impediments which bind a baptized non-Catholic. The Church insists, moreover, that civil authority has no direct power over the validity of Protestant marriages. *The marriages of all baptized persons are sacramental in character,* and the State possesses no power whatever to specify the conditions required for the valid reception of any sacrament.

Regarding the marriage of baptized persons, the State has the authority to make laws concerning such effects as are merely civil. It is for this good reason, as well as to avoid punishment by civil law and to aid the State in the maintenance of vital statistics, the the Church urges both Protestants and Catholics to obey all reasonable civil laws on marriage.

The charge that the Church places a low estimate on the dignity of Protestant marriages, or is harsh in its legislation toward them, is clearly without any basis. Actually, the Church insists on the sacramental character of Protestant marriages and on their objective independence of civil law. It thus bestows on them a dignity in every way comparable to that possessed by a Catholic marriage.

Furthermore, the Church is more lenient toward Protestant marriages than it is to any other type of marriage. For example, the Church maintains that the marriages of nonbaptized persons must be governed, not only by Natural Law and Divine

Positive Law, but also by Civil Law. The Church demands that the marriages of Catholics must conform, not only to Natural Law and Divine Positive Law, but also be free from *all impediments* to marriage imposed by Her own Ecclesiastical Law. In contrast, the Church teaches that a valid Protestant marriage need only fulfill the requirements of Natural Law, Divine Positive Law, and be free from those ecclesiastical impediments from which the baptized non-Catholic has not been specifically exempted.

Marriage of Unbaptized Persons

The Church recognizes the marriages of all unbaptized persons, such as pagans, Mohammedans, and Jews, as valid when contracted in conformity with the requirements of both Natural Law and local Civil Law.

Whenever both parties to a marriage are unbaptized, the Church has no direct authority over the marriage. She may, however, have to pronounce on their validity, as in the case of converts, or in the case of infidels seeking to marry Christians after a previous marriage. When both parties to a marriage are unbaptized, they are directly subject to the requirements of Natural Law. However, since Natural Law is frequently vague and indefinite on many points, unbaptized persons must conform to the detailed requirements for validity specified by Civil Law.

Unlike consummated Christian marriage, the purely natural marriage of two unbaptized persons can sometimes be dissolved. We learn of this possible exception to the usual indissolubility of marriage from the Church's infallible interpretation of the teaching of Saint Paul (I Cor. VII, 13-15). The *Pauline Privilege,* as it is known, might be summarized as follows:

Should there exist a marriage between two unbaptized persons, and one of the two parties be converted to the true faith and be baptized, he or she is able in certain cases to remarry in the Church, thus dissolving the existing natural marriage.

Before the Pauline Privilege may be used, the converted person must ask the unbaptized person whether he or she is willing to be converted and receive baptism, or at least willing to live in peaceful wedlock, without offering any hindrance to the converted person's practice of the true religion. The Pauline Privilege may only be used if the unconverted spouse refuses to adopt the true religion or at least to allow the other partner full freedom and respect in the practice of the true faith.

God, as the Author of the institution of marriage, has the power to dissolve it. In those instances in which living with an antagonistic pagan spouse would risk the spiritual welfare of a convert to the true faith, God has seen fit to sanction a dissolution of the marriage with the unbaptized person "in favor of the faith" of the convert.

The Purpose of Marriage

As an institution of nature, the primary purpose of marriage is the generation and rearing of children. It has already been stated that the very essence of the marriage contract is the mutual right to conjugal relations, and to all that is normally associated with them, such as love, assistance, and cohabitation. And every intelligent person realizes that the sexual powers are chiefly ordained for the procreation of new life. The personal pleasure involved in the marital act is merely nature's enticement to man and woman to assure a use of these powers in a manner sufficiently widespread and frequent as to guarantee the conservation of the race.

The primary purpose of marriage includes not only the procreation of children but also their proper rearing. In this respect, man can learn much even from the animals in lower creation. Natural instinct compels the beast to exhibit a tender care and self-sacrificing solicitude for its young. Not until offspring are developed to the point that they can make their own way in life are they left to their own resources. In the case of children, an adequate rearing implies not only the providing for their bodily needs, but also the development of their intellectual, religious, and moral nature.

Marriage has other purposes besides the procreation and rearing of children. There is the pleasure of sympathetic companionship, the joys of ardent love, the mutual assistance which devoted spouses can render to each other in the countless hardships of life, and the satisfaction in a moral way of the strong sexual inclinations of human nature. These benefits of marriage, though secondary, may be lawfully sought, provided the primary purpose of the institution is not deliberately thwarted.

It must not be thought that the Catholic attitude toward marriage is devoid of sentiment. On the contrary, the Church sees in marriage the blossoming of one of the purest and deepest loves that can take root in the human heart. But the Church endeavors to teach Her children that the purest love is unselfish and that marriages will be most happy when the desire to give is greater than the desire to receive. A marriage which has selfish, sensual gratification as its primary basis cannot produce the deep and lasting happiness which flows from the unselfish love which characterizes a truly Christian marriage.

The Indissolubility of Marriage

As the words of the contract indicate, marriage is intended by the law of God and nature to be a stable and permanent union of husband and wife.

The rational basis of the indissolubility of marriage is to be found in the fact that parents have a strict and mutual obligation to rear and educate their children. This parental obligation can be fulfilled properly only if their conjugal union be lasting. The physical, spiritual, moral, and intellectual development of a child is a task which requires long years of sincere effort. As a result, parents are well advanced in age before they have fulfilled their obligations to their children. Throughout the years in which they have reared their children, husband and wife become more and more a part of each other. Decades of married life weld their natures together and their dependence upon each other is not only physical and emotional, but also mental and spiritual.

Nature has implanted instincts in the lower animals to assure their remaining together until their offspring no longer need their help and protection. Surely this degree of permanence is obviously to be expected of the union of husband and wife. But we may now go beyond the permanence imposed by the primary ends of marriage. We must realize that there are also secondary purposes of this institution and that many of these "secondary benefits" become deep and abiding needs of husband and wife precisely because they have lived for years as "two in one flesh" in the pursuit of the primary end of marriage. Nature has created and intensified this dependence of one spouse on the other throughout the years. It is certainly not the mind of the Creator that this bond should be severed in old age when the dependence has become greatest.

It will be objected that, if the indissolubility of marriage is based primarily upon the obligation of parents to care for their children, childless marriages need not be indissoluble.

To grasp the answer to this objection, one must understand that the nature of the marriage contract is specified by God, not by the contracting parties. Marriage is an institution established by the Creator to achieve a *social* objective (the conservation of the race) and it must possess those characteristics or properties which will enable it to achieve its purpose. For reasons already given, the adequate rearing of children and the mutual dependence of husband and wife, require their remaining together until death.

The nature and characteristics of the marriage contract, therefore, lie outside the sphere of human influence. It is certainly true that man may freely choose to enter or refrain from marriage, but if he does elect marriage he cannot alter its divinely-established nature.

In the ordinary affairs of life, individuals frequently make contracts. They bestow upon each other definite rights and assume specific obligations. Such contracts can usually be dissolved by the mutual consent of the parties involved. But such contracts do not parallel the contract of marriage. Such individuals have freely and mutually specified the nature of the contract to which they desired to be bound; they were the sole originators of the contract and thus possess complete authority over it.

In contrast, the nature and properties of the marriage contract are specified by God for all mankind. Men are free to enter marriage or to refrain from it, but they possess no power to alter it. The fact that the love of a husband and wife has turned into hatred for each other, or that their marriage is childless, cannot destroy the truth that they entered a contract which both Natural and Divine Law declare to be indissoluble.

It may be helpful in this regard to recall that all laws have the social objective of assuring the welfare of the community. Yet there are frequent instances in which a law brings no good to a specific individual but actually works a hardship upon him. Unless the proper authority specifically exempts such a person from the observance of the law, the obligation to observe it still rests upon the subject. Since the social welfare hinges upon conformity to law, individuals are not free to decide that they need not be bound by a law because its violation by them in a particular case would not injure the community.

So it is with the institution of marriage. It was established by the Creator to achieve the great social objective of the propagation and conservation of the human race. To achieve this goal adequately and properly, the stability of marriage cannot be subject to individual considerations. It is, indeed, regrettable that some marriages are failures. Where just reasons are present, the separation of spouses is morally permissible, *but the bond of marriage can be severed only by Divine authority.*

A dissolution of the bond of marriage could, of course, be authorized by God. In fact, the Creator has already done so under certain definite conditions.

Under the law of the Old Testament, a man was permitted to divorce his wife and remarry if she had been guilty of some offense against her marriage vows. "If a man take a wife and have her, and she find not favor in his eyes for some uncleanness; he shall write a bill of divorce, and shall give it in her hand, and shall send her out of his house" (Deut. XXIV, 1). Some authorities regard the expression "some uncleanness" as referring only to adultery. The Jews themselves disputed about this expression; some restricted the meaning to adultery, while others included very trivial offenses under it.

The cases in which the bond of marriage can be dissolved in the *New Law,* provided certain conditions are present, are three: (1) If at the time of the marriage both of the parties

were unbaptized and later one receives Baptism, and the other
refuses to dwell peacefully and sinlessly with the convert. This
is the Pauline Privilege which has already been explained in
this chapter. (2) If at the time of the marriage one was a baptized non-Catholic, the other unbaptized. The Church for
sufficiently grave reasons can dissolve such a marriage in virtue
of the supreme power of loosing and binding, conferred on
Her by Christ, which power is known to us by tradition, and
manifested by the practice of the Popes over many centuries.
(3) If at the time of the marriage both were baptized but
afterward never consummated their union.

But neither the Church nor any other power on earth can
dissolve a consummated sacramental marriage.

Over and above the rational basis for the indissolubility of
marriage, God has given us positive precepts on this matter.
"A man shall cleave to his wife" was the command of the Creator at the very institution of marriage. Centuries later, Christ
explicitly asserted "For this cause shall a man leave father and
mother, and shall cleave to his wife, and they shall be two in
one flesh; therefore now they are not two, but one flesh; what
therefore God has joined together, let no man put asunder"
(Matthew, XIX, 4-6). And again, "Whosoever shall put away
his wife and marry another, committeth adultery against her;
and if the wife shall put away her husband and be married to
another, she committeth adultery" (Mark X, 11-12).

In his first epistle to the Corinthians (VII, 10) and in his
epistle to the Romans (VII, 2-3)), Saint Paul repeats the teaching of Christ on the indissolubility of marriage.

Throughout the early centuries, the Fathers of the Church
wrote frequently and emphatically on the indissolubility of
marriage. And throughout her long history, the Church of
Christ has never compromised on this teaching, even when She
knew that the refusal of a divorce to a king would cost Her the
loss of a whole nation.

The Unity of Marriage

The conjugal union of one man and one woman is called
monogamy and it is the only form of marriage which is in
conformity with Natural Law.

Opposed to monogamy is *polygamy,* that is, the marriage of one person to two or more persons of the opposite sex. *Polygyny* is the term used to indicate the marriage of one man to two or more women, whereas *polyandry* is the marriage of one woman to two or more men.

Unquestionably, polygamy is opposed to the natural law. In such a union, the whole-hearted love of husband and wife is impossible; jealousy and envy are rampant in the home; domestic peace is destroyed; and the spiritual ends of marriage are subordinated to gross sensual gratification.

In polyandry, moreover, it is not ordinarily possible for the father to know his child nor for the child to know his father. Such a fact destroys the basis upon which Natural Law erects the mutual rights and duties of parents and child.

Besides these arguments from reason against polygamy, we know that at the very dawn of creation Almighty God made Adam and Eve "two in one flesh" (Gen. 11, 24).

We are further assured that monogamy was the form of marriage specified by God from the fact that, when the race threatened to die out after the deluge, God Himself issued certain temporary dispensations from the unity of marriage. In that crucial period of history, a Divine dispensation from monogamy enabled the institution of marriage to attain the end for which it was established, namely, the conservation of the race. *If monogamy had not been the divinely-appointed form of marriage, there would have been no need for a special Divine dispensation from it.*

During that unusual period, the full benefits of monogamous marriage, such as conjugal affection and a fully unified home based on a single mutual love, had to be sacrificed in the interests of preserving the race. As soon as the unusual circumstances ceased, the Divine dispensation no longer existed. Monogamy became once more obligatory on all mankind.

At His coming, Christ made it clear that the perfect unity of marriage was henceforth binding on all men (Matt. XIX, 4-6). This teaching of Christ has been consistently upheld by the Church throughout the centuries. Thus, the Papal *Encyclical on Marriage* describes the unity of marriage as "the

mutual fidelity of the spouses in fulfilling the marriage contract, so that what belongs to one of the parties by reason of
this contract sanctioned by Divine law, may not be denied to
him or permitted to any third person."

Not only is all external impurity opposed to the unity of
marriage but also all wilful internal thoughts and desires for
such things. Christ clearly expressed this truth when He said:
"Whosoever shall look on a woman to lust after her has already
committed adultery with her in his heart" (Matt. V, 28).

Needless to say, wherever there is true unity of marriage
there is nothing unbecoming in the proper marital relationships of husband and wife. In fact, the sex life of the married
couple is the divinely chosen means through which the propagation of the race is secured. Furthermore, just as marital
intercourse is legitimate between husband and wife, so are all
actions which are naturally preparatory, concomitant, and consequent to it.

The marital relationship between spouses is not merely one
of right but also of duty. The right to sexual intercourse is a
true right of each party, and hence a refusal by either party is
ordinarily a breach of the contract of marriage and a violation
of justice. This obligation is emphasized by Saint Paul: "Let
the husband render the debt to the wife, and the wife in like
manner to the husband" (I Cor. VII, 3). It is understood, of
course, that at times there are justifiable reasons for refusal:
real danger to the health or life of one of the parties, likelihood
of infection from an active venereal disease, uncondoned adultery, intoxication, and other reasons of comparable weight.

The marital relationship of husband and wife should be
characterized by true conjugal chastity. This principle demands
that the use of marital rights be kept under the control of
reason. Moderation is a quality which is just as important to
conjugal chastity as it is to the other virtues. As the Holy
Father says in the Encyclical on Marriage: "If the blessing of
conjugal faith is to shine with splendor, that mutual familiar
intercourse between the spouses themselves must be distinguished by chastity so that husband and wife bear themselves
in all things within the law of God and nature, and endeavor

always to follow the will of their most wise and holy Creator with the greatest reverence toward the work of God."

Still another highly important characteristic of true unity in marriage is mutual charity or love between the spouses. We do not refer here to emotional sentiment or physical attraction, but to a true, deep and lasting spiritual love. It is to this love that the Encyclical on Christian Marriage refers when it says: "The love, then, of which we are speaking is not based on the passing lust of the moment, nor does it consist in pleasing words only, but in the deep attachment of the heart which is expressed in action, since love is proved by deeds."

A final characteristic of conjugal unity is a proper obedience of the various members of the family to the father. The traditional teaching of the Church is that the father possesses the position of supreme authority within the home. It is in the epistle of Saint Paul to the Ephesians (V, 22-23) that we find the scriptural basis for this teaching: "Let women be subject to their husbands as to the Lord, because the husband is the head of the wife, as Christ is head of the Church."

As the Encyclical on Christian Marriage clearly indicates, the subjection of the wife to the husband does not lessen in the least "the liberty which fully belongs to the woman in view of her dignity as a human person, and in view of her noble office as wife and mother and companion; nor does it bid her obey her husband's every request if not in harmony with right reason or with the dignity due to a wife; nor, in fine, does it imply that the wife should be put on a level with those persons who in law are called minors, to whom it is not customary to allow free exercise of their rights on account of their lack of mature judgment, or of their ignorance of human affairs. . . . Again, this subjection of wife to husband in its degree and manner may vary according to the different conditions of persons, place, and time. In fact, if the husband neglect his duty, it falls to the wife to take his place in directing the family." In a word, the wife is the companion of the husband, not his servant; in particular her rôle of mother is most dignified, important, and noble. For these reasons, a deeply spiritual love should be the ever-present basis of the mutual relations of husband and wife.

Artificial Insemination

It is an established scientific fact that it is possible for a woman to become pregnant as the result of "artificial insemination."

On the animal level, artificial insemination is not new. It is known that centuries ago the Arabs relied upon this technique to injure the quality and purity of the horses of their enemies. It is said that they would secretly enter their rival's camp at midnight and inject the semen of defective horses into the purebred animals of the enemy.

In recent years, of course, artificial insemination has been widely used in selective cattle breeding; the semen of a prizewinning animal is procured and then shipped to various parts of the country for breeding purposes. Some idea of how widespread artificial insemination of cattle has become can be appreciated from these facts: in 1939, approximately 7500 cows were artificially bred in the United States; whereas, in 1950, about 2,800,000 cows were produced through artificial insemination. In that eleven year period (1939-1950), the cow population of the country rose twenty per cent, to over forty-one million head; whereas, in the same period, the bull population increased only six per cent, to one million and seven hundred thousand head. (*Wall Street Journal,* March 13, 1951). Some prize bulls have earned over a million dollars in breeding services for their owners; many have produced over five hundred offspring within a year; and, by the use of new and improved methods of artificial insemination, some bulls have sired as many as two thousand calves in a single year.

On the human level, artificial insemination is relatively new. The practice of artificial insemination first began on a major scale in the early 1930s and steady progress has been made in its application since that time. Little publicity is given this matter for obvious reasons, but it is known that there are very many children who have been born as the result of artificial insemination. It was estimated in January, 1948, that there are at least 20,000 children in the United States who have been born through artificial insemination. As early as November 7, 1936, the *Journal of the American Medical Association* carried an article on this subject by Doctors Frances Seymour and Alfred Koerner, of New York City. For more than five years these doctors had been successfully engaged in the practice of artificial insemination on many patients. This article was presented in a condensed form in the November 21, 1936, issue of the *Literary Digest,* and popularized under the heading of "Test-Tube Babies" in the February, 1937, issue of *Reader's Digest.*

More recently, the *Woman's Home Companion* (January, 1945) carried an article which endeavored to point out the value of this scientific discovery to certain childless couples. Great emotional appeal is made on the basis of a woman's desire for a child, the value of a child to a home, and the fact that a woman can never know anything about the background of an adopted child, whereas she can carefully select the type of "proxy father" she desires for her own artificial insemination and then bear a child that is of her own flesh and blood.

From the scientific viewpoint, there are few major difficulties involved in artificial insemination. After the semen is obtained from a suitable donor, it can be kept for several days, at temperatures between forty and fifty degrees, without losing its potency. It is mixed with "buffer fluids" which simulate as nearly as possible the natural medium of motile spermatozoa.

The actual process of insemination is quite simple: with a syringe, a gynecologist introduces a few drops of the semen directly into the cervical canal, the lower part of the uterus.

The most difficult problem for the gynecologist, in his attempt to produce pregnancy, is to discover the exact time of ovulation. Naturally, the active sperm must contact a live ovum to produce conception. For these reasons, artificial insemination is usually attempted during the so-called "fertile period," which usually occurs from ten days to two weeks after menstruation.

Reports on the success of artificial insemination vary quite a bit. Sometimes pregnancy results from the first attempt. In contrast attempts have been made in other cases over a period of a year, even changing donors, without effecting pregnancy. Some doctors report success in only fifteen to twenty per cent of their cases; others get thirty-three per cent results. One gynecologist, in a series of more than fifty carefully selected cases, got better than eighty per cent results. In expert hands, it is believed that an average of sixty per cent success is about what can reasonably be expected.

The scientist insists that not all childless wives should be granted artificial insemination. We are told that an investigation into the physical and mental background of the woman is absolutely necessary. Should such investigation uncover any hereditary condition which would be injurious to offspring, or should physical examination of the woman reveal any pelvic malformation, motherhood is not recommended.

It is said that the examination of the male donor should be even more rigid. He must be free of structural defects, venereal disease, epileptic heredity, or family taint of insanity. It is recommended also that the donor never be a relative, that his blood type correspond to that of the husband (to make proof very difficult for the husband if he should ever be inclined to deny paternity of the child), that he be an educated person with a good mind, preferably a college graduate who has attained success in some worthwhile field of endeavor. It is further suggested that the donor be of the same racial stock, religion, temperament, and physical features as those possessed by the actual husband of the woman.

A final word from the scientist interested in artificial insemination is that sterility on the part of the husband is not the only sufficient reason for recourse to this procedure. We are told that whenever a husband has any hereditary conditions which would handicap a child, consideration of a "proxy father" is advisable.

From the legal standpoint, the practice of artificial insemination presents many difficulties. It is true that no laws have been enacted in reference to this procedure. But one can readily visualize some of the problems which could arise: (1) a husband might sue for divorce from his wife on the grounds of adultery when she bore a child, and he being able to prove that he was sterile; (2) a child born of such a pregnancy might sue for a share in the estate upon the death of his "proxy father"; (3) a "proxy father" might sue the mother for at least partial custody of his child; (4) a mother might sue the "proxy father" for support of their child; (5) according to our civil law, is such a child legitimate? (6) according to our civil law, should the husband adopt this child which is born to his wife? (7) a doctor who performed the artificial insemination, or knew of it, could not honestly assist at the birth of the child and write the husband's name on the birth certificate as the father of the child; (8) could a doctor who had artificially inseminated a woman be held liable for defects in the child which are traceable to the heredity of the donor that he had procured for the woman?

Up to the present time (1953) only a few cases involving artificial insemination have been brought into civil court. As might be expected, the decisions of the courts are not in agreement with each other and are evasive on many points. Thus, in 1921, when artificial insemination was merely a medical curiosity, a case was brought before the Supreme Court of Ontario. The principal point which interests us in this case is the statement of the Court that "if the insemination of the wife had been artificial, as alleged, the wife was still guilty of adultery, and the contention by the wife's lawyer that it was not adultery for a married woman to produce a child by artificial insemination is a monstrous conclusion."

In 1947, a case involving artificial insemination found its way into the law courts of England. In this case, a woman became the mother of her husband's child by artificial insemination. It appears that recourse was had to this method in the face of a psychological condition which prevented the husband from consummating marriage in a normal manner. It was also hoped that the birth of a child might serve in some degree to remedy the condition of the husband. Shortly afterwards, the wife sued for a declaration of nullity of the marriage on the basis of the husband's incapacity for normal marital relations. Meanwhile the child was born. The Court granted the declaration of nullity to the wife and, according to British law, the child was regarded as illegitimate.

In 1948, a case was brought before the Supreme Court of the State of New York. The Court held that a child born of a married woman who was artificially inseminated by another man, with the knowledge and consent of her husband, is not an illegitimate child. The Supreme Court Justice Henry Clay Greenberg declined to pass on the "propriety" of the act. Such a question, he held, "lies in the field of sociology, morals, or religion." The Judge also emphasized that the Court was not rendering a verdict on the legal consequences of artificial insemination in so far as property rights are concerned.

The French law recognizes the use of semen procured from a donor as constituting adultery; and if the use of the semen should be achieved without the consent of the wife the act is legally held as rape. (*Journal of Am. Med. Assoc.*, Nov. 15, 1947, p. 729)

One can readily perceive that the practice of artificial insemination is packed with potential legal dynamite. Countless efforts have been made to avert such legal complications: the written consent, with fingerprints, of both husband and wife is procured; the woman never learns the identity of the "proxy father," nor does he ever learn the identity of the woman who is to bear the child; a doctor is to be procured for the delivery of the child who does not know that it is not a normal pregnancy. These precautions, as well as others of a similar nature, are taken in an effort to avert legal complications. Needless to say, varied types of cases resulting from the practice of artificial insemination will eventually find their way into our courts. One can only await with interest the decisions which will have to be made.

From the moral standpoint, one must state immediately and without qualification that artificial insemination is gravely immoral. It is repulsive to every decent tendency of human nature, and it certainly bears witness to the unnatural extremes to which science based on materialistic philosophy will go. It is impossible to imagine a Christian woman submitting to such an unnatural act.

According to the teachings of sound ethics, it is a principle of Natural Law that a woman has no right to receive into her vagina the semen of any man except her husband.

We have treated this topic of artificial insemination under

the *Unity of Marriage* precisely because it is an evil which is opposed to that property of this divinely-established institution. We can only repeat what has already been said, namely, that this institution is primarily *social* in its objective, and for this institution to achieve the adequate and proper conservation of the race, offspring must be born only of couples united in marriage. The fact that some couples are incapable of having children does not confer upon them an authorization to infringe upon the divinely-established unity of marriage.

A single woman who would submit to artificial insemination would commit a mortal sin against legal justice. A married woman would also commit a mortal sin against commutative justice by infringing on the exclusive right of her husband to fecundate her; for this reason, such an act would contain the specific element of adultery. The fact that her husband has consented to her receiving the semen of another man would not essentially alter the case, since he has no moral power to authorize a violation of the unity of marriage.

For a most complete and most authoritative statement on artificial insemination we are fortunate in being able to quote the words of Pope Pius XII, from his address on artificial insemination to the Fourth International Convention of Catholic Physicians in October, 1949:

> "We have already had many occasions to speak on a good number of special points regarding medical morality, but now we have here a question of the first order, which with no less urgency than other questions requires the light of Catholic doctrine: it is the question of artificial insemination.
>
> We could not allow this opportunity to pass without indicating briefly a general outline of the moral judgment regarding this subject.
>
> *First,* the practice of artificial insemination, when it is applied to man, cannot be considered exclusively, nor even principally, from a biological and medical viewpoint, while leaving aside the viewpoint of morality and law.
>
> *Second,* artificial insemination outside marriage is to be condemned purely and simply as immoral. In fact, the natural law and positive Divine Law are such that the pro-

creation of a new life may only be the fruit of marriage.
Marriage alone safeguards the dignity of husband and wife
—and in the present case, particularly that of the wife—
and their personal well-being. Marriage alone provides
for the good and for the education of the child.

Consequently, there is no possibility of any divergence
of opinion among Catholics regarding the condemnation
of artificial insemination outside marriage. A child conceived in such conditions is, by this fact alone, illegitimate.

Third. Artificial insemination in marriage, with the use
of an active element from a third person, is equally immoral and as such to be rejected summarily. Only marriage partners have mutual rights over their bodies for the
procreation of a new life, and these rights are exclusive,
nontransferable and inalienable. So it must be out of
consideration for the child.

By virtue of this same bond, nature imposes on whoever gives life to a small creature the task of its preservation and education. Between marriage partners, however,
and a child that is the fruit of the active element furnished
by a third person—even though the husband consents—
there is no bond of origin, no moral or juridical bond of
conjugal procreation.

Fourth, with regard to the lawfulness of artificial insemination in marriage, it is sufficient for us at present to recall
the principles of the natural law: the simple fact that
the desired result as obtained by this means does not justify the employment of that method itself; nor yet does
the desire of marriage partners—most legitimate in itself—
to have a child, suffice to prove the lawfulness of a recourse to artificial insemination for the fulfillment of
that desire.

It would be false to believe that the possibility of a
recourse to that method would render a marriage valid
between two persons who are unfitted to contract marriage because of the impediment of impotency. *Moreover,
it is superfluous to indicate that the active element can
never be lawfully obtained by acts that are contrary to
nature.*

Although one may not exclude 'a priori' the use of new
methods simply on the grounds that they are new, never-

theless, with regard to artificial insemination, it is not only a case of being extremely reserved, but it must be rejected entirely. With such a pronouncement one does not necessarily proscribe the use of certain artificial methods intended simply either to facilitate the natural act or to enable the natural act, effected in a normal manner, to attain its end . . .

The medical doctor would not be corresponding fully to the ideal of his vocation if—while profiting from the most recent advances of the medical science and art—he used in his role of practitioner merely his intelligence and ability, and if he did not also make use (and we were about to say, above all) of his heart as a man, and of his loving tenderness as a Christian . . .

Undoubtedly, the doctor's ministrations are to bodies, but to bodies animated with immortal and spiritual souls. By virtue of a mysterious but indissoluble bond between the physical and the moral, he only acts efficaciously on the body when, at the same time, he is acting on the spirit.

Whether he be dealing with the body or the human being in its entirety, the Christian doctor will always have to beware of the fascination of science and the temptation to use his knowledge and his art for ends other than the care of the patients entrusted to him."

All that has been said above on the immorality of artificial insemination holds true even in the improbable supposition that the seed is procured by the aid of a needle directly from the testicles of the donor, without any sexual activity. Ordinarily, the donor procures the seed by self-abuse, and this would add the guilt of impurity to the whole procedure.

Two other acts which might be called "artificial insemination," in a broad sense, merit brief consideration.

First, for a grave reason, a number of excellent moralists permitted the extraction of seed by needle, without any sexual pleasure involved, from the testicles of a husband for implantation in the cervical canal of his wife. Noldin, Ubach, Wouters, and Vermeersch were some of the renowned writers who permitted this act for a grave reason. Their conclusion was based on the fact that no self-abuse nor violation of the unity of marriage is involved. In justice to these writers, it must be said that they expressed this opinion previous to the already-quoted address of Pope Pius XII on artificial insemination. It is now clear that the foregoing opinion is no longer tenable. The Holy Father has sanctioned only such artificial aid to producing conception between husband and wife as could be construed as assistance to a completed act of natural sex relationship. In the words of the address:

> "One does not necessarily proscribe the use of certain artificial methods *intended simply either to facilitate the natural act or to enable the natural act, effected in a normal manner, to attain its end.*"

Two years later in the address to the Congress of the Italian Catholic Union of Midwives (Nov. 26, 1951), the Holy Father emphasized this point still further:

> "To reduce cohabitation and the conjugal act to a simple organic function for the transmission of seed would be converting the home, the sanctuary of the family, into a mere biological laboratory. In our address of September 29, 1949, to the International Congress of Catholic Doctors, We formally excluded artificial insemination from marriage. In its natural structure, the conjugal act is a personal action, a simultaneous and immediate cooperation on the part of the husband and wife which by the very nature of the agents and the propriety of the act is the expression of the mutual gift which according to Holy Scripture brings about 'union in one flesh only.' This is something much more than the union of two seeds which may be brought about even artificially, without the natural action of husband and wife. The conjugal act, ordained and willed by nature, is a personal act of cooperation, the right to which husband and wife give each other when they marry."

The first-quoted words of the Holy Father do, however, provide a firm basis for the permissibility of a method which may be used in cases in which the hyperacidity of the vagina or some physical impediment in the woman prevents the natural progress of the sperm into the cervical canal. In such an instance, after normal and natural marital intercourse has taken place, it is morally permissible for a doctor to aid nature. The semen should not be removed from the vagina, but a doctor may use a syringe to collect the semen and to deposit it at the entrance of the cervical canal.

Conclusion

The doctor and nurse should cherish a deep appreciation of the true nature of marriage. In their work they can do much to help innumerable patients along the path of domestic happiness and good moral living. In no sense do we mean that they should set out on the moral reformation of all of their patients. Such action would serve only to antagonize many patients and displease hospital authorities. A direct approach to a patient on spiritual or moral matters is a task usually reserved for the priest.

The good influence of the doctor and nurse will most frequently result from their fine example, their respectful speech and attitude toward marriage, their realization that the union of husband and wife is most sacred, their reverence for motherhood, and their care and love for children.

In occasional instances, the good influence of doctor and nurse may, of course, be more direct. At times their instruction and advice will be sought by patients who have learned to trust and respect them and who realize that they themselves lack a proper knowledge of either marriage itself or of some of its obligations. Often a word of encouragement is all that is needed to strengthen such patients in the determination to lead a moral marital life. In most cases, however, doctors and nurses must be prudent enough to realize that their patients require counsel and guidance from a mind better trained in spiritual and moral matters than their own. In these instances, they should do all in their power to bring their patients into contact with a capable spiritual adviser.

But whether the doctor or nurse does spiritual good by direct counsel, by example, or by bringing their patient into contact with a competent spiritual adviser, their work is equally valuable. It is then that they are doctors and nurses in the true sense of the word, because they have helped to care for the soul as well as the body of their patient.

Problems for Discussion

1. As a nurse, you have witnessed the attitude of a husband and wife toward each other after they have been blessed with a child. Discuss the value of children to the stability of marriage.

2. Do you know anything about the difference in divorce rates between marriages blessed with children and those which are childless?

3. If the primary purpose of marriage is the procreation and rearing of children, is it morally permissible for a woman to marry who is physically incapable of ever having a child?

4. Do you think that young people overemphasize the physical basis of marriage? Do you think that sufficient consideration is usually given to the spiritual basis of marriage?

5. What is "marriage by proxy"? What are the requirements laid down by the Church for it? Can you think of any cases in medical practice where marriage by proxy provides a helpful solution to a difficult problem?

6. A girl is to be married within two months. She is brought into the hospital and it is discovered that surgery which will render her incapable of ever having children must be performed. Must she tell her future husband of this fact before their marriage?

7. In the Gospel of Saint Matthew (XIX-9) we read: "Whosoever shall put away his wife, *except it be for fornication,* and shall marry another, committeth adultery." Does the New Testament here authorize divorce and remarriage in the case of marital infidelity? (Reference: Fr. Connell's pamphlet on *Matrimony,* p. 19, listed in the recommended reading for this chapter.)

8. Is it easier for those who have been married in the Church to live up to the moral ideals of their state in life than it is for those who have been married before some civil magistrate? Explain your answer.

9. Is divorce followed by remarriage a violation of the unity of matrimony as well as of its indissolubility?

10. Do you think that it is the duty of the State to make "artificial insemination" an act punishable by law?

References for Reading

POPE PIUS XI: *Christian Marriage* (encyclical), Paulist Press, N. Y., 1931.

POPE PIUS XII: *Moral Questions Affecting Married Life* (the two addresses on Morality in Marriage), N.C.W.C., 1952.

BECK, SR. BERNICE: *The Nurse: Handmaid of the Divine Physician,* pp. 137-157, Phila., 1945.

BONNAR, A.: *The Catholic Doctor* (2nd ed.), pp. 43-53; 82, N. Y., 1939.

CLIFFORD, J.: "Marital Rights of the Sinfully Sterilized," *Theological Studies,* June, 1944, pp. 141-158.

CONNELL, F.: "Impotence," *American Ecclesiastical Review,* August, 1945, p. 148.

CONNELL, F.: *Matrimony* (pamphlet), Catholic Truth Society, Brooklyn, 1937.

————: *Marriage: Human or Divine* (pamphlet), Paulist Press, N. Y., 1940.

————: "Artificial Insemination," *American Ecclesiastical Review,* pp. 140-141, Feb., 1945.

————: "Moral Aspects of Marriage by a Person with Venereal Disease," *American Ecclesiastical Review,* pp. 54-59, July, 1940.

————: "State Legislation on Venereal Diseases," *American Ecclesiastical Review,* pp. 445-446, May, 1939.

————: "Marriage and Venereal Infection," *American Ecclesiastical Review,* pp. 331-334, April, 1939.

————: "Venereal Disease and Marriage," *American Ecclesiastical Review,* p. 68, July, 1939.

————: "May the State Forbid Marriage Because of Social Disease," *American Ecclesiastical Review,* pp. 507-518, Dec., 1938.

DOMS, H.: *The Meaning of Marriage,* N. Y., 1939.

FOERESTER, F.: *Marriage and the Sex Problem,* N. Y., 1936.

GEIS, R.: *Principles of Catholic Sex Morality,* N. Y., 1930.

GERRARD, T.: *Marriage and Parenthood,* N. Y., 1937.

HANLEY, T.: "The Natural Law on Marriage," *American Ecclesiastical Review,* pp. 195-208, March, 1943; pp. 298-308, April, 1943.

HEALY, E.: *Marriage Guidance,* Chicago, 1948.

HILDEBRAND, D.: *In Defense of Purity*, N. Y., 1936.

HOPE, W.: *Life Together*, N. Y., 1943.

JOYCE, G.: *Christian Marriage*, N. Y., 1943.

KELLY, G.: "The Morality of Artificial Fecundation," *American Ecclesiastical Review*, pp. 109-118, August, 1939.

KELLY, G.: "Artificial Insemination," *Theological Studies*, March, 1947, pp. 106-110; "The Moral Aspects of Artificial Insemination," *The Linacre Quarterly*, Jan., 1947, pp. 19-24.

LECLERCQ, J.: *Marriage and the Family*, N. Y., 1941.

LORD, D.: *Questions I'm Asked About Marriage*, Queen's Work, St. Louis, 1938.

MCCARTHY, J.: "The Morality of Artificial Insemination," *The Irish Ecclesiastical Record*, May, 1946, pp. 328-333; Nov., 1946, pp. 345-346.

MERSCH, E.: *Love, Marriage and Chastity*, N. Y., 1939.

MOORE, T.: *Principles of Ethics*, pp. 207-215; 232-239, Phila., 1935.

NOWLAN, E.: "Double Vasectomy and Marital Impotence," *Theological Studies*, Sept., 1945, pp. 392-427.

——————: "Marriage and Venereal Infection," *American Ecclesiastical Review*, pp. 323-331, April, 1939; pp. 27-53, July, 1940.

O'BRIEN, J.: *The Church and Marriage*, Fort Wayne, Indiana, 1934.

POTTER-WILLSON: "Artificial Insemination as a Means of Preventing Erythroblastosis," *Journal of the American Medical Association*, pp. 458-459, Feb. 24, 1945.

SCHMIEDELER, E.: *Christian Marriage* (analysis and commentary on the encyclical), N. C. W. C., Washington, D. C.

——————: *The Sacred Bond*, N. Y., 1940.

SUTHERLAND, H.: *Laws of Life*, N. Y., 1936.

VERMEERSCH-BOUSCAREN: *"What is Marriage?*, America Press, N. Y., 1932.

"Artificial Insemination," *American Ecclesiastical Review*, p. 434, April, 1934; p. 423, April, 1937; pp. 628-630, June, 1937.

"Impotency and Marriage," *Homiletic and Pastoral Review*, p. 628, Dec., 1942.

CHAPTER 4

Contraception

A brief survey of the spread of organized contraception in the United States within the past twenty-five years should serve as an enlightening introduction to this topic.

The first American birth control clinic still in continuous operation was opened in 1923. In 1928, there were 21 birth control clinics in operation; by 1930, there were between 40 and 50; in 1935, there were 150; in 1937, there were 356 birth control centers. In September, 1938, 447 clinics were in operation. In January, 1940, there were 553 birth control centers functioning in the country, an increase of 400 in five years. In January, 1942, there were approximately 620 such clinics in the nation and, only six months later, in June, 1942, there were 805 birth control clinics in 44 states.

In 1945, there were approximately 600 birth control clinics in the country. As compared with the earlier years, this figure indicates a notable decrease. The reasons given for the decrease are associated with the war. Three factors, in particular, were said to be responsible: (1) the war created a shortage of doctors and nurses on the home front, and this fact necessitated the closing of many of the clinics; (2) the economic status of much of the country's population improved under war-time salaries, and former "clinic patients" were therefore in a financial position to go to regular physicians; (3) many husbands and wives were separated by virtue of the demands of military service.

The reasons offered for the decrease in the number of clinics are apparently valid and a return to pre-war conditions will probably result in a rapid increase in the number of clinics throughout the country.

The number of birth control clinics in the nation in 1949 is actually lower than at any time since 1940. At the present time there are 557 clinics in the nation. Of this number, 242 are in Public Health Departments; 62 are in hospitals; 210 are extra-mural clinics; and 43 are referral services. A state-by-state breakdown of these clinics is not available at the present writing, but it is not substantially different from the chart (p. 79) which presents the May, 1945, distribution of these clinics.

Statistics are available on the number of people who are frequenting the clinics. During the past four years, there have been approximately 600 clinics in the country and the statistics from more than half of these centers present the following picture:

	1945 (350 Reports)	1946 (317 Reports)	1947 (349 Reports)	1948 (347 Reports)
New Patients	44,060	48,436	50,397	49,133
Old Patients	82,228	86,263	86,167	82,573
Total	126,288	134,699	136,564	131,706

In the above table, a "new" patient is a person who is visiting the clinic for the first time; an "old" patient is one who has previously attended the clinic. Only one visit per person per year is recorded in the above figures. These figures do represent a decline in the attendance at the clinics, and those who maintain these clinics account for this decline by saying that there are more private physicians who are giving contraceptive advice to their patients rather than sending them to local clinics.

The advocates of contraception take great pleasure in stating that about twenty-six per cent of the women who visit their clinics declare themselves to be Catholics. Similarly, they state that, in 1936, the *Ladies' Home Journal* asked its women readers if they believed in birth control, and fifty-one per cent of the Catholic women who were polled answered in the affirmative. Later, in the summer of 1943, *Fortune* asked its readers if knowledge about birth control should be made available to all married women, and sixty-nine per cent of the Catholic women contacted gave their approval. The accuracy and im-

Number and Types of Birth Control Clinics

State	Extra Mural	Public Health	Hospital	Referral
Alabama	4	63	—	—
Arizona	2	—	—	—
Arkansas	2	2	1	1
California	17	4	6	1
Colorado	4	—	1	2
Delaware	2	—	—	—
Dist. of Columbia	2	—	1	—
Florida	12	39	2	—
Georgia	—	5	3	—
Idaho	—	1	—	—
Illinois	13	—	2	4
Indiana	5	—	—	—
Iowa	8	—	—	—
Kansas	1	—	1	—
Kentucky	2	—	2	—
Maine	6	—	—	—
Maryland	6	4	4	—
Michigan	14	1	4	4
Minnesota	4	—	—	—
Mississippi	—	15	—	—
Missouri	7	7	3	1
Nebraska	2	—	—	—
New Hampshire	1	—	—	—
New Jersey	9	—	4	—
New Mexico	1	—	—	—
New York	57	—	10	2
North Carolina	—	50	—	—
Ohio	16	2	3	—
Oklahoma	3	—	—	—
Oregon	—	1	—	—
Pennsylvania	22	—	4	20
Rhode Island	1	—	—	—
South Carolina	1	47	2	—
South Dakota	1	1	—	—
Tennessee	3	—	7	—
Texas	14	1	1	—
Vermont	2	—	—	1
Virginia	4	3	4	—
Washington	1	—	—	—
West Virginia	4	1	—	—
Wisconsin	1	—	—	1
	254	247	65	37

partiality of these polls may be questioned, but such is the propaganda which is being used to entice wavering Catholic women into the practice of contraception. It is a familiar tactic: "everyone else is doing it, including most of those in your own Church, so why be old-fashioned and scrupulous about it?"

The above statistics on birth control clinics and their clientele are particularly alarming when one realizes that, for the most part, contraception is a vice that is practiced on the individual level, rather than through contact with a clinic. Almost all of those who practice contraception do so on their own initiative or upon the advice of private physicians. The Birth Control clinics usually handle only those persons who cannot afford to pay an ordinary doctor.

Too much emphasis cannot be placed on the point that we have recorded only the organized aspect of the contraceptive program. Everyone realizes only too well that the number of wives who attend birth control clinics, vast as this number is, constitute only a small percentage of those who are practicing contraception in the United States. It has, for example, been estimated that 375,000,000 male contraceptives were produced in 1937 alone. It is likewise known that women in the United States spend $200,000,000 each year on contraceptive drugs, solutions, and appliances.

Such statistics do not even touch the practice of contraception through withdrawal, which is acknowledged by all medical authorities to be the most prevalent of all forms of contraception.

These unsavory facts give one a rough idea of the extent to which the vice of contraception is spreading like a cancer through the entire body of American society. To apply the term "race suicide" to so widespread an evil is not oratory. It is the statement of a very grim fact.

The Legal Status of Contraception

As interpreted in court decisions, *Federal* laws do not prohibit the mailing of contraceptive supplies and information to doctors, or to other persons upon a doctor's recommendation, for medical use. The Federal statutes relate chiefly to "non-mailable matter" and do not concern themselves with medical practice in a clinic or doctor's office, except in the District of Columbia, Puerto Rico, and the Territories of Alaska, Hawaii, the Philippine Islands, and the Virgin Islands.

The laws of nineteen states make no reference whatever to the prevention of conception. These nineteen states are: Alabama, Florida, Georgia, Illinois, Kentucky, Maryland, New Hampshire, New Mexico, North Dakota, Oklahoma, Rhode Island, South Carolina, South Dakota, Tennessee, Texas, Utah, Vermont, Virginia, and West Virginia.

Thirteen states in the nation have statutes which restrict the distribution and dissemination of information regarding the prevention of conception, *but expressly exempt medical practice*. In these states, the restrictions prohibit the display and advertising, sometimes the sale, of contraceptives *outside of medical practice*. These thirteen states are: Colorado, Delaware, Idaho, Indiana, Iowa, Minnesota, Montana, Nevada, New York, Ohio, Oregon, Wisconsin, and Wyoming.

The statutes of fourteen states are aimed at the indiscriminate advertising and distribution of information regarding the prevention of conception, *but exempt medical practice by implication or construction*. These fourteen states are Arizona, Arkansas, California, Kansas, Louisiana, Maine, Michigan, Mississippi, Nebraska, New Jersey, North Carolina, Pennsylvania, and Washington.

Needless to say, there is a vast distinction between law and the enforcement of law. Twenty-seven states have prohibitions of various types on the display, advertising, and sometimes on the sale, of contraceptives outside of medical practice. It is only too well known, however, that contraceptives are displayed occasionally, advertised constantly, and sold almost everywhere.

Only two states in the nation, Massachusetts and Connecticut, have had the courage to hold their ground against the powerful influences demanding the lifting of the barriers. In these two states, an adequate law exists and diligent effort is made to enforce it. In the November, 1948, election the people of Massachusetts again voted to retain this law.

The Massachusetts law reads as follows:

Whoever knowingly advertises, prints, publishes, distributes or circulates, or knowingly causes to be advertised, printed, published, distributed or circulated, any pamphlet, printed paper, book, newspaper, notice, advertisement or reference, containing words or language giving the conveying any notice, hint, reference to any person, or to the name of any person, real or fictitious, from whom, or to any place, house, shop or office where, any poison, drug, mixture, preparation, medicine or noxious thing, or any instrument or means whatever, or any advice, direction information or knowledge, may be obtained for the purpose of causing or procuring the miscarriage of a woman pregnant with child, *or of preventing, or which is represented as intended to prevent, pregnancy,* shall be punished by imprisonment in the state prison for not more than three years or in jail for not more than two and one-half years or by a fine of not more than one thousand dollars.

Whoever sells, lends, gives away, exhibits, or offers to sell, lend, or give away an instrument or other article intended to be used for self-abuse, or any drug, medicine, instrument or article whatever *for the prevention of conception,* or for causing unlawful abortion, or advertises the same, or writes, prints or causes to be written or be printed a card, circular, book, pamphlet, advertisement or notice of any kind stating when, where, how, of whom, or by what means such an article can be purchased or obtained, or manufactures or makes any such article, shall be punished by imprisonment in the state prison for not more than five years or in jail or the house of correction for not more than two and one-half years or by a fine of not less than one hundred nor more than one thousand dollars.— (Mass. Gen. Laws, 1932, Pt. 4, tit. 1, ch. 272, sec. 20, 21.)

The Connecticut law simply states:

Any person who shall use any drug, medicinal article or instrument *for the purpose of preventing conception* shall be fined not less than fifty dollars or imprisoned not less than sixty days nor more than one year or be both fined and imprisoned.— (Conn. Gen. Stat., Rev. 1930, tit. 59, ch. 329, sec. 6246.)

Two additional facts which reflect the attitude of the states toward contraception are worth noting.

In 1937, eighteen per cent of the birth control clinics in the country derived all or part of their support from tax funds; by 1940, forty per cent of these clinics were wholly or partially maintained by state funds.

Alabama, Florida, Mississippi, North Carolina, South Carolina, and Texas are states that have integrated or are integrating "contraceptive services" as part of their Public Health programs.

Attitude of Medical Association

For many years the American Medical Association adopted a cautious attitude toward the practice of contraception. As might be expected, powerful influences were exerted upon the Association in an effort to obtain its approval of contraception. But not until 1937 was any comment forthcoming from the Association. In June of that year the Association held its annual convention at Atlantic City, New Jersey. At that time the Committee on Contraception presented a threefold recommendation which was unanimously adopted by the House of Delegates at the Convention.

The recommendations of the Committee were as follows:

(a) "That the American Medical Association take such action as may be necessary to make clear to the physicians their legal rights in relation to the use of contraceptives."

(b) "That the American Medical Association undertake the investigation of materials, devices, and methods recommended or employed for the prevention of conception, with a view of determining physiologic, chemical, and biologic properties and effects, and that the results of such investigations be published for the information of the medical profession."

(c) "That the Council of Medical Education and Hospitals of the American Medical Association be requested to promote thorough instruction in our medical schools with respect to the various factors pertaining to fertility and sterility, due attention being paid to their positive as well as their negative aspects."

To these three recommendations, the Reference Committee added a fourth, on its own initiative. It reads as follows:

"The Reference Committee further recommends that information and advice concerning the prevention of conception, given in dispensaries, clinics, and similar establishments, should be given only in such dispensaries, clinics, and similar establishments legally licensed to treat the sick and under medical control."

The leading editorial of the June 19, 1937, issue of the *Journal of the American Medical Association* voiced its approval of the above recommendations.

Again, in the editorial of the June 26, 1937, issue of the above journal, approval of the recommendations was voiced and it was stated that "the intelligent, voluntary spacing of pregnancies may be desirable for the health and general well-being of mother and children."

In an editorial of a much later date (September, 1937), in commenting upon the safe period method, it was stated that contraceptives "have not met any of the critical criterions." But in its December 18, 1943, issue, the journal carried an extensive article by Robert L. Dickinson, M.D., on the comparative reliability of the various types of contraceptives.

One is reluctant to believe that the American Medical Association would approve a practice which is both immoral and unscientific. It is possible to imagine certain far-fetched explanations of the above recommendations which would not make them synonymous with approval of contraception. But, all things considered, it does appear that the American Medical Association has given a limited approval and a certain amount of coöperation to the contraceptive movement.

The Arguments for Contraception

It is fitting that some consideration be given to the arguments which are offered in defense of the practice of contraception. These arguments are reducible to four general types: the *economic* argument, the *eugenic* argument, the *medical* argument, and the *moral* argument.

(a) The *economic* argument for contraception emphasizes

that parents should have only as many children as they can adequately support. Proper food, clothing, shelter, recreation, and education should be the heritage of every child. Whenever the number of children in a family exceeds its financial income, deprivation of the necessities of life is the inevitable and unfortunate consequence.

What is the solution of this ever-present and pressing problem? Certainly, says the advocate of contraception, married couples cannot be expected to refrain from the exercise of their marital rights, nor should they bring children into the world who cannot be given the physical, mental, and social requirements for a happy and successful life.

The obvious solution to the problem, according to the proponent of birth control, is "planned parenthood." Widespread training in contraception should be made available to all married persons, particularly to those of the poorer classes.

The individual family, we are told, will profit from the knowledge and practice of contraception. The marriage will not be haunted by the constant fear of unwanted pregnancy. Children will not be born into homes where they are not desired and in which they cannot possibly receive the necessities of life.

Society, too, will derive certain advantages from the widespread practice of contraception, especially among the "lower" classes. Poverty will be decreased, unemployment will be lessened, health conditions will be improved, and better positions with higher pay will be available to the average person.

The answer to the economic argument should not be difficult to understand.

First, it is not an argument on the *moral* character of contraception. It simply states that certain valuable economic benefits would be derived from the widespread practice of contraception among the poorer classes. The argument then proceeds to draw the conclusion that contraception is, therefore, morally permissible.

Since when did we begin to evaluate the *morality* of an act by what we can get out of it? Since when is an act morally good simply because the doing of it will assure the acquisition

of material benefits? By such a standard, lying, murder of the
hopelessly insane and incurable, stealing from the wealthy, and
countless other acts should be classified as morally permissible.

The defect of the economic argument for contraception is
that *it does not even attempt to evaluate the moral character of
the act itself.* It simply proceeds on the assumption that the
act is permissible because it will secure certain needed material
advantages. *This refusal to consider the nature of the act in
itself is characteristic of each of the four basic arguments for
contraception. This same ethical fallacy is inherent in each of
the arguments, namely, an attempt is made to evaluate the
morality of an act solely in terms of its material and temporal
effects.*

More extensive consideration will be given this ethical
fallacy in our chapter on *Direct Abortion.* For the moment,
it is sufficient to say that there is something about the very
nature of an act, over and above its temporal effects, which
makes it conformable or opposed to the nature of man. It is
a fundamental ethical principle that "the end does not justify
the means"; that is, the morality of an act cannot be evaluated
solely in terms of the temporal goods it may produce. The
rejection of this principle would result in the destruction of
the foundations of all ethics. A stable and unchangeable moral
mode would be an impossibility. Morality would be determined simply by expediency.

In addition to the above reflections on the economic argument, one might note that it is well known that contraception
is far more common among the higher than among the lower
classes. The continued spread of contraception, therefore, will
not lessen the number of the poor so much as it will decrease
the number of children among the wealthy.

The obvious remedy for poor living conditions and low
wages is a better organization of society. There is sufficient
work and wealth in the world for all. Social legislation which
will prevent the concentration of wealth in the hands of a
comparative few, without destroying individual rights, is the
great need of our age. Some worthy action should also be
taken by the State to make the road of life easier for large
families.

In this reference, one might call attention to the aid given by Canada to the family. Canadians of all walks of life agree that family allowances, which have been in effect since 1945, have substantially contributed to the well-being of the people. The Government-paid allowances range from $5 a month for each child under six years to $8 a month for each child between the ages of thirteen and sixteen. It is generally acknowledged that this program has had the following effects on families of low or moderate income: (1) better child nutrition, (2) better clothing for children, (3) increased child health care, (4) increased school attendance—since children must obey school attendance regulations for the families to be eligible for the allowances, (5) more recreational and cultural activities for young people, (6) greater family security, benefiting child and adult alike. The allowances are paid out of general tax revenues; cases of fraud are infinitesimal in number; and administrative costs amount to only one and one-half per cent of the whole program. Canada also has an excellent program of hospital assistance. Thus, the public press reported in March, 1951, that the government had contributed ten million dollars to the hospitals in Montreal; three million was given to St. Justin's Hospital, which was making a public appeal for ten million dollars; two million was given to Notre Dame Hospital, which was making a public drive for seven and a half million dollars. There is surely food for thought in the fact that many nations which lack our wealth, such as Spain and Canada, find it possible to do much more than we do for low and moderate income families.

(b) The *eugenic* argument for contraception is interested in the physical betterment of the race. The proponents of this argument regard a two- or three-child family as most desirable CR among all classes. Their deep-rooted conviction is that the fewer children there are in a family, the better the children will be in quality. It is also the hope and determination of the eugenicist that the spread of contraception among the lower classes will serve to eradicate these people whom they are pleased to regard as inferior.

The so-called eugenic argument is so defective that it merits little attention.

First, even if contraception would produce better citizens, it could not be tolerated. Contraception is an intrinsically immoral act and hence no good that it might produce could ever justify its practice.

Second, there is no basis for the assumption that the fewer children there are in a family the better they will be in qualities of mind and body. It is true, of course, that parents should be able to provide the necessities of life for their children. But, if average, sincere, industrious parents find it impossible to do this, the fault is not with them, but with the State. The solution of the problem is not to curtail the function of the family, but to force the State to fulfill its task of securing the temporal welfare of its citizens.

In a home where the necessities of life are available to all, a large family does not imply the presence of an inferior type of child. In fact, the experience of most people would point to the contrary. There is no substitute for the home with its numerous vital contacts. The child of a large family has far more opportunity to develop a well-rounded personality and countless social virtues than has an "only child."

Third, the whole spirit of materialistic eugenics is obvious. It places a premium upon worldly wealth and identifies economic poverty with inferiority. Despite this attitude, man remains a creature of body and soul. His highest faculties are those of his spiritual nature and the greatest "superiority" possible among men is a highly developed spiritual nature. Happily, this spiritual excellence is not uncommon among the poor. Unfortunately, it is not too common among the wealthy. The only sense in which the critics of the poor are "superior" is in the possession of more wealth, fuller secular knowledge, and an arbitrary code of etiquette. A reformation of his own personal conscience and a grasp of the true scale of values is the remedy most needed by the materialist.

(c) The *medical* argument for contraception is based upon the fact that there are many conditions in which pregnancy endangers the health or even the life of the woman.

The health conditions which serve as pretexts for the use of contraceptives are so numerous that there is hardly any point in listing them.

Among the medical indications which are suggested as necessitating contraception are the following: first, any gynecological or obstetrical condition which might make childbearing hazardous, such as a past history of dangerous pregnancies, toxemia, eclampsia, hyperemesis gravidarum, prolonged or instrumental labors, deformity of the pelvic bones or a previous Cesarean section; second, certain diseases of the heart; third, many cases of tuberculosis; fourth, high blood pressure and certain kidney diseases; fifth, miscellaneous conditions, such as diabetes, toxic goiter, venereal infections, extreme obesity, severe malnutrition, and general debility; sixth, the presence of certain nervous and mental diseases, such as insanity, feeble-mindedness, epilepsy, hemophilia, hereditary deafness or blindness (the contraceptionist prefers permanent prevention of conception through sterilization for this group of conditions); seventh, as a means of spacing children, in order to avert strains on health which might result from frequent pregnancy.

The ethical answer to these problems is comparatively simple: the woman may avoid pregnancy by any moral means but certainly not by an immoral act. She may avoid conception either by total sexual abstinence or by an expertly-guided following of the safe period method. But, as has been explained, contraception is intrinsically immoral and no end whatsoever can justify the commission of an immoral act.

(d) The *moral* argument claims that the practice of contraception strengthens the marriage bond. It professes that the practice of contraception will lessen the number of divorces and abortions and will better preserve the dignity of woman. The contention of this argument is that the avoidance of pregnancies which would involve serious physical or economic hardship is tantamount to avoiding a factor which is disruptive of the family unit.

The answer to the supposedly moral argument is evident. Everyone is interested in removing any element which makes more difficult the burdens of married life. But we may not act immorally to lessen such difficulties. Married persons are no more justified in committing an immoral act of contraception to lessen domestic difficulties than they are in committing an act of theft to lighten their economic burden. One may never do an immoral act regardless of the benefits which may be derived from it.

The Immorality of Contraception

It is not always easy, especially for the untrained mind, to reason out the immorality of certain acts. Fortunately, the Christian does not depend solely on reason to provide a complete and accurate moral code. Sacred Scripture and the teaching of Christ's Church are also a constant source of true moral ideals. The doctor and nurse will not find it difficult to reason out the immorality of contraception, but they should then confirm the accuracy of their rational conclusions by a study of the teaching of Revelation.

From the sciences of psychology and sociology, as well as from personal experience, we have learned that man is by nature both an individual and a social being. Quite logically, therefore, certain natural endowments and tendencies of man have for their purpose the conservation and development of the individual, while others are primarily social in character.

Most of man's organs, such as the heart and lungs, obviously exist for a purely individual objective, namely, the conservation of the health of the individual man. Other organs exist primarily for a social objective; thus, the faculty of speech has been given to man in order that he may communicate his thoughts to fellowmen.

Even the first year student of biology should be able to understand that the reproductive powers of man and woman exist primarily for a social objective, namely, the propagation and conservation of mankind. The Creator has so fashioned the nature of man and woman that one is the complement of the other. Important endowments, both physical and psychical. of each sex have a significance only when viewed in relationship to those of the opposite sex. For these reasons, the sexes are, by Divine Plan, attracted to each other, and the natural use of their reproductive powers assures the propagation of the race.

It is necessary to bear in mind the fact that the reproductive endowments of human nature exist primarily for a social objective, an end outside of the individual, namely, the maintenance of the race. The whole spirit of our age is to reverse the purposes of marriage. Instead of marriage being set up by the Creator for the conservation of the race, the spirit of our age is to hold that its purpose is primarily individual. Its objective is to provide man and woman with a source of various types of pleasure, and children are to be desired only when their presence will further the happiness of husband and wife. Such persons apparently believe that God placed us in this life simply to enjoy ourselves and fashioned our natures in such a way as to make this objective easier of attainment.

The doctor and nurse must appreciate that, in marriage, husband and wife are playing vital rôles in a Divine Plan. They must understand that the primary objective of life is not sensual happiness and that it is a truly great honor for a husband and wife to coöperate with God in the production of a human being.

Consideration of the faculty of speech will bring to light a second point helpful to a proper grasp of the present topic. The faculty of speech has been given to man by the Creator in order that he may use it to manifest his thoughts to his fellowmen. When man uses the gift of speech for this purpose, he is using it in a natural manner. He is using it in the way and for the purpose for which God bestowed it upon him.

In contrast, when man deliberately tells a lie he is abusing the faculty of speech. He is acting in a manner contrary to the will of his Creator. Instead of using speech to manifest his true thoughts, he perverts its purpose and uses it to portray precisely the opposite of that which is in his mind. In brief, he uses speech, not in a natural manner, but in an unnatural manner. Thus, a lie is an abuse of a faculty, a deliberate perversion of a great gift. And so we regard a lie as immoral, as contrary to the law of man's nature and opposed to the evident will of the Creator.

The above thoughts on the abuse of the faculty of speech should help to make clear the immorality of contraception. For, just as the Creator has bestowed the faculty of speech on man, so has that same Creator given man a power of reproduction. Just as the purpose of speech is evident, so is the purpose for which man is given the organs of reproduction. Just as the gift of speech has been given to man for the *social* purpose of communicating thoughts to his fellowman, so has the power of reproduction been given to him for the *social* objective of propagating the human race. *In brief, any use of speech is immoral when it is opposed to the very purpose for which the endowment was made a part of our nature. Similarly, any use of man's reproductive powers is immoral when the use is of such a nature that it impedes the very purpose for which God created these powers.*

In an act of contraception, man, so to speak, says to God, "perhaps You have so fashioned our natures that the use of our reproductive powers at this time should produce a new human being, but we say 'it shall not'; we shall take deliberate steps to make certain that the exercise of this faculty does not now produce the effect which You, through Your laws of nature, would have produced."

The Creator has attached a certain amount of pleasure to the use of the powers of reproduction in order, thereby, to induce married couples to engage in this act. By attaching this natural attraction to the act, the Creator has intended to assure the conservation of the species. *The important point to remember is that this pleasure is subordinate to the primary purpose of the reproductive powers.* The basic reason for the presence of pleasure in this act is a *social* one, namely, that it will serve to attract husband and wife to an act which will propagate the race.

An analogy will serve to clarify this latter point. Hunger and thirst are natural urges which incline man to partake regularly of sufficient food and drink to preserve health. Hunger and thirst are natural tendencies which have a purely *individual* objective, namely, the preservation of the person's health. The natural pleasure derived from eating and drinking must always be subordinated to the end for which the tendency exists. Hence, *if the urge to eat and drink is made an end in itself to the extent that the purpose for which this inclination exists is no longer achieved, there is a perversion of nature which is both morally wrong and destructive of the physical organism.*

In brief, we may eat and drink and take pleasure in these acts provided we do not eat and drink to the point of injuring health, since the preservation of health is the basic reason for which the urge to eat and drink exists.

Similarly, husband and wife may take pleasure in the marital act; *but they may not make such pleasure an end in itself; that is, they may not seek this pleasure in any way which would destroy the very purpose for which this pleasure exists, namely, the propagation of the race.*

In contraception, man completely perverts the order of nature and acts contrary to the will of the Creator. Pleasure becomes, not a means to a higher end, as intended by God, but an end in itself. Its social purpose is disregarded, and man makes it exclusively individual. He seeks this pleasure not only as an end in itself but actually take deliberate steps to make certain that the basic purpose of this pleasure, the propagation of the race, shall not be attained.

Contraceptive Pills

During the year 1952, a new form of immorality gained nationwide attention. Dr. Benjamin Sieve, of Boston, produced a pill which, it is said, will prevent conception by rendering the man or woman who takes it temporarily sterile. At the moment, it is impossible to evaluate the physical effectiveness of this pill which is composed of phosphorylated hesperidin.

A report was made to the New York Academy of Sciences on the "new birth control chemical" (preceptin gel) in which it is stated that this substance is 98.2 per cent effective in rendering a woman sterile for approximately a month.

It must not be thought that the taking of such drugs is any less immoral because they are not used to pervert the nature of the conjugal act itself. The fact remains that these drugs, whether taken orally or in any other manner, are aimed at preventing the conjugal act from achieving its natural end and as such, their use constitutes a perversion of nature.

As Father Francis Connell has said:: *"Any* positive means employed for the direct purpose of rendering a person sterile and of thus frustrating the primary effect of conjual relations is forbidden by God's laws. It matters not whether it is a sterilizing operation or medication used before coition, or a contraceptive action or device used at the time of coition, or a means of removing the seed from its proper place used after coition; it matters not whether its sterilizing effect is temporary or permanent. In any event, it is a violation of the natural law, and every instance of its use or application is a mortal sin." *(Am. Ecc. Rev.,* Jan. 1952, p. 64). And again: "It is just as truly a frustration of God's plan of conception. . . . The act of coition between husband and wife is the occasion on which, in God's plan, He coöperates with His creatures toward the sublime work of the creation of a human being, destined to immortal happiness. Hence, to thwart God's plan in so important a matter is mortally sinful, even if it occurs only once."

Neither does it alter the morality of the act simply because it produces only a temporary, not a permanent sterility. As our Holy Father remarked in his October 29, 1951 address to the Italian Catholic Union of Midwives, the Church has already condemned the direct sterilization of man or woman, whether it be permanent or temporary. In his words:

> "Ten years ago, when sterilization began to be more widely practiced, the Holy See saw the need of speaking out clearly on the matter. We then declared publicly that direct sterilization, *either permanent or temporary,* in the case of man or of woman is illegal. And this is by the power of the natural law, from which, as you are well aware, the Church has no power to dispense (Decree of the Holy Office, Feb. 22, 1940). Every effort should be made to oppose these unnatural trends and to refuse any coöperation with them."

The above thoughts should make it very clear that any act of contraception is a grave abuse of a great gift. It is the unnatural use of a power which God has bestowed on man for a specific objective. It is a perversion of this great social power in the sense that man's individual pleasure is made a supreme end in itself. But, even worse, it is a pleasure which is attained in a manner which explicitly outlaws the very purpose for which God created both this pleasure and the powers from which it springs. No perversion of a God-given faculty could be more clearly opposed to the will of man's Creator.

The doctor and nurse, however, are not dependent upon reason alone for their knowledge of the immorality of contraception. Both in Revelation and in the teaching of Christ's Church, they possess infallible sources of moral truth.

In the Old Testament we may read of the terrible punishment inflicted by God upon Onan for this sin. Sacred Scripture speaking of his abuse of the sexual act, says: "He spilled his seed upon the ground and . . . therefore the Lord slew him, because he did a detestable thing" (Gen. XXXVIII).

In the New Testament, Saint Paul severely condemns those who were guilty of unnatural uses of man's reproductive powers. Thus, in the first chapter of his epistle to the Romans, he says that they have "dishonored their bodies," that they have changed the natural use of this God-given power into a use which is against nature.

The constant teaching of Christ's Church has been equally emphatic throughout the ages. Thus, in his *Encyclical on Christian Marriage,* Pius XI says: "Any use whatsoever of matrimony exercised in such a way that the act is deliberately frustrated in its natural power to generate life is an offense against the law of God and nature, and those who indulge in such are branded with the guilt of grave sin."

This grave moral offense is extremely degrading to both husband and wife. They are mutually robbed of their true dignity and abased into instruments of mere sexual gratification. Any pure and sincere person has a natural repugnance for such an action. The degradation is felt especially by the noble-minded woman of high moral ideals; her deepest moral sense rebels against the rôle she is called upon to play in the abuse of marriage.

It is unquestionably true that the practice of contraception has, among other things, ruined countless nervous systems and induced sterility. The worst consequences fall to the lot of the woman. A famous gynecologist has wisely said "women suffer less illness from the children whom they bear than from those they have not borne." The regrettable physical conditions created by the practice of contraception are well known to the experienced worker in this part of the medical field. Such facts should not surprise anyone. Nature is a stern Mother and those who violate her laws usually suffer for their offenses in this life.

The present writer, however, prefers to omit deliberately any detailed mention of the innumerable physical evils which attend the use of contraceptives. Emphasis on physical evils can create a false impression. Contraception is gravely immoral for the reasons already given, and it would remain gravely immoral even though its practice never involved the slightest physical harm. Emphasis on the physical evils which follow its use might tend to create the impression that if the practice could be made physically harmless, the moral character of contraception would be altered. Nothing could be farther from the truth. Ability to engage in contraception without physical harm has no more influence on its immoral character than does our ability to tell a lie without getting a sore throat alter the immorality of lying.

Sterility Tests

Since the basic immorality of contraception consists in the abuse of the reproductive powers, it is proper at this point to consider the morality of several tests of sterility, some of which violate this same moral principle.

Recent medical research has indicated that one out of every ten married couples is incapable of having children. In itself, this fact is rather surprising. But when one recalls that infertility in marriage is commonly attributed to a deficiency on the part of the woman, it is still more revealing to learn that more than one-third of the sterile marriages are so because of the husband.

Sterility in woman presents a scientific problem which taxes the knowledge and skill of the specialist. In the vagina, it may be due to hyperacidity of the secretions, fungus infections, and vaginitis; in the uterus, endocervicitis, thickened mucous plug, infantilism, malposition, atresia, or tumors; in the fallopian tubes, occlusions, torsions, pus, strictures, and tumors. No particular moral problem, however, is created by the study of female sterility.

Sterility in man presents both a scientific and a moral problem. Over and above psychic factors, male sterility may be due to the following physical causes: testicular deficiencies either in structure, placement, or function; irregularities in penile anatomy; endocrine dysfunction; the after-effects of social disease, bilateral mumps, or tuberculosis; from venereal diseases, chronic toxic conditions, general debility, insanity, or injury to the reproductive organs.

The above causes of male sterility affect the formation, quality and volume of the semen. Investigation of such sterility actually covers the genesis, morphology, physiology, and chemistry of spermatozoa. *Quite obviously, a sample of the semen of the husband is the first requirement of such a study. Herein lies the moral problem.*

A brief summary of the morality of the accepted methods of investigating male sterility will suffice:

(a) Masturbation is the technique commonly employed to procure specimens of semen. This act is intrinsically evil and may never be resorted to as a means of obtaining samples of semen.

(b) All forms of onanism, either instrumental (condom) or noninstrumental (withdrawal), are immoral and may never be used as methods of procuring semen.

(c) It is probably permissible to extract *some* semen from the vagina, or the cervix, after one to three hours have elapsed since normal and natural marital intercourse.

(d) The "expression" of semen from the testicles or the epididymis, by aspiration, or from the vesicles by rectal massage, is probably permissible.

(e) It is stated by one author that the use of a perforated condom for procuring a specimen of semen appears morally permissible, provided it permits the escape of sufficient semen to effect generation. (J. J. Clifford, S.J., "Sterility Tests and

Their Morality," *American Ecclesiastical Review,* pp 358-367, Nov., 1942). Others object that such a method involves the direct purpose to eject some of the semen into a place not intended by nature. (F. J. Connell, C.SS.R., "The Catholic Doctor," *American Ecclesiastical Review,* p. 446, Dec. 1944).

(f) It appears morally permissible to use a vaginal cup, inserted *after* marital intercourse, to recover such semen as does not naturally proceed into the cervix (that is, the excessive semen which would simply lie unused in the vagina).

(g) It appears morally permissible to use a perforated condom to correct hypospadias, which is sometimes the cause of sterility.

(h) A final method of sperm examination is presented by Dr. Joseph B. Doyle, Director of the Sterility Clinic at Saint Elizabeth's Hospital, Boston. An account of this method will be found in his article entitled "The Cervical Spoon: an Aid to Spermigration and Semen Sampling," in the *Bulletin of the New England Medical Center,* X, 1948, pp. 225-231.

Doctor Doyle uses a concave lucite spoon, which is inserted into the vagina before coitus in such a way that the spoon itself is directly under the cervix. The purpose of this procedure is to protect the semen from the acid of the vagina and to provide the best possible conditions for the largest number of spermatozoa to penetrate through the cervical os. This procedure is carried out on the day which our best scientific tests would indicate to be the probable day of ovulation. Marital relationship takes place at home, after the husband has inserted the spoon according to the directions of the doctor. Approximately one hour after coitus, the spoon is withdrawn. Much of the semen which did not enter the cervix has been caught by the spoon and protected from the acids of the vagina. It is placed in a jar and brought to the doctor's office for examination. Finally, if there are appreciable numbers of active sperm still present, these are replaced in the vagina.

This method of aiding nature in the effecting of conception and of securing the material for semen analysis appears to be both practicable and moral. Emphasis must be placed on the point that the spoon must not be withdrawn too soon. If the spoon is left in place at least a half hour, preferably an hour, after coitus, the procedure appears to be morally permissible.

(i) The fact that masturbation is the technique commonly employed to procure samples of semen has created certain further moral problems for those who are asked to conduct the sterility tests. The question immediately arises: *may a doctor examine a semen specimen without inquiring whence or how it was obtained?* In the *Australasian Catholic Record,* April, 1951, Monsignor Madden answers in the affirmative with the proviso that the doctor's action "is not likely to be accepted as approval of what is sinful." Father Donovan gives an affirmative answer for the laboratory technician who might be called on to make such tests of semen; in fact, he adds that, even when the technician knows that the specimen was obtained immorally, the act is still one of *material* coöperation and therefore allowable for a sufficient reason. (Refer to the chapter on *Assistance in Immoral Operations* for an explanation of material coöperation.) Father Donovan apparently supposes the same proviso made by Monsignor Madden, namely, that there is no sign of approval of the illicit procurement of the semen. (*Theological Studies,* March, 1952, pp. 83-84.)

Problems of Cooperation

The immorality of contraception provides both doctor and nurse with numerous and serious moral difficulties. These moral problems arise primarily out of demands made upon them to assist in one way or other in the spread of contraception.

A thorough study of the principles underlying "assistance in immoral operations" will aid them in the solution of the moral problems created by such demands.

The following ethical conclusions will be of practical value: no instruction on the methods of using contraceptives of any type may be given to any person, regardless of religion, by a doctor or nurse. All mankind is bound by both Natural Moral Law and Divine Law. Instruction on the use of contraceptives is therefore instruction on how to commit a gravely immoral act. Such instruction would be *formal* coöperation in the sin of the other party. No reason whatsoever could justify the rendering of this formal participation in the sinful act of the other person.

No advice or encouragement to use contraceptives may be given to any person, regardless of religion, by a doctor or nurse. Such advice would obviously be a deliberate attempt to persuade another to sin. Such persuasion would constitute *formal* coöperation in the sin of another and is never justifiable.

No books, pamphlets, or literature of any type which teach and encourage contraception may be sold or distributed by any doctor or nurse. Such diffusion of contraceptive information constitutes *formal* coöperation in sin and as such is always grave sin.

Doctors and nurses are confronted with a special moral problem when asked to administer a spermicidal douche. The following principles will serve as an adequate guide in such cases: (1) it is gravely sinful to use a douche with a view to kill or frustrate the semen, since the intention in such a case is to defeat the purpose of nature. (We are not considering here the case of rape; special treatment of that type of case is considered in the chapter on *Direct Abortion*). (2) If the purpose of the douche is cleanliness, health, or other reasonable good, no moral objection is made to the use of a douche after three or four hours have elapsed since marital intercourse, for during that time the process of nature would normally have had its effect. (3) In serious and extraordinary cases, where reasons of health demand it, the use of a douche one hour after marital intercourse may be permitted.

No doctor or nurse may coöperate in the establishment of a clinic designed *solely* for the giving of contraceptive information and instruction. Neither may a doctor or nurse accept a position in a clinic of this type. These acts would constitute *formal* coöperation in the sinful work of the clinic and would be gravely sinful, and never justifiable.

When a doctor or nurse is approached for information or instruction on contraception, the request must be refused. If prudent judgment indicates that the mind of the questioner may be open to moral instruction, there is a splendid opportunity to present the true nature and purpose of marriage. Should circumstances indicate clearly the necessity of a limitation of children, the doctor or nurse should encourage the patient to consult her spiritual adviser, who may suggest the Safe Period Method. If the patient has questioned a nurse and refuses to consult a priest, the nurse should encourage the patient to discuss the problem with a conscientious doctor.

Doctors and nurses may take positions in an ordinary hospital or ordinary Maternity Clinic even when contraceptive information and instruction is given there by other doctors or nurses.

A double warning must be issued to personnel working in such an institution: first, they themselves must never give such advice or instruction; second, the danger of scandal must be averted. The precise steps which they would be obliged to take to avoid scandal would have to be determined by the circumstances of each particular case.

Doctors and nurses should remain on hospital committees, if it can be done without scandal, even when such committees favor by a majority vote the giving of information and instruction on contraception. It is to be hoped that active opposition to contraception by these doctors and nurses will curtail or even halt this immoral program.

Nurses and medical students may, for a sufficient reason, attend classes or lectures in which contraceptive methods are explained. Such attendance will not usually result in scandal. But an accurate knowledge of the immorality of contraception and a clear grasp of the answer to its subtle and attractive arguments should be possessed by these medical students and nurses. Attendance at these classes or lectures without this knowledge would be equivalent to exposing oneself to an occasion of sin.

The Christian doctor and nurse must never forget that very special moral obligations fall upon them. They have been blessed with the gift of faith and enjoy membership in the

Church of Christ. In moral matters their infallibly guided Mother, the Church, is ever at their side to counsel and direct them.

Doctors and nurses are forced to live and work in a world which is not a Christian world. The ideals of the contraceptive movement are primarily materialistic and pagan, and its interest is focused solely on the material and physical aspects of life.

The truly Christian doctor and nurse possess a deeper and fuller outlook on life. The primacy of the spiritual over the material is basic in their Christian scale of values. The intrinsic moral goodness or badness of an act is of vital concern to them. And when any act is immoral by its very nature, such as contraception, they know that it may never be done for any reason. In fact, they perceive the utter foolishness of committing a moral evil simply to procure a purely temporal physical benefit.

There are few fields in which the doctor and nurse may do more spiritual good than in the combating of the modern evil of contraception. With a true realization that each child born is a potential citizen of Heaven and with a deep faith in the Providence of God, they will be able to do an incalculable amount of good. It is to be hoped that they will not fail to take advantage of this splendid opportunity.

Problems for Discussion

1. What recommendations of an economic and social nature would you suggest which would provide at least a partial answer to the *economic* argument for contraception? Do you believe in giving a "bonus" to families for each child born?

2. What recommendations of a medical nature would you suggest which would provide at least a partial answer to the *medical* argument for contraception? Comment on the value of proper medical treatment of various conditions before marriage which, if allowed to develop, may later create a serious complication of pregnancy during married life. Comment on the value of adequate prenatal care as a means of avoiding certain serious complications of pregnancy.

3. By what standards do those who propose the *eugenic* argument for contraception determine the real value and destiny of a human being?

4. Do you think that the so-called "moral" argument for contraception is an argument in its own right, or is it simply a variation of one or several of the other arguments?

5. Precisely what do you mean by the expression: "the end does not justify the means."

6. Is the principle that "the end does not justify the means" really vital to a sound ethics? Why?

7. Is it possible for a married person who is a Catholic to be unaware of the sinfulness of contraception? (Reference: *American Ecclesiastical Review*, Sept., 1944, p. 229.)

8. Discuss the following thought that the medical profession is being very unjustly treated on the matter of contraception. The reasons which underlie the practice of contraception are almost always economic and social, seldom medical. The State fails in its duty to provide man with an environment in which he can earn a living for himself and his family. Men, in turn, frequently subvert the true scale of values by placing social pleasures above the primary purpose of marriage. As a result of these combined factors, the medical profession is "put on the spot" to provide a solution (such as contraception) for problems which are created by economic disorders or individual selfishness. In a word, the medical profession is frequently asked to shoulder a problem which properly belongs to the State or to the individual conscience.

9. Discuss this statement: "I practice contraception, and I do not think I am doing wrong because my act does not destroy human life (since that life has not yet come into being)."

10. Discuss this case: "My husband is a non-Catholic and does not believe that contraception is immoral. I have had one child and it almost cost me my life. Specialists assure me that I may lose my life if I become pregnant again. My husband insists that he will not risk my life and therefore practices contraception. I would like to have children, but I cannot enjoy this privilege without risking my life. Along with my husband, I regard contraception as the only reasonable way of preserving our marriage. I cannot see that it is immoral for me to preserve my marriage and my home by allowing my husband to engage in this practice."

11. Are you familiar with the laws of your own State on the manufacture, sale, display, and advertising of contraceptives? If your State has such a law, is it enforced? If the law exists and is not enforced, what value do you attach to protests to proper authorities by individuals or groups?

References for Reading

BONNAR, A.: *The Catholic Doctor* (2nd ed.), pp. 54-64; 83, N. Y., 1939.

CLIFFORD, J.: "Sterility Tests and Their Morality," *American Ecclesiastical Review*, pp. 358-367, Nov., 1942.

CONNELL, F.: *Birth Control—the Case for the Catholic* (pamphlet), Mission Church Press, Boston, 1939.

CONNELL, F.: "The Use of Contraceptives when Conception is Impossible," *American Ecclesiastical Review*, July, 1945, p. 62; Nov., 1946, p. 389; "Pre-marital Intention to Practice Contraception," *American Ecclesiastical Review*, Dec., 1947, pp. 469-470.

————: "The Sorrow Required for the Reception of the Sacrament of Penance by Those Who Practice Onanism," *American Ecclesiastical Review*, pp. 55-64, July, 1942.

————: "The Sale of Contraceptives," *American Ecclesiastical Review*, p. 70, July, 1942.

————: "The Sale of Contraceptives in the Army," *American Ecclesiastical Review*, pp. 440-441, Dec., 1942.

————: "The Intrinsic Evil of Condomistic Relations," *American Ecclesiastical Review*, pp. 36-39, Jan., 1943.

————: "The Use of Contraceptives During Pregnancy," *American Ecclesiastical Review*, pp. 62-63, July, 1945.

————: "The Use of Contraceptives When the Wife is Sterile," *American Ecclesiastical Review*, pp. 62-63, July, 1945.

CUMMINS, D.: "The Birth Control Platform," *American Ecclesiastical Review*, pp. 164-173, Feb., 1935.

DONOVAN, J.: "The Use of a Douche After Criminal Attack," *Homiletic and Pastoral Review*, pp. 1132-1134, August, 1941.

————: "Contraceptives Used in Fornication," *Homiletic and Pastoral Review*, pp. 1132-1134, August, 1941.

FOERESTER, F.: *Marriage and the Sex Problem*, N. Y., 1936.

GEIS, R.: *Principles of Catholic Sex Morality*, N. Y., 1930.

GERRARD, T.: *Marriage and Parenthood*, N. Y., 1937.

GUCHTENEERE, R.: *Judgment on Birth Control*, N. Y., 1931.

HILDEBRAND, D.: *In Defense of Purity*, N. Y., 1936.

LECLERCQ, J.: *Marriage and the Family*, N. Y., 1941.

LUCEY, R.: *Artificial Birth Control* (pamphlet), Catholic Truth Society, Brooklyn, 1935; also to be found in *Graduate Nurses,* edited by L. Fink, pp. 109-132, N. Y., 1938.

MOORE, T.: *Principles of Ethics*, pp. 185-204; 216-231, Phila., 1935.

PRUEMMER, D.: *Birth Control* (pamphlet), Paulist Press, N. Y., 1933.

QUIGLEY, J.: "Cooperation by Husband in Wife's Practice of Contraception," *American Ecclesiastical Review*, pp. 386-389, Nov., 1943.

ROCHELLE-FINK: *Handbook of Medical Ethics*, pp. 65-78, Westminster, Md., 1943.

RYAN, J.: "Cooperation by Wife in Husband's Practice of Contraception," *American Ecclesiastical Review*, pp. 70-73, July, 1931; p. 77, Jan., 1941.

SCHMIEDELER, E.: "The Death-Rhythm of the Family," *American Ecclesiastical Review*, pp. 181-195, Sept., 1942.

SCHWITALLA, A.: "The American Medical Association and Contraception," *Graduate Nurses*, pp. 26-44, N. Y., 1938.

SUTHERLAND, H.: *Laws of Life*, N. Y., 1936.

VERMEERSCH-BOUSCAREN: *What is Marriage?*, American Press, 1932.

"Contraceptives May Never Be Used," *American Ecclesiastical Review*, pp. 413-414, Oct., 1935.

"Use of a Serum to Prevent Conception," *American Ecclesiastical Review*, pp. 633-634, Dec., 1930.

"Marriage Instructions Regarding Birth Control," *American Ecclesiastical Review*, pp. 401-405, April, 1937.

"Cooperation by Wife in Husband's Practice of Contraception," *American Ecclesiastical Review*, p. 503, May, 1931; pp. 189-190, Feb., 1936.

"The Sale of Contraceptives," *Homiletic and Pastoral Review*, p. 282, Dec., 1939.

"The Use of a Vaginal Douche," *American Ecclesiastical Review*, p. 624, June, 1934; pp. 68-72, Jan., 1935; p. 530, May, 1935; p. 410, Oct., 1935; p. 542, May, 1937; p. 483, Nov., 1937; p. 73, Jan., 1938; p. 164, Feb., 1938; and in the *Homiletic and Pastoral Review*, p. 72, Oct., 1941.

"The Marital Obligation of Sexual Relationship," *American Ecclesiastical Review*, pp. 142-143, Feb., 1942.

The Safe Period Method

The modern development of biological science coupled with various other factors, such as the economic conditions of the twentieth century, has given rise to widespread interest in family limitation. It was for this reason that the entire problem of contraception received a lengthy treatment in the previous chapter. It is for this same reason that our attention in the present chapter must be concentrated upon the Safe Period Method.

The moral aspects of the Safe Period Method will receive due consideration in the second half of this chapter. For the present, the following brief historical sketch of the scientific discoveries on this subject should provide the necessary background for an understanding of the subject.

Historical Background

It appears that even in ancient times it was known, at least vaguely, that there are certain times during the menstrual cycle in which conception cannot occur. Thus, the fifteenth chapter of the Book of Leviticus prescribed that all Jewish women should abstain from marital relationships for approximately twelve days following the onset of menstruation. These twelve days roughly approximate the first unfertile or "safe" period, as we know it today from modern science, in the normal length menstrual cycle. The Jews therefore were refraining from marital relations during what we know today to be the first unfertile period and were resuming these relationships each month at a time when conception was most likely to occur. In view of this fact, it is easy to explain the exceptional fertility of the Jewish people throughout the centuries. The Talmudic scriptures also indicate that the Jews had definite ideas on the duration of time during which the male element of generation (spermatozoa) retain their fertilizing capacity. The medical writings of the Hindus reveal that they also knew that woman is capable of conception only once during the menstrual cycle, specifically, during the period immediately following ovulation. (A more detailed presentation of the knowledge possessed by ancient peoples on this topic can be found in Dr. J. G. Holt's work entitled *Marriage and Periodic Continence,* published in 1937, in London.)

During the latter part of the nineteenth century a great deal of scientific effort was directed towards a formulation of a biological theory on the probable time of conception. Many erroneous views, however, such as the judgment that menstruation and ovulation coincide, rendered all of these theories inaccurate. Thus, Dr. Gallus Pouchet published a widely-circulated book on the topic, in 1842, in which he contended that menstruation and ovulation were simultaneous. (This error of the nineteenth century scientists was occasioned by the fact than many animals actually bleed during the so-called "rutting" period, which is the time when ovulation occurs and the time at which conception is most likely to take place; in fact, in the case of many animals this is the only time at which the female will accept the male. These facts led the nineteenth century scientists to conclude that menstruation in women is analogous to "rutting" in the lower animals.) These same ideas seem to have been accepted by most of the physicians of the late nineteenth century. These crucial errors were embodied in the so-called Pflüger theory which was published in 1863. Dr. Carl Capellmann's well-known book on pastoral medicine indicates that he adhered to the Pflüger theory. Hence, in this work Capellmann erroneously states that the fertile periods are the fourteen days immediately following menstruation and the three or four days just preceding the next menstruation. He goes on to state that these "facts" were general knowledge in his time (1890). The Pflüger theory was refuted by Knauer in 1898 and by Halban in 1901, bringing the medical world to the realization that the relation between menstruation and ovulation was still a mystery.

Present day scientists have devoted strenuous efforts to the solution of this vexing problem. The basic errors which marred the older theories have long since been eradicated. But it appears that science still has much to learn on this topic: It still does not know the *exact* time of ovulation, nor has it yet offered *a wholly accurate and practical method of detecting ovulation.* Much progress, of course, has been made and it should not be minimized. A hasty summary of these scientific efforts would necessarily include mention of the following: Allen, Pratt, Newall, and Bland recovered human ova by washing the oviducts on the fourteenth, fifteenth, and sixteenth days; these men concluded that, if the ovum requires seventy-two to ninety-six hours to pass through the oviduct, ovulation apparently occurs *between the twelfth and fourteenth day.* Rock and Hertig removed uteri containing very early embryos at known times of the menstrual cycle, and estimated that ovulation occurs *between days 13.5 to 19.5* of the cycle. Schroeder, Shaw, Fraenkel, Ogino, and Meyer reported ovulation to have taken place between the *thirteenth and nineteenth days,* as indicated by macroscopic and microscopic study of the ovary. Dickinson, by manual examination of selected women under very favorable circumstances, detected changes in the ovary at the time of ovulation. Papanicolaou and deAllende, Shorr and Hartman have studied the changes in the vaginal smear in relation to ovulation. Wollner described physical changes in the cervix at the time of ovulation; he found that long before ovulation the cervical canal was dry, whereas at ovulation it exhibited a thick, glairy, mucous discharge. Siegler, from endometrial biopsy studies, concluded that menstruation takes place at a period from twelve to sixteen days after ovulation. Knaus observed that posterior pituitary extract (pituitrin) had no effect on the myometrium during the period that the corpus luteum was active; he assumed that ovulation occurs two to three days before the uterus becomes refractory to the drug, and concluded that *ovulation takes place exactly fifteen days before the ensuing menstruation.* Ogino confirmed these conclusions of Knaus by observing signs of recent ovulation at laparotomy. D'Amour assayed urine daily for both estrogen and gonadotrophin and described a gonadotropic peak at the time of ovulation. Burr, Hill, and Allen used an electrometric technic for registering the time of ovulation. Mittelschmerz, intermenstrual spotting, and other signs are recognized as indications that ovulation is taking place. (Wharton, on the basis of these signs, places ovulation between the ninth and the sixteenth day after the onset of menstruation; Siegler, on the basis of these indications, places ovulation between the tenth and eighteenth day in cycles which vary between twenty-four and thirty-three days.) Farris measured the walking activity of a group of healthy women for one to six months; all of these individuals experienced an increase in activity at the mid-period. Finally, an attempt to determine the time of ovulation by the use of the Schorr-Lamport millivoltmeter method of registering direct current potentials is described as inconclusive by Dr. Herbert Newman in the November, 1948, issue of the *American Journal of Obstetrics and Gynecology*.

Many of the methods mentioned above for determining the time of ovulation have certain obvious disadvantages. Some of these methods, such as laparotomy, have only academic interest. Others lack value due to the fact that too much reliance is placed on the subjective feelings of patients and because conception frequently fails to take place when the theory indicates the so-called ovulation time is at hand. Endometrial biopsies and hormonal assays measure ovulation *after* the event has occurred. For these reasons, most of the above methods lack either sufficient accuracy or practicability.

At the present time three methods of determining the "safe" period deserve special attention because of the *general* validity which medical specialists attribute to them and because of the widespread public interest in their use. The three methods are: *the Rhythm Method, the Basal Body Temperature Method,* and *the Farris Rat Test Method.*

The Rhythm Method

The first fairly accurate and practicable presentation of a safe period method is to be attributed to Dr. Herman Knaus of

Prague (1929) and to Dr. Kyusaku Ogino of Japan (1930). These two scientists did not collaborate in their work but their conclusions were practically identical. In the words of Doctor Ogino:

> Human conception can occur in a certain limited period between two menses (from the twelfth to the nineteenth day before the subsequent menses) and this conception period can be predicted practically in most cases.

The application of the Rhythm Method obviously involves the keeping of an accurate record of the length of a woman's menstrual cycles over a period of some months. In this way the pattern of the cycles will become clear. It may show, for example, in the case of a certain person, that the cycles are rarely shorter than twenty-seven days nor longer than thirty days in duration. With this information at hand, it would be possible to estimate *the earliest date* on which the next cycle would begin, as well as *the latest date* on which the next cycle would begin (that is, it would not begin sooner than the day after twenty-seven elapsed days nor later than the day after thirty elapsed days). One would then have recourse to the conclusion of Ogino and Knaus that ovulation occurs on approximately the fifteenth day before the start of the next cycle (that is, the fifteenth day before the next anticipated menstruation). By "counting back" fifteen full days from the *earliest* date on which the next menstruation is expected to occur, one will arrive at the *earliest probable day of ovulation in the present cycle;* by "counting back" fifteen full days from the *latest* date on which the next menstruation would be expected to begin, one will arrive at *the latest probable day of ovulation in the current cycle.* This procedure would set up four consecutive *probable* days of ovulation in the cycle. Two days are then usually added *before* these four days to allow for the life of the spermatozoa (that is, it would be possible to have marital relations occur a day or so before the earliest day of ovulation; and, if the spermatozoa were to retain its fertilizing capacity for a day or thereabouts, conception would occur when the ovum came in contact with the already-present spermatozoa).

Dr. John Rock of the Free Hospital for Women in Brookline, Massachusetts, states that male sperm cells live only a short time after entering the female reproductive tract. His estimate is that they probably do not live more than forty-eight hours.

Two days are next added *after* the four *probable* days of ovulation to allow for the life span of the ovum (that is, it would be possible for marital relations to occur a day or so *after* the latest day of ovulation; and, if the ovum were to retain its ability to be fertilized for a day or thereabouts, conception would occur when the spermatozoa came in contact with the already-present ovum).

According to Dr. Abraham Stone of New York: "Investigations indicate that a woman can conceive only on or about the day she ovulates." "It is very generally accepted, too," says Dr. Stone, "that ovulation occurs only once each month, and that the egg retains its capacity of being fertilized for a short time, probably not more than forty-eight hours."

The rhythm method, therefore, rests on the verification of three simple facts: *the time of ovulation in the menstrual cycle, the life span of the sperm,* and *the life span of the ovum.* In the light of known facts it appears clear, therefore, that in the case of the average woman there are at most four days in a month when intercourse would probably result in pregnancy. These days would be the two days before ovulation, the day of ovulation, and the day following ovulation. Since the menstrual cycle usually varies about three or four days in its length it is necessary at our present level of science to allow a four day span for the probable time of ovulation. In this way a fertile period of approximately eight days is set up within the menstrual cycle. The days preceding these eight days and the days following these eight days are the so-called safe periods of the cycle.

The above exposition of the manner in which the safe and fertile periods may be estimated is not offered as detailed presentation of the Rhythm Method. A comprehensive treatment of this phase of the topic need not be given here. This brief explanation of the Method will, however, give the reader a sufficiently accurate idea of the matter under consideration in this chapter.

THE RELIABILITY OF THE RHYTHM METHOD. It is most interesting to note the reversal of attitude towards the Rhythm Method which has recently taken place among the advocates of contraception. A few years ago they asserted that the theory lacked a sound scientific basis; that the method was so complicated that the average married couple could neither understand nor successfully apply it; that it was being exploited as a source of financial gain by those who were selling for a dollar or more calendars and charts which were worth only a few cents; that the method was only an "escape" to which the Church was having recourse in the face of the ever-increasing practice of contraception. It was explained that the Church has always condemned contraception as unnatural and immoral and could not now consistently authorize a practice which it had so long condemned. The Birth Controllist insisted that the Church had eagerly grasped the new theory, declared it to be essentially different from contraception, and then offered it to her children as a "moral" solution to the problems of married life.

In contrast to the above attitude, we find that the Margaret Sanger Research Bureau has now incorporated a "Safe Period Service" in its clinic in New York City. In the words of their own literature: "For women who wish to rely upon the safe period for conception control, a specific safe period service has been established. Fertile and sterile periods are calculated individually for each woman upon the basis of her completed menstrual cycle. Her "safe" days for the ensuing month are indicated on a special card, which she is asked to return by mail upon the onset of her next period. The safe-period for the following cycle is again calculated at the Bureau and the card returned to the patient."

The establishment of this *Safe Period Service* in connection with these clinics has resulted in a far greater respect for the Rhythm Method than the advocates of contraception were willing to concede a few years ago. In fact, Dr. Stone states that at the Margaret Sanger Research Bureau, where women have been instructed by doctors to chart safe and unsafe periods, the method has been successful in ninety-five per cent of the cases. The availability of this Safe Period Service at these clinics also poses several moral problems: may a woman, in the light of the materialistic philosophy which is at the very core of a Birth Control Clinic and in view of the danger of scandal, go to these clinics for guidance on the Rhythm Method? Does the establishment of this Safe Period Service by the advocates of contraception further emphasize a need for agencies, whose policies are based on a sound spiritual philosophy, to handle this matter for our people?

Whether or not the Rhythm Method is reliable is, of course, a question for science to answer. The advocates of the Rhythm Method are probably prejudiced in favor of it and, consequently, overenthusiastic about it. Some advocates of contraception still see in the Rhythm Method a rival to their own program and, as a result, are prejudiced against it. In the face of this conflict, the impartial procedure is to go to the testimony of specialists in this field.

In the June, 1933, issue of *Surgery, Gynecology, and Obstetrics* (official organ of the American College of Surgeons), Drs. A. D. Miller, C. H. Schulz, and D. W. Anderson report the results of their investigation of the Rhythm Method. These physicians relied on the coöperation of ninety-seven married couples in the establishment of their conclusions. Ninety-five per cent of these couples previously had children; eight nationalities were represented in the group; the women had twelve different types of menstrual cycles; examinations were made to make certain that there were no physical conditions which might prevent pregnancy. From every scientific viewpoint, this group was certainly ideal.

The results of this scientific investigation were wholly conclusive. Eighty-seven of the married couples had normal marital relations 725 times *only* during the prescribed sterile or "safe" periods, and *not a single pregnancy resulted.*

Doctors Ogino and Knaus, who are credited with the modern scientific establishment of the Rhythm Method, had equally perfect results in hundreds of cases.

As early as February, 1934, the *Journal of the American Medical Association* editorially stated:

> There is being developed scientific evidence to warrant the possibility that this method for the prevention of conception or birth control is sufficiently accurate to be dependable and at the same time psychologically, socially, and esthetically sound. It calls for a certain amount of civilized restraint. In view of the nature of the evidence now brought forward and rather well confirmed it would seem desirable that large clinics especially interested in studying the prevention of conception might concentrate their efforts temporarily on a study of this method from all different points of view that have been mentioned. *The possibilities seem more promising than promoting the sale of various mechanical devices, chemical substances, and other forms of intricate manipulation which have not met any of the critical criterions.*

Seven months later, the September, 1934, issue of the *Journal of the American Medical Association* editorially stated:

> *Enough evidence has already been established to indicate that the strict observance of the method is assurance of sterility, even beyond that associated with the employment of most of the contraceptive appliances and medicaments.*

Dr. Leo J. Latz has reported in the *Journal of Obstetrics and Gynecology* on an eighteen month study of one thousand women in the United States and Canada. He guided these women in keeping calendars of safe and fertile periods and his cumulative figures show that fifty thousand (50,000) sexual contacts resulted in only two pregnancies, and these were desired ones. He concluded that abstinence during the fertile period does prevent conception.

More recently, a study of 225 patients was made at the Rhythm Clinic of the Free Hospital for Women, Brookline, Massachusetts. Failures of the method amounted to only three per cent, while only six per cent of the women found it impossible to adopt this method. (It is admittedly impossible to apply this method to abnormally irregular menstrual cycles.)

Contrary to the general impression, the reports of reliable investigators in this field indicate that the most effective artificial birth control methods fail in from seven to ten per cent of all cases. Many other types of contraceptives are admitted to be effective in only about seventy per cent of the cases.

In fairness, it is to be acknowledged that the thousands of cases in which the safe period was tested probably benefited by more direct skilled advice than is usually available to those relying on artificial birth control methods. To allow for this probability, we might reasonably conclude that, in the hands of persons of average intelligence, under normal guidance, both methods are about equally reliable.

The objective truth is that either method is *usually* reliable *in the average case*, if it is *carefully* followed. Neither method is reliable if it is not rigidly observed.

The statistics quoted above establish the fact that the Rhythm Method is very reliable when properly applied. A certain percentage of failure will inevitably result from obvious causes: some persons who are incapable of working out the theory for themselves will fail to seek the guidance of competent physicians; others will not rigidly follow the skilled advice when they have received it; still others will ignore the fact that the theory is based on the laws of human nature and the calculation of their personal safe period measured in terms of the normal, healthy functioning of the body (hence, whenever the vital functions of the body have been notably disturbed by severe sickness or great emotional distress, the method should not be relied upon).

A further cause of "failure" of the Rhythm Method is the attempt to use it shortly after the birth of a child. For a certain period of time after pregnancy, the menstrual cycle is often most irregular. Sometimes the length of the cycle is altered by pregnancy. Hence attempts to use the Rhythm Method within a few months after childbirth, on the basis of evidence belonging to an earlier date, often meet with failure.

It is probably true that there are some persons who could never rely upon the Rhythm Method. The method is based upon a physiological law of human nature, and it is only too well known that there are always some individuals who never conform to a normal and average pattern. Human nature is not a machine. It may be true that ovulation *usually* occurs in the average person at a certain midmonth point indicated by the Rhythm Method. But no one who knows the fickleness and variability of Mother Nature should be surprised to encounter the testimony of science to the effect that *ovulation and conception have been known to occur at all times in the menstrual cycle.*

Science has much work yet to do on the Rhythm Method. At the moment, it would seem fair to say that the so-called safe periods indicated by the Rhythm Method are *usually* sterile *for most women* who are *in good health* and *free of intense emotional disturbances.* A careful use of the Rhythm Method in these normal cases is about as reliable as any artificial contraceptive in averting pregnancy.

In view of the present state of scientific knowledge on the matter, it would not seem prudent to suggest the Rhythm Method to one whose life would be endangered by pregnancy. Such cases, however, are rare. Often the coming of a child is not desired for sound economic or health reasons; but, if conception were to occur in these cases, a disaster would not be in the offing.

In a word, the Rhythm Method provides a moral solution to a difficult problem for many people. It may be of no help in a minority of cases; it may be of no value to women whose bodily functions do not seem to conform to the normal pattern; it may be of questionable value to one for whom pregnancy involves a truly grave economic or physical hardship. But it may be of great value to most women, whose natures conform to the normal pattern, who do not desire a child at a certain time, but for whom pregnancy would not involve a grave loss.

After pointing out that the Rhythm Method is not always reliable, it is only fair to state that certain factors will always result in a definite percentage of failure in the effectiveness and reliability of artificial contraceptives. These factors are so numerous that the percentage of inefficiency of artificial contraceptives will certainly equal, if not surpass, the percentage of failure which will result from reliance on the Rhythm Method.

Some of these factors may be briefly mentioned:

A certain number of male contraceptives, defective in material construction, with resultant ineffectiveness, will always be encountered. One manufacturer markets what are admittedly "seconds," that is, products defective in manufacture.

Many contraceptives become defective through use, and a certain number of people will always fail to discard them before they become ineffective.

Exploiting manufacturers place some solutions on the market that are merely antiseptic, under the guise of their being spermicidal and, therefore, contraceptive in character.

Certain female contraceptives must be accurate in size to be effective, and there will always be some mistakes made on this score.

The effective use of all contraceptives is dependent on their use in a very definite and careful manner, which will always be neglected in a certain percentage of instances. The effective use of many contraceptives makes it necessary that they be in place before marital relations and not removed too soon afterward, and one can be sure that there will always be some error of judgment in this matter.

These are a few of the factors which will inevitably render artificial contraceptives ineffective in a fair percentage of cases. These factors are so numerous and so humanly unavoidable that the percentage of failure will always equal, if it does not surpass, the amount of failure which will characterize the use of the Rhythm Method.

The Basal Body Temperature Method

Van de Velde pointed out in 1904 that the body temperature of women varies during the phases of the menstrual cycle; but very little attention was given to this important factor in determining periods of fertility and sterility until recent years. Recently, however, many excellent scientific contributions have been made on this topic. Thus, in 1932, Harvey and Crockett presented the temperature records of one patient over a period of thirteen months and analyzed the variations observed. Zuck, in 1938, and Williams and Simmons, in 1942, made clinical use of the method. In 1939, Dr. R. B. Rubenstein, through a study of vaginal smears, first attempted to correlate the changes in temperature with the phases of the menstrual cycle. Barton and Vollmann, in 1940, presented excellent bibliographies on the subject. In 1940, Mocquot and Raoul Palmer reported the effect of endocrine therapy on basal temperature. Raoul Palmer and Devillers in 1939, Allan Palmer in 1942, and Williams in 1943 illustrated their reports with graphs. In 1943, Lyon discussed the evaluation of dysmenorrhea by temperature records. In 1943, D'Amour compared temperature records with other means of determining the time of ovulation. In this same year (1943), Martin made an accurate correlation between the phases of the endometrium and the temperature curve. Then, in 1944, Tompkins published a series of graphs which greatly intensified interest in the subject.

Body temperature variations in healthy persons, young and old, have therefore been known to medical science for many years. Body temperature is a sensitive barometer of physical as well as mental activity, metabolic activity, and other physiologic functions. Muscular work, eating, mental excitement, and extraneous stimuli tend to raise the level of temperature of the healthy person. It is even possible to set up graphs which demonstrate the fluctuations in body temperature during a given twenty-four hour period under varying environmental conditions. These graphs follow a diurnal pattern.

A comparison of the temperature graphs of the male and female shows that *in the male* there is no variation in the daily pattern other than those induced by the above-mentioned extraneous factors. *In the female,* however, ovarian activity and corpus luteum development raise the level of the basal (normal) temperature during the latter half of the menstrual cycle.

It is a fairly well established fact that basal temperatures are reliable indices of ovarian activity in at least three out of four women. In the case of the remaining one-fourth, the curve is atypical and irregular. In the case of three-fourths of all women, the temperature curves are typical, and an accurate correlation between basal temperatures and physiological activities can be established.

A brief presentation of the facts involved would be as follows: Twenty-four to thirty-six hours before the onset of menstruation, the temperature drops and reaches a low level within a day or two after the beginning of the menses. This low level continues during the entire menstrual phase and to the mid-interval (when ovulation occurs in the woman who has a twenty-seven to thirty-one day cycle). Typically, there is a further sharp drop in temperature from the base line just prior to the time of ovulation (though this drop is not always apparent). The temperature then rises abruptly and appreciably during the next twenty-four to thirty-six hours and finally reaches a plateau where it remains until a day or two before the onset of the next menstruation. The abrupt rise in temperature after ovulation is a clear-cut phenomenon and the temperature curve after the rise is in sharp contrast to that preceding it.

By way of illustration, the following data is a summary of the studies made by Dr. W. W. Williams on thirty-five women. He states that in the first half of the cycle an average temperature level of 98°F. is usually maintained. This low temperature level is frequently followed by a further abrupt drop of 0.3 to 0.4 degree and then a sudden shift to a high temperature level of between 98.5 and 99.1° F. *The time of shift from the abnormally low to the abnormally high temperature plateau marks the time of ovulation.* This pattern is constant on normally ovulating women.

Doctor Tompkins, of Philadelphia, devised a special grid graph on which to record the temperature curve during the menstrual cycle. Temperatures taken orally or rectally upon awakening in the morning are recorded on the graph. There is a slight variation between temperatures taken orally and those taken rectally, but the variation is constant. The important feature of the curve, as mentioned above, is the rapid rise at ovulation. It is necessary to continue the graph for at least a few menstrual cycles before it is of much value. After this time, it is usually possible to predict when the temperature will rise. If the low temperature level in the early part of the menstrual cycle is followed by a sudden rise of 0.4 or 0.6 degree around the mid-month point, and if this corresponds with a similar rise in the previous menstrual cycle, it can then be assumed that ovulation is occurring.

In the studies of the various investigators, it has been assumed that the sudden drop prior to the abrupt rise in temperature indicates ovulation and, therefore, the most fertile period in the cycle. In case histories, *most pregnancies took place immediately after this sudden drop in temperature or immediately after the temperature reached its upper plateau.* (Dr. M. E. Davis thinks that the rise is brought about by ovulation and that the elevated basal temperatures are maintained by the corpus luteum.)

When pregnancy does occur, the basal temperature remains at its high postovulatory level until the end of gestation. In the postpartum period, there is little variation in temperature until ovulation has been resumed. (Basal temperature curves reveal that the first menstrual cycle after childbirth is rarely ovulatory in character and that the second menstrual period is associated with ovulation in approximately half of the cases.)

Barton and Wissner in their work on *Waking Temperature in Relation to Female Fecundity* state that a level of 99° F. or higher which is sustained for more than sixteen days is highly suggestive of pregnancy. In contrast, even though the period is long overdue, it is very unlikely that pregnancy exists if the waking temperature is at a subnormal level (below 98.6° F.). These investigators found that their diagnosis of pregnancy based on high waking temperatures was correct in 97 per cent of the cases and that there was no error in their diagnosis of non-pregnancy on the basis of a low temperature level.

It can therefore be said that the persistence of the postovulatory elevated temperature over a period of sixteen days or more constitutes excellent early data on the existence of pregnancy. Whenever the temperature fails to drop during the first week of a missed menstrual period, this failure constitutes strong evidence of existing pregnancy.

In reference to the Body Temperature Method, the attention of the reader is called to an interesting article by Dr. Edward

F. Keefe of St. Vincent's Hospital, New York City, printed in the November 1, 1949, issue of the *New York State Journal of Medicine*. In this article he describes in detail a new open-scale Ovulindex thermometer designed specifically for timing human ovulation. Its range is from 96 to 100 degrees temperature, only two degrees to the inch; in contrast, the standard clinical thermometer contains nine degrees to the inch, with its range of 94 degrees to 110 degrees crowded into less length than is used for only four degrees by the Ovulindex thermometer. Since the application of the Body Temperature Method depends upon the accurate detection of variations in temperature within the range of a degree, the value of the detailed Ovulindex is evident.

It should be frankly stated at this point that there are some outstanding authorities who are unwilling to acknowledge that there is a definite relationship existing between basal body temperature and the time of ovulation. An excellent article by Dr. Edmond J. Farris expressing this point of view is to be found in the October 23, 1948, issue of *The Journal of the American Medical Association*. In justice, however, to those who have done so much work on the Body Temperature Method, two comments might be made on the article of Doctor Farris: first, the cases which he cites are relatively few in number; and, second, even in the cases which he mentions, conception did occur somewhere near the shift from a low to a high temperature level in the cycle. He points out that conception sometimes occurred a few days *before* the rise and at other times conception took place *as the temperature rose*. His evidence would therefore seem to indicate a need for a refinement of the theory, rather than its substantial inaccuracy.

In the light of the above explanation, it seems probable that temperature curves can be employed in determining the safe and fertile periods in a menstrual cycle. Many authorities believe that this is a more accurate means of determining ovulation than that which is used by the Rhythm Method. In the woman with a typical temperature curve, the fertile period can be narrowed down to three days or less. In a woman with an atypical temperature curve, the fertile period could be calculated from the ninth day of the cycle until forty-eight hours after the temperature rise has reached the high postovulatory plateau. In a normal temperature curve, fertility can be construed to exist from the preovulatory drop in temperature until forty-eight hours after the rise has reached the high plateau.

Observation of the temperature curve during the period of the climacteric has also provided valuable information. It has established that ovulation was associated with fewer and fewer periods (obviously conception could not occur in the absence of ovulation). When that point in life is reached at which menstruation ceases completely, ovarian activity is at a very low ebb and the temperature curve therefore assumes the typical diurnal pattern witnessed in the male.

The above evidence indicates clearly that an accurate graphic record of morning basal temperatures taken orally or rectally will provide valuable data on ovarian activity and ovulation. This information can be very helpful in gynecologic endocrine studies, in sterility investigations, as an aid in determining the safe period, and as a help to a married couple who are desirous of bringing about conception.

The Farris Rat Test Method

Any treatment of the latest scientific methods of determining the time of ovulation would be incomplete without at least brief mention of the work of Dr. Edmond J. Farris of the Wistar Institute of Anatomy and Biology in Philadelphia. It is true that the method which he has devised involves laboratory work and is therefore too expensive and impractical for popular use. Nevertheless, the exceptional accuracy which Doctor Farris has been able to achieve merits mention of his work. Married couples who are very desirous of having a child, and who have not been blessed with one, would probably be very willing to undergo whatever inconvenience and expense these tests might involve. Certainly these tests would determine in a very precise way the days on which conception would most likely occur. Similarly, in the case of a married couple for whom pregnancy might constitute a grave risk, the inconvenience and expense of the tests might be very willingly accepted.

A brief statement of the test will suffice for our purposes: The occurrence of human ovulation is detected by the reaction of an immature rat's ovary to the hypodermic injection of the urine of the woman. If ovulation is not taking place in the woman, her urine has no effect upon the ovary of the rat. On the other hand, if ovulation is taking place, the urine injected into the rat produces hyperemia of the animal's ovaries. Ovulation time is tested, in the average woman, for two or three consecutive months. The first month is regarded as simply a "control" month and the data acquired during that month is used only to determine whether ovulation took place, whether the activity was normal or abnormal, and, if normal, at what time in the menstrual cycle ovulation occurred. After the first month, a positive reaction in the tests will indicate the presence of ovulation and point out the best time to bring about conception. When the reactions to the tests become negative, there is sound assurance that the unfertile period has been reached.

The astonishing accuracy of these tests and a more detailed presentation of them will be found in the excellent scientific articles on the subject by Doctor Farris. (*American Journal of Obstetrics and Gynecology*, issues of August, 1944; July, 1946; September, 1947; August, 1948.)

The Morality of the Safe Period Method

The discovery of the safe period is of great interest to the student of ethics because of the questions which it creates.

Does this method of birth limitation differ essentially from artificial contraception? Are married couples justified in exercising their marital rights during the "safe periods"? Are married couples justified in exercising their marital rights only during the safe periods? These questions are important and deserve sound consideration in the field of Ethics.

According to sound principles of Ethics, the use of the safe period by married couples is not *in itself* morally wrong. In the use of the safe period, married persons do not interfere in any way with the operation of nature. Their marital relationship is carried out in the strictly natural manner. Conception does not result from their action, not because they have prevented it, but because the Creator has so fashioned human nature that their action does not result in conception at this particular time. No unnatural action is committed by those who exercise their marital rights in a truly natural manner during the safe period. Conception does not take place, simply because the Author of Nature does not deign to cause a new life to come into being from the marital act at this particular time.

In marriage, both parties acquire mutual *permanent rights* to marital relationship. This fact indicates that they have the right at all times. Generally speaking, however, *they do not have the obligation to exercise their rights at any specific time.* It is clear, then, that though the parties have these rights during every day of the month, they have no obligation to exercise these rights on any particular days. In general, then, if they agree to exercise their rights in a perfectly natural manner during the safe period, they cannot be accused of any moral wrong.

In the above treatment, it is assumed that the use of the marital rights is restricted to the safe period by the mutual and free consent of both parties. It is understood that each party is morally obliged to consent to the reasonable request of the other party for marital relationship at any time.

We may now ask the question: *would it be morally wrong for a married couple always to exercise their marital rights during the safe period and never exercise them at a time when conception would take place?*

In answer, it must be said that, due to extrinsic factors, the exclusive use of the safe period could be sinful. One must remember that by marriage the two parties have entered an institution of Nature, an institution whose primary purpose is the procreation and education of children. It is for this latter purpose that the Author of Nature has given man the powers of reproduction. It is also true that the Creator has attached a certain amount of pleasure to the use of these powers, so that there would be a natural inducement and tendency for man to use these powers and thereby propagate the race.

In view of these facts, it appears evident that those who enter this institution and who avail themselves of its privileges and pleasures have a moral obligation to achieve to some degree the primary purpose of marriage and the primary purpose of the pleasure which they enjoy.

This latter thought certainly does not pertain to those who are prevented by serious reasons from having children.

It should be emphasized, however, that the resolution to follow the safe period habitually and exclusively is not without many spiritual dangers. There is the danger of incontinence to one or both parties created by the resolution to refrain from marital relationships during the fertile period; this hardship may be particularly severe for the woman, since some reputable physicians hold that the desire in woman for sexual relations is especially strong during the fertile period. Again, there is danger that the relationship of husband and wife would become degraded into one which is based primarily on selfish interests and sensual pleasure. It is for these good reasons that many reputable moralists, as well as certain private responses from the Holy See, advocate a fitting caution and restraint in the spread and encouragement of the safe period method.

It should not be necessary to tell married couples whom God has blessed with good health and a sufficiency of worldly goods that they should have children. A Christian outlook on life and an appreciation of all that a child means should be more that sufficient to make such parents desire this greatest gift of God from the depths of their hearts.

The sincere doctor and nurse will do all in their power to reflect the true Christian viewpoint on this vital matter to all with whom their work brings them in contact.

We must acknowledge, however, that in the case of some women the bearing of children in too rapid succession may be seriously detrimental to health. In other cases, a woman may be afflicted by a condition in which the bearing of a child might cause even permanent invalidism. Again, there are diseases which might cause death if they were to be complicated by pregnancy. Economic factors may also make it desirable to stop, at least temporarily, the bearing of children. Admittedly, parents frequently have very sound reasons for desiring to space their children.

Whenever prudence dictates a limitation of children, the first and obvious solution to the problem is a mutual agreement to the practice of Christian continence. The modern world will ridicule such a solution as impracticable; but, throughout the centuries, countless faithful followers of Christ have proved that it can be done. When, however, either party desires the exercise of marital rights, or whenever sexual abstinence would create a danger of incontinence for either spouse or a lessening of conjugal love, recourse may be had in such cases to the habitual and exclusive use of the safe period method.

In reference to all the above conditions, we know only too well how they are abused by many people. No one would urge parents to have a child when its birth might endanger the permanent health or the life of the mother. But we know, also, that the normal hardships of motherhood are frequently magnified into an excuse for not having any children. Similarly, no one would urge parents to have a child if it were obvious that they would be economically incapable of giving the child the true necessities of life. But we know very well that for many married couples the "economic incapability" of rearing children frequently means simply that a child would involve the sacrifice of some luxuries, a curtailment of some pleasures, and a little more home life.

The advocates of contraception charge that the safe period method at best solves the marital problem during only a portion of the month. This observation is quite pertinent and it provides us with a splendid opportunity to note that temperance is still a Christian virtue. Those who lack a spiritual outlook on life can hardly be expected to grasp the nature and value of the Christian virtue of temperance.

Fortunately, however, the Christian knows that the lower nature of man must be kept subject to his higher spiritual faculties of intellect and will. Control by the intellect and will of the lower nature of man is demanded of a Christian. Moderation in the use of sense pleasures is of the very essence of the Christian virtue of temperance.

The safe period method covers approximately two-thirds of a month; it is a sad commentary on the spiritual development of anyone who finds a comparatively short period in a month too long to hold lower nature under the control of reason.

In his Catechism on *What Is Marriage,* Father Vermeersch gives us the following pertinent thought:

> Let us observe that there is a great difference between the practice of birth control and the restricted use of marriage of which we speak. The abuses of birth control can be practiced constantly, they give free rein to passion, they do not demand the exercise of any moral force whatsoever; whereas this limited use of marriage requires, for the voluntary abstinence on certain days, a moral force the exercise of which is not without its social value.

The discovery of the safe period is, then, fortunate for many people. Many, if not all contraceptive methods, are repulsive except to the most calloused. To women of refinement, possessed of noble sensibilities, contraceptives are unaesthetic and revolting. We know that they are immoral. And the medical profession warns us that the practice of contraception can be harmful: it has frequently resulted in nervous disorders, sterility, chronic invalidism, and even death.

The discovery of the safe period gives us an aesthetic, scientific, fairly reliable, and moral method whereby religiously sincere persons may live a normal marital life and yet not have children, if circumstances necessitate their sacrifice of one of God's greatest gifts.

Pius XII and the Use of the Sterile Periods

It is most fortunate when theologians are presented with a clear and detailed analysis of a moral problem by the Holy Father. For more than twenty years, from the first scientific formulation of knowledge on the sterile period in 1929 until 1951, no detailed analysis of this matter was forthcoming from the Holy See. A single sentence in the *Encyclical on Marriage,* issued by Pope Pius XI on December 31, 1930, was the only official, public guidance available. This sentence read:

> "Nor are those considered as acting against Nature who
> in their married life use their right in the proper manner,
> although on account of natural reasons of time or of cer-
> tain defects, new life cannot be brought forth."

This directive was so brief that it was inevitably interpreted
in different ways by various theologians. Some even contended
that it did not refer to the sterile periods in the menstrual
cycle but rather to the sterile period in a woman's life after
her child-bearing years had passed. Much was written on the
morality of using the sterile periods by outstanding authors
during this twenty year period. Finally, however, we have been
blessed with a detailed treatment of the topic in two allocu-
tions delivered by Pope Pius XII.

On October 29, 1951, the Holy Father delivered an address
to the Congress of the Italian Catholic Union of Midwives on
Morality in Marriage. Some of his thoughts were misunderstood, so he availed himself of a second opportunity, about a
month later, on November 26, 1951, to clarify his thoughts
in an address to two national Italian family associations. These
two talks are so clear and so authoritative that it is most fitting
that we should present them as the best possible analysis of
the moral problems involved in the use of the sterile periods.
We can do no better than to quote directly from His talks on
each point.

First, the Holy Father states that married couples are not
morally obliged to restrict the use of their rights to the fertile
days in the menstrual cycle, and that the use of their rights on
the sterile days is in no way comparable to avoidance of pregnancy through contraception:

> "If the carrying out of this theory means nothing more
> than the couple can make use of their matrimonial rights
> on the days of natural sterility too, there is nothing against
> it, for by so doing they neither hinder nor injure in any
> way the consummation of the natural act and its further
> natural consequences. It is in this respect that the applica-
> tion of the theory of which we have spoken differs from
> the abuse already mentioned which is a perversion of the
> act itself."

Second, the Holy Father notes that if the married couples contemplate the restriction of their relationships *only* to the sterile periods of the month, a more difficult moral problem is created and necessitates a more careful analysis:

> "If, however, it is a further question—that is, of permitting the conjugal act on those days exclusively—then the conduct of the married couple must be examined more closely."

In response to this problem, the Holy Father first explains that a true marriage contract necessarily involves the mutual bestowal of *permanent rights* to sex relationship. Any attempt on the part of a couple to enter marriage by bestowing on each other the *right* to sex relationship *only* during specific periods in the month, would be no marriage at all. As explained earlier in this chapter, a distinction must always be made between *a right* and *the use of a right.* Frequently we possess a permanent right to perform a certain act but we are often free to exercise the right only at such times as we choose. For this reason the Holy Father explains that a couple entering marriage must bestow *permanent rights* to sex relationship upon each other—otherwise their attempted marriage is invalid. Any discussion of restricting sex relationship to the sterile periods must, therefore, imply that the *right* to such relationship is possessed on every day of the month; the morality of restricting the *use* of the rights only to certain days in the month can be the only point under consideration.

> "If at the time of marriage at least one of the couple intended to restrict the marriage right, not merely its use, to the sterile periods, in such a way that at other times the second party would not even have the right to demand the act, this would imply an essential defect in the consent to marriage, which would carry with it invalidity of the marriage itself, because the right deriving from the contract of marriage is a permanent, uninterrupted and not intermittent right of each of the parties, one to the other."

Third, the Holy Father emphasizes that if the couple have bestowed *permanent rights* upon each other, and contemplate only the *restriction of the use of the right* to sterile days, their marriage is certainly a valid one. This fact, however, does not mean that such restriction of sex relationship is always morally permissible.

"On the other hand, if the act be limited to the sterile periods in so far as the mere use and not the right is concerned, there is no question about the validity of the marriage. Nevertheless, the moral licitness of such conduct on the part of the couple would have to be approved or denied according as to whether or not the intention of observing those periods constantly was based on sufficient and secure moral grounds. The mere fact that the couple do not offend the nature of the act and are prepared to accept and bring up the child which in spite of their precautions came into the world would not be sufficient in itself to guarantee the rectitude of intention and the unobjectionable morality of the motives themselves.

The reason for this is that marriage obliges to a state of life which, while conferring certain rights also imposes the fulfillment of a positive work in regard to the married state itself.

The marriage contract which confers upon husband and wife the right to satisfy the inclinations of nature, sets them up in a certain state of life, the married state. But upon couples who perform the act peculiar to their state, nature and the Creator impose the function of helping the conservation of the human race. The characteristic activity which gives their state its value is the 'bonum prolis' (having children). The individual and society, the people and the state, the Church itself, depend for their existence in the order established by God on fruitful marriage. Therefore, to embrace the married state, continuously to make use of the faculty proper to it and lawful in it alone, and, on the other hand, to withdraw always and deliberately with no serious reason from its primary obligation, would be a sin against the very meaning of conjugal life."

In view of the last-quoted words of the Holy Father, it appears evident that the prolonged use of the rhythm method without a serious reason would be gravely sinful. A span of five years would seem to be a reasonable *maximum* estimate as to what length of time would constitute a 'prolonged' period. Habitual recourse to the use of only the sterile periods without sufficient reason for a shorter duration of time would be venially sinful (barring serious proximate danger of incontinence, which would render even a brief use of the sterile periods gravely sinful).

With reference to married couples *who have no serious reason for curtailing the number of their children,* a vital question is asked: *Is there any limit to the number of children which parents must have?*

In an attempt to answer this question, Father Gerald Kelly, S.J., makes a distinction between *duty* and *action beyond the call of duty.* He states that such parents have a *duty* to have four or five children (a figure arrived at by the application of the sociological norm that families of that size would be adequate for the conservation of the race—which is, of course, the primary purpose of marriage). He believes that these parents do not have any moral obligation to have a greater number of children but should be encouraged to do so in conformity with true Christian *ideals* on the value of a large family. (*America,* May 3, 1952, pp. 128-130.)

In contrast to the above view, the opinion of Fr. Francis Connell, C.Ss.R., is that the divinely imposed obligation to procreate remains substantially unmodified, even when a couple have had seven or eight children, presuming that they wish to make use of their rights and have no serious reason for not having any more children. (*American Ecclesiastical Review,* August 1952, pp. 136-141.)

Fourth, the Holy Father explains that the duty on the part of married couples to have children is of the affirmative type. In ethics, a distinction is always made between moral duties based on negative Natural Law and those derived from affirmative Natural Law.

Negative Natural Law is concerned with prohibitions—such law orders us not to do certain acts which in themselves are evil. Negative Natural Law is most rigid: it binds us every instant of our life and it never admits of relaxation or dispensation. It is a basic principle of ethics that "the end never justifies the means"—hence no loss that we might endure or hardship that we might thereby suffer would ever entitle us to do an evil act prohibited by Negative Natural Law.

In contrast, affirmative Natural Law orders us to perform certain good acts. Such law is not nearly so rigid as the former type both because it binds us only to the periodic performance of certain good acts and because it does not compel us to achieve the good at a specific time if by so doing we would have to suffer a grave hardship. It is expected that the observance of law will entail ordinary inconvenience and sacrifice; but it is never the mind of proper authority, whether Divine or human, to compel us to do a good act at a time when such observance of the law would subject us to a grave loss.

On the basis of the above principles, the Holy Father explains that the positive obligation to have children does not bind a married couple when having offspring would involve grave hardship of any type.

> "The reason for this is that marriage obliges to a state of life which, while conferring certain rights also imposes the fulfillment of a positive work in regard to the married state itself. In such a case, one can apply the general principle that a positive fulfillment may be omitted when serious reasons, independent of the good will of those obliged by it, show that this action is not opportune, or prove that a similar demand cannot reasonably be made of human nature. . . .
>
> There are serious motives, such as those often mentioned in the so-called medical, eugenic, economic, and social "indications," that can exempt for a long time, perhaps even the whole duration of the marriage, from the positive and obligatory carrying out of the act. *From this it follows that observing the non-fertile periods alone can be lawful only under a moral aspect. Under the conditions mentioned it really is so. But if, according to a rational and just judgment, there are no similar grave reasons of a personal nature or deriving from external circumstances, then the determination to avoid habitually the fecundity of the union while at the same time to continue fully satisfying their sensuality, can be derived only from a false*

appreciation of life and from reasons having nothing to do with proper ethical laws. . . .

Unfortunately, there are many cases where speaking, even cautiously, of children as a 'blessing' is sufficient to provoke contradiction or even derision. Very often the idea and remarks about the great 'burden' of children dominate. How opposed is such a frame of mind to God's plan and the language of Holy Scripture and even to sound reason and the sentiment of nature. If there are conditions and circumstances where, without violating God's law, parents can avoid the 'blessing' of children, nevertheless these cases of 'force majeure' (pressing circumstances) do not authorize the perverting of ideas, the disparaging of values and the despising of the mother who has the courage and the honor to bring forth new life."

The Holy Father re-emphasized this point in his second allocution (November 26, 1951). In this talk he stated:

"Since, too, the primary office of matrimony is to be at the service of life, the expression of Our principal gratification and of Our paternal gratitude goes to those generous mothers and fathers who, for love of God and with trust in Him, courageously raise a large family.

On the other hand, the Church knows how to consider with sympathy and understanding the real difficulties of the married state in our day. Therefore, in Our last allocution on conjugal morality, We affirmed the legitimacy and, at the same time, the limits—in truth very wide—of a regulation of offspring, which, unlike so-called 'birth-control, is compatible with the law of God."

The following examples of these "justifications" for practicing rhythm have been given: (a) Childbirth would be dangerous, or one of the parents is too ill to help in the rearing of the children *(medical reasons);* (b) The real likelihood of mental abnormality or serious hereditary defect in children, or mental weakness on the part of the parents *(eugenic reasons);* (c) Lack of housing facilities, over-population, the husband's employment in a public office, such as military service, which is at least temporarily incompatible with family life *(social reasons);* (d) The inability to provide decently for children according to the papal standard of a family living wage (*economic reasons*). (Kelly G., *America,* May 3, 1952.)

Fifth, the Holy Father acknowledges some "hardship cases" are encountered which, for one reason or another, are not able to be handled by recourse to the sterile periods. In such cases, he emphasizes that a couple may never have recourse to the immoral act of contraception as the solution of their problem and, secondly, that complete sexual abstinence is wholly possible and may be the necessary moral solution for some severe cases.

"Now you might insist observing, perhaps, that in the exercise of your profession you sometimes come across very delicate cases in which the risk of motherhood cannot be run or must be avoided completely, and in which, on the other hand, observing the sterile periods either does not give sufficient security or has to be abandoned for other reasons. And then you ask how one can still speak of an apostolate in the service of maternity.

If in your reliable and experienced judgment, conditions absolutely demand a 'no', (that is, that maternity must be excluded) it would be a mistake and a wrong to impose or counsel a 'yes'. Here we are dealing with concrete facts, with a medical not theological question, one, therefore, which you are competent to handle. But in such cases couples do not ask you for a medical answer, which is necessarily negative, but for approval of a 'technique' of the conjugal act which insures them against the risk of motherhood. Here is another occasion on which you are called to exercise your apostolate, in so far as you do not leave any doubt that even in such extreme cases every preventive step and every direct attempt upon the life and development of the germ is in conscience prohibited and excluded, and that there is but one way open, that of complete abstinence from every complete exercise of the natural faculty. Here your apostolate obliges you to clear, sure judgment and calm firmness.

But it will be objected that such abstinence is impossible, that such heroism cannot be attained. Today you will hear and read this objection on all sides, even from those who on account of their duty and ability should be able to judge very differently. The following argument is brought forward as a proof: 'No one is obliged to do the impossible and no reasonable legislator, it is assumed, wishes by his law to oblige people to do the impossible. But, for married couples long-term abstinence is impossible. Therefore they are not obliged to abstain. The Divine law cannot mean this.'

Thus, from partly true premises a false conclusion is deduced. In order to convince yourself of this, invert the steps of the argument. 'God does not oblige people to do the impossible. But God obliges married people to abstain, if their union cannot be fulfilled according to the laws of nature. Therefore, in this case abstinence is possible.' In confirmation of this argument we have the Council of Trent which, in its chapter on the observance, necessary and possible, of the commandments teaches us that, as St. Augustine said, 'God does not command impossible things, but when He commands He warns us to do what can be done and to ask what cannot and gives you help so that you can.'

Therefore, do not allow yourselves to be confused in the practice of your profession and your apostolate by all this talk about impossibility, either as regards your own inner judgment or in what concerns your outward conduct. Never do anything contrary to the law of God and your consciences as Christians. It is wronging men and women of our times to deem them incapable of continuous heroism. Today, for many reasons—perhaps with the goad of hard necessity or even sometimes in the service of injustice—heroism is exercised to a degree and to an extent which would have been thought impossible in days gone by. Why, then, should this heroism, if the circumstances really demand it, stop at the borders established by the passions and inclinations of nature? The answer is clear. The man who does not want to master himself is incapable of so doing. He who believes he can do so, counting merely on his own strength without seeking sincerely and perseveringly help from God, will remain miserably disillusioned."

Finally, it is clear from the Holy Father's second allocution (November 26, 1951) that knowledge of the sterile periods is regarded as a fortunate discovery of modern medical science, and the hope is expressed that further research will perfect this knowledge so that married couples who truly require it may have a moral solution to their problems.

> "One may even hope (but in this matter the Church naturally leaves the judgment to medical science) that science will succeed in providing this licit method with a sufficiently secure basis, and the most recent information seems to confirm such a hope."

The Attitude of Doctor and Nurse

The doctor and nurse will constantly encounter the problem of family limitation and they should never lose sight of their duties in this serious and vital matter.

First, they must remember that in no instance may they give advice or instruction on contraception. Such an action would be formal coöperation in sin. A detailed treatment of this point will be found in the chapter on *Assistance in Immoral Operations.*

Second, they should remember at all times that the birth and education of children is the primary purpose of marriage. They should have a deep appreciation of the designs of the Creator in this matter and realize that a child is the greatest gift God can bestow on a married couple. In the procreation of a child, parents play a most dignified rôle; they are, in a sense, co-creators with God in the begetting of an immortal soul. The child cements the love of husband and wife whose right and privilege it is to lead this child along the path to eternal happiness. Doctors and nurses should never lose an opportunity to present these noble ideals to those with whom they come in contact.

Third, the doctor or nurse may know that in certain circumstances it is not advisable for parents to have more children. Reasons of health or economic conditions can create obvious situations of this type. But they must be cautious and prudent at all times. They must certainly not become advocates of needless sterility. Should circumstances indicate clearly the necessity of limitation of children, they should encourage the patient to consult a spiritual adviser, who may suggest exclusive use of the sterile periods. If the patient has first consulted a nurse, and refuses to consult a priest, the nurse should encourage her to discuss the problem with a conscientious doctor.

The doctor and nurse who oppose contraception at all times, who teach capable parents the value of a child, and who recommend the habitual and exclusive use of the sterile periods only to those who truly need it, bring honor to their profession by their efforts to strengthen the family which is the foundation-stone of our society.

Problems for Discussion

1. Comment on this statement: "I've tried the safe period method and it is not reliable—I must use contraception."

2. Comment on this statement: "I can't see any difference between contraception and the safe period method; both represent steps taken to avert pregnancy."

3. Do you think that widespread knowledge of the safe period method would result in an increase in immorality among unmarried persons?

4. Do you think that widespread knowledge of the safe period method would make married couples more sensual minded and both encourage and provide an escape from the normal duty of parenthood?

5. Are the advocates of the safe period method over-enthusiastic in evaluating its assurance of sterility? Are the advocates of contraception unprejudiced in their evaluation of the safe period method?

6. Has science offered any means for detecting the actual time of ovulation?

7. Would you recommend that the Church foster the spreading of knowledge of the safe period method to married couples for whom it is physically or economically unwise to have children? If so, what channels would you suggest for the distribution of this knowledge?

References for Reading

BONNAR, A.: *The Catholic Doctor* (2nd ed.), pp. 65-71, N. Y., 1939.
CONNELL, F. J.: "Rhythm in Pre-Marital Instructions," *American Ecclesiastical Review*, August, 1949, p. 153.

FARRIS, E.: "A Test for Determining the Time of Ovulation and Conception in Women," *American Journal of Obstetrics and Gynecology*, July, 1946, pp. 14-27; "The Prediction of the Day of Human Ovulation by the Rat Test," *American Journal of Obstetrics and Gynecology*, August, 1948, pp. 347-352.

FOERSTER, F.: *Marriage and the Sex Problem*, N. Y., 1936.

GERRARD, T.: *Marriage and Parenthood*, N. Y., 1937.

GRIESE, O.: *The Morality of Periodic Continence*, Catholic University, Washington, D. C., 1942.

"Objective Morality of Rhythm Practice," *American Ecclesiastical Review*, June, 1949, pp. 475-479.

HARTMAN, C.: *Time of Ovulation in Women*, Baltimore, 1936.

HILDEBRAND, D.: *In Defense of Purity*, N. Y., 1936.

HOLT, J.: *Marriage and Periodic Continence*, London, 1937.

KAISER, A.: "Abuse of the 'Safe Period' in Marriage," *Fortnightly Review XLI*, pp. 123-124, 1934.

KELLY, G.: "The Safe Period Method," *Theological Studies*, March, 1947, pp. 104-106.

————: "The Safe Period," *American Ecclesiastical Review*, pp. 284-288, March, 1935.

LATZ, L.: *The Rhythm of Sterility and Fertility in Women* (6th ed.), Latz Foundation, Chicago, 1939.

LATZ-REINER: "Natural Conception Control," *Journal of American Medical Association*, pp. 1241-1246, 1935.

————: "Failures in Natural Conception Control and Their Causes," *Illinois Medical Journal*, March, 1937.

————: "Further Studies on the Sterile and Fertile Periods in Women," *American Journal of Obstetrics and Gynecology*, XLIII, pp. 74-79, Jan., 1942.

LECLERCQ, J.: *Marriage and the Family*, N. Y., 1941.

MURPHY-FARRIS: "Conception Following the Prediction of the Day of Ovulation with the Rat Test," *American Journal of Obstetrics and Gynecology*, Sept., 1947, pp. 467-474.

MCCARTHY, J.: "The Morality of Using the Safe Period Method," *The Irish Ecclesiastical Record*, April, 1946, pp. 259-263.

O'BRIEN, J.: *Natural Birth Control*, Champagne, Ill., 1938.

O'CONNELL, J.: "On the Erection of 'Safe Period' Clinics," *American Ecclesiastical Review*, pp. 246-254, Sept., 1939.

O'DONNELL, R.: "Contraception and Rhythm," *The Nebraska Medical Journal*, XXII, pp. 132-134, April, 1937.

PURVIS, M.: "Detection of Ovulation by the Basal Temperature Curve," *American Journal of Obstetrics and Gynecology*, July, 1943. Additional references on the basal body temperature method: *Journal of the American Medical Association*, March 11, 1944; Feb. 16, 1946; April 6, 1946; and June 21, 1947.

ROCHELLE-FINK: *Handbook of Medical Ethics*, pp. 79-84, Westminster, Md., 1943.

TOMPKINS, P.: "The Use of Basal Temperature Graphs in Determining the Date of Ovulation," *Medical Clinics of North America*, Nov., 1945.

VERMEERSCH-BOUSCAREN: *What is Marriage?*, America Press, N. Y., 1932.

CHAPTER **6**

The Christian Philosophy of Suffering

In their daily work, both doctor and nurse come into constant contact with intense and prolonged suffering. Bitter pain, both physical and mental, is the common lot of those whom they call their "patients."

Repeated association with so much suffering can have either of two effects upon them. On the one hand, they may allow themselves to become so accustomed to pain that they become calloused, unsympathetic, and wholly insensible to the possible value of suffering. On the other hand, repeated contact with pain may both deepen their understanding of the purpose of life and develop in them those finer qualities which are so invaluable in the character of those dedicated to the service of man.

Both for the benefit of their patients and for their own sake, it is vitally essential that doctors and nurses possess a proper outlook on the significance and value of suffering.

Patients will constantly seek from them an explanation of why suffering forms such a predominant part of life.

"Why," they will ask, "does a good and just God send so much pain to His creatures? Why does God permit physical and mental suffering, and the moral evil of sin, in a world which He Himself created and governs? Why do the good seem to suffer so much and the wicked frequently enjoy a carefree life?"

These questions will invariably arise both in their own minds and in the minds of their patients, and they must be prepared to answer them.

The presence of suffering in the world has created a problem which has baffled the intellects of many renowned philo-

140

sophers. Down through the ages, great minds have struggled with this problem and found it difficult of solution. In the face of bitter suffering, even those blessed with the gift of Faith have at times been tempted to question the goodness of God.

For the materialist, who does not believe in God, there can, of course, be no problem. Nature is for him nothing more than a mass of cruel, irresistible, physical forces. For him, disease and death represent merely the triumph of stronger physical powers over weaker man.

This materialistic philosophy of the modern world has resulted in its frequent advocation of euthanasia or, as it is more popularly called, "mercy-killing." Along with suicide, this evil implies an absolute ignorance and lack of appreciation of the basic moral truths underlying the Christian philosophy of suffering.

Euthanasia is no new evil in civilization. As one might well expect, it is as old as the materialistic philosophy of life which underlies it. Thus, in ancient Sparta, not only those who were regarded as incurable, or physically unfit, but all who were deemed useless to the State were killed, or permitted to die.

In our age, certain doctors and some organizations, under the guise of "humanitarianism" have clamored for the legalization of euthanasia. The following incidents reflect typical expressions of this attitude.

In a press interview, Doctor Alexis Carrell, winner of the Nobel Prize, elaborated on certain passages in his volume entitled *Man the Unknown*. He was reported as saying: "Sentimental prejudices should not stand in the way of civilization; it is my opinion that not only incurables, but imbeciles, habitual criminals, as well as the hopelessly insane, should be quietly and painlessly disposed of."

A similar plea for the acceptance of euthanasia was attributed by the press to Doctor Frederick Bancroft, member of the New York City Cancer Committee. While admitting that there are certain difficulties involved, he says: "I do not see why a person should be condemned to agony; I do not see why we should not give humans the same treatment we accord to animals."

According to an International News Service Dispatch of February 4, 1936, the Rev. Dr. C. F. Potter advocated the use of the lethal gas chamber for incurable imbeciles.

In 1937, a poll by the Institute of Public Opinion reported that the medical profession itself was so much influenced by the arguments for euthanasia that fifty-three per cent of the doctors polled, favored "mercy killing."

Bills to legalize euthanasia were introduced without success in the British Parliament in 1936 and in the legislature of the State of Nebraska in 1937.

Doctor Foster Kennedy, head of the Neurological Division of Bellevue Hospital, New York City, also advocated a qualified legalization of euthanasia. His thoughts were contained in an article "To Be or Not to Be," written for the May 20, 1939 issue of *Collier's*. (The editors apparently thought so much of this materialistic article that they reprinted it ten years later, in the April 22, 1950 issue, when the Saunders "mercy-killing" case in New Hampshire attracted national attention.) In this article, Doctor Kennedy objects to widespread euthanasia but feels that in the case of those who are born with a hopelessly damaged brain "we surely might be allowed legally to grant a dreamless and unending sleep; let us try to relieve of living the young person or child who should never have lived at all."

In a later scientific article, Doctor Kennedy stated: "I believe that when the defective child shall have reached the age of five years—and on the application of his guardians—that the case should be considered under law by a competent medical board; then it should be reviewed twice more at four month intervals; then if the Board, acting, I repeat, on the application of the guardians of the child, and after three examinations of a defective who has reached the age of five or more, should decide that that defective has no future nor hope of one; then I believe it is a merciful and kindly thing to relieve that defective—often tortured and convulsed, grotesque and absurd, useless and foolish, and utterly undesirable—of the agony of living." (*American Journal of Psychiatry*, 1942-1943, Vol. 99, p. 13.)

Doctor Kennedy admits that one time in his life he was in favor of an unqualified legalization of euthanasia. Now he says: "My face is set against the legalization of euthanasia for any person who, having been well, at last becomes ill; for, however ill they may be, many get well and help the world for years after." He adds that he is now "in favor of euthanasia for those helpless ones who should never have been born—nature's mistakes; in this category it is, with care and knowledge, impossible to be mistaken in either diagnosis or prognosis." (loc.cit.)

In 1946, a group of non-Catholic ministers in New York stated that voluntary euthanasia "should not be regarded as contrary to the teaching of Christ or to the principles of Christianity." (*New York Times,* Sept. 28, 1946.)

In 1947, a bill was proposed unsuccessfully in the New York General Assembly. This bill read as follows: "Any person of sound mind over twenty-one years of age who is suffering from severe physical pain caused by a disease, for which no remedy affording lasting relief or recovery is at this time known to medical science, may have euthanasia administered" at his own request and after a judicial hearing.

It is encouraging, however, to note that in recent years there has been a strong counter-action against the euthanasia movement and also an evident decrease in public interest in it.

Thus, as one would expect, the Church strongly condemned euthanasia on December 2, 1940. On this occasion the Church was asked whether the State may directly kill persons who had committed no capital crime but who are useless to the nation and who constitute a public burden by reason of their physical or mental defects. The Holy Office answered on the above date that such an act would be in direct violation of both natural law and Divine positive law.

Less than three years after this condemnation by the Church, Pope Pius XII issued his encyclical letter on *The Mystical Body of Christ.* In this papal encyclical, he writes:

"Conscious of the obligations of Our High Office We deem it necessary to reiterate this grave statement today, when to Our grief We see at times the deformed, the

insane, and those suffering from hereditary disease
deprived of their lives, as though they were a useless burden to society; and this procedure is hailed by some as a
manifestation of human progress, and as something that is
entirely in accordance with the common good. Yet who
that is possessed of sound judgment does not recognize
that this not only violates the natural and divine law written in the heart of every man, but that it outrages the
noblest instincts of humanity. The blood of these unfortunate victims who are all the dearer to our Redeemer because they are deserving of greater pity cries to God from
the earth."

The ebbing of public interest in the matter is reflected in
the steady decrease in the number of articles which have appeared on the topic in the nation's principal magazines. Thus,
as seen by a survey of the *Periodical Index,* twelve articles were
carried by the nation's magazines on mercy-killing in the five
year period between 1930-1934; twenty-two articles were carried in the next five year period from 1935-1939; then, only
five articles were published in the five years between 1940-
1944; while not a single article on the subject was carried
between 1945-1950.

Worthy of mention also is the fact that the World Medical
Association, of which the American Medical Association is a
member, recently condemned euthanasia. At its Second General Assembly Meeting in Geneva, Switzerland, in September,
1948, it endorsed a modern version of the Hippocratic Oath
which includes this thought: "The health and life of my
patient will always be my first consideration."

At a more recent meeting, the World Medical Association
was more specific in its opposition to euthanasia: "Whereas,
the Council of the World Medical Association believes that
the practice of euthanasia is contrary to the public interest and
to medical ethical principles as well as to natural rights, and
whereas, such practice is contrary to the spirit of the Declaration of Geneva, therefore be it resolved, that the Council of
The World Medical Association in session at Copenhagen,
Denmark, April 24-28, 1950 recommends to the national medi-

cal associations that they condemn the practice of euthanasia under any circumstances."

The specious arguments advanced in favor of euthanasia have already been presented in this chapter by direct quotation from the writings of its proponents. Briefly, these arguments contend that there is no point in forcing certain physically and mentally defective persons to live a miserable existence. The kinder and more humane thing to do, says the advocate of euthanasia, is to release them painlessly from existence. To refuse a "mercy" death to the hopelessly incurable or insane is to condemn them to a life of agony. It is to refuse to man the alleviation from pain that we would grant an animal. It is to place unbearable physical, emotional, and financial burdens upon the family of the unfortunate person as well as upon society. The more sensible and happier solution for all parties concerned is to grant a painless death to such unfortunates. Such are the specious and attractive arguments advanced in favor of legalized euthanasia.

From the scientific point of view, there are many defects in the arguments advanced in favor of euthanasia. Actually these flaws are only of secondary importance—since the problem is basically a moral one, not a scientific one. For the sake of completeness, however, we shall mention some of these flaws:

(a) Erroneous medical judgments as to the hopelessness of many cases would be inevitable. Medical science has been advancing by 'leaps and bounds'. New drugs and new techniques accomplish results today which would have been regarded as fantastic a few years ago. For example, the "basket amputees" of a few years ago were regarded as hopeless; today, prosthesis, coupled with determination on the part of the victim to relearn, bestows functioning legs and arms on the patient, and he returns to society as an adjusted and useful citizen.

(b) If a statute authorizing voluntary euthanasia were ever enacted, it would not be long before there would be urgent demands to broaden its provisions so as to authorize its *compulsory* application to certain types of unfortunate people. Thus, those persons who are incurably ill, mentally deficient, insane or aged, and who are without parents or guardians and confined to state institutions, would soon be 'painlessly disposed of'. We have seen this trend at work in the realm of eugenic sterilization. Certain State laws at first authorized only voluntary sterilization upon the consent of parents or guardians; but, before much time elapsed, we soon saw State Medical Boards set up and empowered to render the desired decision.

(c) It is self-evident that incorrigible criminals are more of a hazard and burden to society than physically incurable persons. It would be a simple and logical step for the State to decide that, in the interest of the common good, it had the power to dispose also of habitual criminals.

(d) The legalization of euthanasia would destroy the soul of medical science. This field is dedicated to the conservation of life, not to its destruction. State-authorized euthanasia would gradually, but inevitably rob this profession of its appreciation of the sacredness of human life.

(e) Mercy-killing would do incalculable harm to the minds of men. It is a psychological fact that the deliberate killing of a fellow-man, even in self-defense, leaves a permanent mark upon the mind of anyone who has done it.

(f) State-authorized euthanasia would destroy the faith and confidence which must exist between patient and physician. Imagine the terror in which seriously ill persons would live if they believed that their doctor might possibly be planning to dispose of them as hopelessly incurable? Imagine how many seriously ill persons would refuse to seek medical aid because of their fear of this profession?

(g) Friends and relatives would often profit from a person's death. The pressure which would be exerted on the doctor to avail himself of a euthanasia law would often be difficult to resist.

(h) State-sanctioned mercy-killing would destroy the initiative for medical science to do research on diseases currently regarded as incurable.

As stated earlier, these and other scientific considerations are of secondary value in evaluating mercy-killing. Fundamentally, the problem is a moral one and must be evaluated as such.

Almighty God, as the Creator of the universe, is its one supreme Lord and Master. In the most absolute sense, all things belong to Him. The life of each single individual is a creation of the Almighty, and supreme mastery over such life belongs to the Creator alone.

If, perchance, certain individuals are born with physical or mental deficiencies, who is man to pass judgment on the creative act of God? Is the creature to say that the Almighty has erred; that He should never have bestowed life upon some unfortunate persons? Certainly not. Rather, it is man's obligation to conserve human life as one of the noblest creations of God. For man is merely the custodian of life, not its Master.

In the words of Pope Pius XII (October 29, 1951):

> "The direct destruction of what they call 'worthless life', born or unborn, practiced a few years ago on many occasions, can be justified in no way. For this reason, when this practice began, the Church formally declared that the killing, even by order of public authority, of those who although innocent are not only useless to the nation on account of physical or psychic defects but also a burden upon it, is contrary to positive natural and divine right and therefore, illegal."

In many instances, the mind of man will unquestionably find it difficult to understand why God allows certain physically and mentally defective persons to be born. Such mystery is, however, to be expected when the created intellect attempts to fathom the Mind and Purposes of the Almighty. It is man's duty to accept the decisions of God, not to pass judgment on them. If God has created and bestowed life upon man, it does not fall within the right of man to destroy it.

The fundamental immorality of euthanasia, therefore, lies in its direct violation of the supreme dominion of God over His creation.

The advocates of euthanasia moreover disregard the supernatural destiny of man and the rôle which suffering can play in the achievement of sanctity. They do not realize the ability of man, aided by God's grace, to bear suffering patiently. They do not know how resignation to pain can serve as penance and temporal punishment for personal moral failings. Lacking a true belief in the supernatural, they have no respect for the power of faith and prayer to produce miracles in even the most hopeless cases. Neither do they understand how the Communion of Saints makes possible vicarious suffering, that is, the ability of man to endure pain for the spiritual good of fellowman. The proponents of "mercy-killing," steeped as they are in a materialistic philosophy of life, cannot grasp the significance of these profound vital truths of Christianity.

These thoughts have been given clear expression by Doctor Bernard Ficarra in his recent book:

> "This sentimentalism loses sight of the essential difference in man and beast which comes from the human immortal soul. It degrades man to the level of the brute, and makes the physician a veterinary. It overlooks the noble virtues that are practiced by the pain-ridden and by those who care for them. It supposes that pain and happiness are mutually exclusive, and that material productivity is the measure of a man's worth. It denies the supernatural, and negates the practice of penance, the heroism of the martyrs, and the blood of the Redeemer. Preaching pleasure instead of virtue, it makes earthly life the final purpose of man instead of a time of probation for the eternal life in God." (Ficarra, B. J., *Newer Ethical Problems in Medicine and Surgery*, pp. 93-94.)

Up to the present time the campaign for the legalization of euthanasia has not succeeded. In both American and English civil law, "mercy-killing" is still regarded, as it should be, as simple murder.

The agitation for euthanasia cannot, therefore, be justified under the principles of the common law, which looks to the Divine and Natural Law as supreme on all vital concerns. But in recent years there has arisen a school of jurisprudence which refuses to acknowledge either Divine or Natural Law as having any binding force. Motivated by a spirit of materialistic pragmatism, this school of thought would erect a legal structure with only one consideration in mind: *any course of action which will alleviate the material burden on individuals and society, and thus contribute to the general well-being of society, should be allowable.*

The most respected authority in the realm of civil law is, of course, Sir William Blackstone; and it is quite pertinent at this point to note how accurately he portrayed the relationship which should exist between Divine and Natural Law, and the laws enacted by civil authority. In his *Commentaries on Law*, he wrote:

> "*The Law of Nature*—This law, being coeval with mankind and dictated by God Himself is obligatory on all. No human laws are of any validity if contrary to this, as they derive their force and authority from this original. We must discover what the law of nature directs in every circumstance of life, by considering what method will tend the most effectively to our own substantial happiness.
>
> *Revealed Divine Law*—In compassion for the imperfections of human reason, God has mercifully at times discovered and enforced His laws by direct revelations. These are found in the holy scriptures. These precepts, when revealed, are really a part of the original law of nature. The revealed law is of greater authenticity than the moral system framed by ethical writers, termed the natural law, because the one is the law of nature, as declared to be by God Himself; the other is only what, by the light of human reason, we imagine to be that law.
>
> *Foundations of Human Law*—Upon these foundations, the law of nature and the law of revelation, depend all human law; that is, no human law should contradict them.
>
> *Murder*—This crime is expressly forbidden by the Divine Law, and demonstrably by the natural law, and from these prohibitions arise the true unlawfulness of the crime. Those human laws that annex a punishment to it do not increase its moral guilt. If, therefore, any human law should allow or enjoin the commission of such crime, we should disobey such law, or we would offend both the natural and the divine." (Blackstone's *Commentaries on Law*, Gavit's Edition, p. 27.)

Unfortunately, however, the manner in which the State has enforced its law is hardly worthy of praise. In some instances, a fitting penalty is given the culprit; in other cases, emotion and a false humanitarianism result in the complete acquittal of those who admit that they have been guilty of this crime.

Thus, in April, 1940, at Allentown, Pennsylvania, a nurse received a life sentence for the "mercy-killing" of her own sister. But in May, 1939, in New York City, a father was freed without any penalty after the acknowledged "mercy-slaying" of his imbecile son.

The State must realize that it is the purpose of civil law to mirror, amplify, and clarify the Natural Moral Law. It is the obligation of the State, not only to make laws which serve this purpose, but also to see to it that such laws are enforced. Law without penalty for its violation is useless.

The ever-recurring acquittal of those who admit having committed euthanasia is most lamentable. Such an acquittal not only grants freedom to a confessed murderer, but also seriously injures society by setting a precedent which tends to induce others in similar circumstances to commit the same offense.

In the face of periodical pressure for the legalization of euthanasia, the State must remain firm. It must remember that it has no direct power over the lives or bodies of its citizens. It is true that it has an indirect power over life in the sense that it can declare that a person has forfeited his life by the commission of a grave crime. Obviously, however, the incurable or insane are not criminals, and the State has absolutely no authority to sanction the destruction of their lives.

Human life belongs to the Creator alone as its Supreme Lord and Master. Neither man himself nor the State has any right to destroy it. Their obligation is to take all ordinary means to conserve this great gift of God.

Throughout their entire professional career, a doctor or nurse may never be asked to play any rôle in the commission of a "mercy-killing." But they may reasonably expect to meet certain problems related to this general topic. The following principles will aid them in the solution of such difficulties.

It is never permissible to give a drug which would hasten the death of a suffering patient. The fact that the patient is certain to die soon does not alter the problem.

It is never permissible to hasten the death of any product of human conception. The degree of deformity does not change the situation. There is no obligation to take *extraordinary* measures to prolong such life, but baptism should be administered and the *ordinary* steps to conserve life must be taken.

⌐In the case of those dying in great pain *without being spiritually prepared for death*, it is not morally permissible to administer any drug which would take away consciousness. ⌐ Such an act obviously grants alleviation from pain at the expense of possible reconciliation with God.

In the case of those dying in great pain, who are known to be spiritually at peace with God, a drug may be administered which will alleviate pain and also take away consciousness. The practice is, however, not to be recommended.⌐ It is often difficult to be certain that a person is spiritually prepared to die, and the loss of consciousness deprives the dying person of the spiritual merit which might be derived from resignation to suffering. The ideal solution, if possible, would be to use a drug which would alleviate pain but not totally destroy consciousness.

The following passage from the recent work by Doctor Bernard Ficarra contains some appropriate thoughts on the problem of alleviation of pain:

"In his practice, the practitioner is often confronted with a serious dilemma in this matter. If he does not administer the drug for relieving pain, the patient must continue to endure pain and that mere fact may hasten the patient's death. If, on the other hand, the physician administers the drug, the condition of the patient himself may be such that the effect of such administration is simply unpredictable and often enough, the drug itself might accelerate the coming of death. In such a moment, the physician must fall back upon his own personal philosophy of life and upon his own philosophy of medical practice. If death is looked upon as a merely biological phenomena, it might conceivably make little, if any difference, other things being equal, whether a patient's life is prolonged for ten minutes or shortened by ten minutes. If, on the other hand, it is realized, as certainly a physician, above all people should realize, that the moment of death is the most important moment of life, the moment upon which

depends the patient's fate for an immortal eternity, then
surely, the gravity of the physician's decision is simply
overwhelming. The dominant controlling and limiting consideration cannot be whether or not the patient is going
to continue in suffering or whether he will be relieved
but rather, whether, as far as the physician can be held
responsible, the patient will be in such a condition at the
moment when death comes that he will face that indescrib-
ably important moment in full consciousness and in the
full possession of his senses even though he be in pain and
suffering.

The right to deprive a patient of his consciousness
even for the purpose of relieving his pain, is not an absolute and unlimited right. It is contingent upon circumstances, upon the physician's intentions and perhaps on
many other considerations. The physician must have a
laudable and worthy purpose or at least not a vicious one,
to deprive a patient of consciousness. Hence, if, as happens
at the moment of approaching death, other considerations
must prevail, in fact, must be given dominant consideration over the relief from pain, then surely, the physician
who insists that even under such circumstances he will
administer a drug, may be guilty of a real crime which may
have the fartherest reaching consequences. Unless the
assurance is all but certain that a patient has used all the
means to ensure a death, as far as he is able to achieve it,
in the friendship of God, it certainly cannot be questioned
whether any physician has the right to administer a nar-
cotic with a definite foreknowledge that the patient will
probably die in the ensuing narcosis. It is sometimes said,
especially in non-Catholic hospitals, that Catholics desire
to receive all the sacraments of the dying first, before subjecting themselves to a terminal narcosis. A physician who
disregards such a wish is, of course, unjust and uncharitable
to his patients. As a matter of fact, however, a physician,
Catholic or otherwise, who fails to safeguard the spiritual
welfare of his patient, even at the cost of the severest pain,
under such conditions, must be held accountable for the
serious consequences which may ensue with reference to
the patient's eternal welfare." (Ficarra, B. J., *Newer Ethical Problems in Medicine and Surgery,* pp. 75-77.)

A true appreciation of the immortal destiny of man and the absolute supremacy of God makes evident the grave immorality of euthanasia. But calm consideration of the problem of pain reveals with equal clarity the folly of allowing the presence of suffering in the world to lead us to doubt either the existence or the goodness of God.

As a matter of fact, it is only when we already accept the existence and goodness of God that we are confronted with a problem.

We certainly possess abundant convincing evidence of the existence of an all-good and all-wise God. We know also that physical and mental suffering are very true realities in life. These are two firmly established facts. And if we are to arrive at a solution to our problem, it must be based upon a reconciliation of what we already know to be true.

The solution is obviously not in denying the goodness of God any more than it is in denying the reality of pain. One is certainly not justified in questioning the goodness of God simply because he has encountered pain in the world.

How then are we to reconcile His goodness with the presence of suffering in the world?

Anyone studying the problem of pain must, of course, fully realize that God is infinitely above man. With our weak, finite intellects, we can never expect to understand fully the actions of the Almighty. His infinite Mind and Purposes can never be wholly comprehended by us. In the words of Sacred Scripture: "How incomprehensible are His judgments, how unsearchable His ways" (Rom. XI, 33).

It would be strange indeed if a lowly creature could fathom the designs of the infinite Creator of the universe. It is far more reasonable for us to expect some mystery when we attempt to comprehend the actions of God.

Both doctor and nurse will have innumerable opportunities to fortify the minds of their patients with a sound Christian attitude toward suffering. We do not mean to imply that they need set out on a program of spiritual regeneration for all of their patients. The fact of the matter is that their patients will often come to them for such help.

The suffering man almost invariably yearns for a sympathetic understanding of his condition. The frailty of human nature causes the pain-racked body and the worried mind to thirst for consolation and comfort. It is only the deeply spiritual soul that fully realizes the futility of human consolation and turns its gaze solely on things eternal. For the most part, men will never cease reaching out in their pain for the reassuring hand and words of their fellow creatures.

The comfort and consolation which the doctor and nurse can give is frequently very meager. It will ever be one of their unfortunate experiences that they will have to behold men in an agony which they are powerless to relieve. At times they will have to turn from a bedside where a broken body pleads and screams to be put out of its pain. In a thousand bitter experiences of their careers they will stand helpless before pain; and, as they stand, they shall realize only too well the weakness of man's power and the limitations of his science.

They must, however, never forget that their ever-recurring inability to relieve innumerable cases of physical and mental suffering is only an inability to provide a purely human and temporary consolation. It is true that they cannot always banish physical pain and free the mind of torturing worries. *But they are always capable of providing the patient with a far more valuable comfort.*

No greater benefit can be conferred upon suffering man than to imbue his mind with a knowledge of the inestimable value of suffering and the divine purposes which it can be made to serve. A doctor or nurse who brings to a suffering patient such a new insight into the meaning of life has bestowed a priceless gift upon him. No act of theirs which might soothe physical or mental pain can begin to compare with imparting to the patient a deeper insight into life.

Before they can teach such a profoundly spiritual lesson, they must, of course, create in their patient a feeling of confidence. The patient must be made to regard them as an invaluable source of not only medical skill but also of spiritual strength. The sufferer must not be allowed to feel ashamed at seeking such human sympathy and understanding. It may be found very inadequate, but it is the most human thing that a suffering man could do.

The strongest Man this earth has ever seen sought human consolation in His suffering, and the meager sympathy He received was pitiably incapable of relieving Him. In the hour of His most bitter agony, those whom He had saved, counselled and consoled, utterly neglected Him. They slept on calmly as He suffered and prepared to die for them. Amidst utter desolation, Christ was abandoned by men and left alone to suffer the greatest physical and mental pain that any man has ever endured. It is true that He was Divine, but He was perfectly human as well. And His human heart, filled with a tenderness beyond our weak comprehension, sought in vain for a word of human consolation.

The patient must therefore see in the suffering Christ, One to Whom he may go with full confidence. The Saviour Himself in His hour of trial sought human consolation, experienced its failure, and then turned to His Divine Father.

The suffering patient who learns to turn to Christ will find in Him the great Consoler of mankind. Just as His loving hands were constantly outstretched throughout His earthly life to restore health to disease-ridden bodies, sight to blind eyes, strength to paralyzed limbs, and even life to the dead, so now does He remain the one great Physician of the universe.

The modern world, steeped in its glorification of all that is material and transitory, never thinks of going direct to God for consolation. But the modern world has not offered, and cannot offer, any worthwhile substitute to the soul that is sunk in the depths of intense and incurable suffering.

Without a spiritual outlook on life, the suffering soul is tempted to turn to suicide, an ugly escape from reality. Such unfortunate souls neither know the strength of God's love nor realize that the life He has bestowed upon them has an eternal destiny.

When suffering teaches a man to go to God, it has taught a priceless lesson. At the moment a man learns that he really needs God, he has begun to grasp the real purpose of life. It is a bitter lesson, but a profitable one, when man begins to see that suffering is in reality an invitation to turn to God.

The doctor and nurse must hold it constantly before the eyes of their suffering patient that no one is too small or unimportant to be the concern of God. The outstretched arms of Christ on the crucifix beckon every sufferer to come to Him.

Response to this call of Christ will cause pain to be seen in a wholly different light. Suffering will become a medium of union with the Saviour of mankind. And the more completely and confidently the suffering soul places itself in the arms of the Crucified, the more certainly will it be using pain as a stepping-stone to its eternal union with God.

It is evident that suffering is a path to spiritual greatness only in so far as it is accepted with the proper attitude. A person might be afflicted with intense physical and mental pain from the cradle to the grave, and it might serve no spiritual purpose. The opportunity to acquire spiritual merit through suffering can be wasted just as any other opportunity in life can be thrown away.

Resignation to the will of God is the one vital element which must characterize an individual's suffering before it can possess any spiritual value. Resignation is admittedly a word which can fall easily from our lips, while the attitude which it represents is most difficult for man to adopt. This difficulty unquestionably arises from man's inability to grasp in all its fullness the purpose of life.

Even the man who knows that his goal is beyond the stars, that his destiny is eternal, finds it almost impossible to break away completely from the love of this earthly life. A wholly spiritual outlook on life is very rare among men and admittedly most difficult to attain. Resignation is therefore not so much a virtue in itself as it is the fruit of all virtues. It is born of a deep realization that only the thoroughly purified soul can be united to the sinless Saviour of the world and that it is by the voluntary acceptation of pain that man is able to be purified.

Resignation to suffering thus serves as a chastisement for past offenses, as an inducement to a more spiritual outlook on life, and as an opportunity to submit to the will of the Creator in all things. Just as man is able to look beyond the darkness of night to a beautiful day, and beyond the dreariness of winter to a glorious spring, so does resignation to suffering enable him to look beyond the material and temporal to things eternal.

The two thieves on their crosses to the right and left of Christ present us with a most astounding lesson on the necessity of resignation to suffering. Both thieves suffered the same agony beside our Crucified Saviour. Yet one thief received a Divine promise of entry into Paradise on that very day, while the other died in his bitterness without any such promise.

A striking difference between the two thieves appears to have been one of resignation. One accepted his lot, thought of his spiritual destiny, turned to Christ, and received an infallible assurance of eternal happiness. The other rebelled against his lot, despised Christ, and died without any promsie of salvation.

The value and necessity of resignation could not be more forcibly portrayed than in this closing event of Christ's life.

It is an unfortunate fact that doctors and nurses will encounter innumerable patients who suffer enough to become saints and yet, because of a rebellious attitude toward their lot, their suffering serves no useful purpose.

Wasted suffering, man's rebellion against that which he must accept, uncovers one of the most lamentable of human inconsistencies. Such antagonism cannot possibly relieve man's condition; it serves only to deprive him of the supreme value which is so intimately connected with suffering. If he could avoid pain by rebelling against it, his action would not be spiritual but it would be at least understandable. But when he cannot avoid suffering, it is obviously most foolish to revolt against it and thus lose inestimable spiritual benefits.

It may be objected that this philosophy of suffering is on a very high plane.

Our only answer is that man was created on a very high plane. The Almighty fashioned him with a spiritual soul and bestowed upon him an eternal destiny. And Christ, the God-Man, revealed to him the priceless value and the supernatural significance of suffering. Impelled by infinite love, He chose suffering in its bitterest form to raise mankind to the supernatural life.

For these reasons, the true follower of Christ sees in suffering a stepping-stone to holiness, a divine invitation to spiritual greatness.

We must not expect to find it easy to teach the Christian philosophy of suffering. The presence of pain greatly affects the accurate functioning of man's mind. Just as emotion and prejudice disturb the operations of reason, so does the presence of suffering make it extremely difficult to form clear judgments. It is no easy matter for man to arrive at an impartial judgment on suffering, especially at the very moment when his body is tortured by it.

We must be sympathetic to the hardship under which a patient is laboring. We must not be surprised or discouraged when a suffering patient, even though he be a good Christian, finds it hard to grasp the supernatural value of pain. Indeed, it should be a matter of great surprise to a doctor or nurse if they should succeed easily in imparting a lesson of such profound spiritual depth.

Following the age-old example of Holy Mother Church, members of the medical profession will do all in their power to banish and to relieve both physical and mental pain. No sacrifice will be too great for them if through it they may better the lot of their fellowman. But even when, in the face of intense and incurable pain, human science and skill admit defeat, they will not consider their work done. They will bring to such suffering souls a deeper insight into life and a realization that they may use pain as means of spiritual union with God. Certainly such a rôle is truly great and noble.

Problems for Discussion

1. How would you talk to an incurable patient who felt that life was no longer worth living?
2. How does your philosophy of suffering contrast with that of the materialist?
3. How does your philosophy of suffering contrast with that of the Christian Scientist?

4. Our State Laws regard "mercy-killing" as murder. How do you account for confessed "mercy-killers" being acquitted?

5. How would you talk to someone who was at the point of casting aside his belief in God because, after having led an ideal moral life for many years, he was afflicted with an incurable disease? He cannot believe that a good and just God would allow evil persons to enjoy good health, while so many truly good persons are afflicted with incurable diseases.

6. When a patient is dying, what do you think of the use of drugs which will relieve pain but render the person unconscious?

7. Judging from your own personal experience, what influence does a person's philosophy of suffering have on the amount of happiness they enjoy in this life?

8. Judging from your own personal experience, what influence does a person's philosophy of suffering have on his physical recovery?

9. How has contact with suffering and death affected your own personal outlook on these phases of life?

10. A patient has been in a sanitarium suffering from tuberculosis. X-rays have definitely shown that the condition is incurable and that the patient is in the last stage of the disease. The patient is frequently delirious and, at such times, evidences suicidal tendencies. There are not enough nurses in the sanitarium to make it possible for one to stay with the patient at all times. Morphine will quiet the patient but if given in the last stages of the disease appears to bring the end a little sooner than it would ordinarily come. May the nurse administer the morphine?

11. A patient is dying in great pain. Death is certain and inevitable. A certain stimulating drug may prolong life for another hour or two. Members of the patient's family tell the doctor and nurse that the patient has suffered enough already and request that the drug not be given. Comment on the case.

12. A mother gives birth to a monstrosity which appears to be still-born. The nurse carries the child to the scrub-room to administer conditional baptism. When the water touches the head of the child, it cries, and the nurse places it in the heating bassinet. The doctor, hearing the cry of the child, asks the nurse to remove the child from the bassinet and to allow it to die. She refuses to do so, and the child lives for twenty-four hours before dying. Comment on the case.

13. An apparently normal baby was born, but it was soon discovered that it had congenital atresia. By artificial means, an esophagus could be made. If this was done, the child would always have to be fed through this opening. The pediatrician regarded this as a cruel way to live and thought that the baby should be allowed to starve to death. The parents are wealthy and could readily meet any expenses which would ever result. Must this technique of preserving the child's life be adopted, or may it be allowed to die?

14. Have you carefully studied the philosophy of suffering portrayed in the *Foreword* to this book?

References for Reading

ARNOLD, F.: "Are 'Mercy-Killings' Justifiable?" (pamphlet), Sunday Visitor Press, Huntingdon, Ind.; also contained in *Graduate Nurses*, pp. 101-108, N. Y., 1938.

CONNELL, F.: "Anesthesia of a Dying Person," *American Ecclesiastical Review*, Sept., 1946, pp. 221-222.

Cox, I.: *Mercy Killing is Murder* (pamphlet), Paulist Press, N. Y.

FICARRA, B. J.: *Newer Ethical Problems in Medicine and Surgery*, N. Y., 1951.

GARESCHE, E.: "The Philosophy of Pain," *Graduate Nurses*, pp. 14-25, N. Y., 1938.

LEWIS, C.: *The Problem of Pain*, N. Y., 1944; (before use, consult an analysis of this book in the *American Ecclesiastical Review*), pp. 312-313, Oct., 1944.

ROCHELLE-FINK: *Handbook of Medical Ethics*, pp. 164-170, Westminster, Md., 1943.

SCHWITALLA, A.: "The Moral Aspects of Euthanasia," *The Linacre Quarterly*, April, 1947.

SIMONART, P.: "The Catholic Hospital and the Neglected Mentally Ill," *Hospital Progress*, August, 1948, pp. 269-271.

WOYWOD, S.: "The Use of Morphine and Other Opiates in Death Agony," *Homiletic and Pastoral Review*, pp. 1197-1201, August, 1937.

CHAPTER 7

Direct Abortion

The crime of abortion is an evil of long standing among mankind. It is a crime which has been committed from the earliest days of the human race. History attests to the fact that it was known in the ancient civilizations of Egypt, Greece, Rome, China, and Palestine. It is said that there exists in writing a Chinese medical formula for abortion which dates back to the period 2737-2696 B. C.

When we possess written evidence that this crime is more than forty-six centuries old, how old must it be in reality? The science of Anthropology contributes much evidence on its presence among primitive peoples; these people, steeped as they are in ignorance, magic, and superstition, utilize unbelievably cruel and fantastic methods of procuring abortion.

It is always well to understand at the outset the precise nature of the topic under discussion.

We, therefore, give the following definition of our topic: *Abortion is the expulsion of a living fetus from the uterus before viability.*

Viewed from the physical standpoint, this expulsion of the living fetus may be either *spontaneous* or *induced.*

Spontaneous abortion is that which results from accident or disease. *Induced,* or *voluntary,* abortion is that which results from man's intentional interference with the normal course of pregnancy.

In the present chapter, we are not concerned with spontaneous abortion. In the case of the truly spontaneous abortion, the expulsion of the fetus is not an effect which is intentionally produced. Since knowledge and freedom are essential to a moral act, it is clear that there can be no moral guilt involved

161

in a purely spontaneous abortion. In the present chapter we shall be concerned, therefore, only with the morality of induced or voluntary abortion.

Induced abortion may be of two types: *direct* and *indirect* abortion.

By *direct* abortion we mean any instance in which means are specifically employed to procure the expulsion of the fetus.

Certain medical authorities divide direct abortion into "criminal" and "therapeutic" abortion. A "criminal" abortion is one which is done simply because a child is not desired and the termination of the pregnancy is not necessary for the preservation of health or life. "Therapeutic" abortion is that which is directly induced as a means of safeguarding the health or life of the mother.

By *indirect* abortion we mean any instance in which a treatment or operative procedure is performed for some other purpose but incidentally and secondarily does cause the expulsion of the fetus.

The present chapter is concerned only with direct abortion.

Some Statistics on Criminal Abortion

Estimates by competent authorities testify to the fact that the crime of abortion is unbelievably prevalent in our country. One can readily understand why it is most difficult to formulate an accurate estimate of the number of crimes of this type.

Doctor Frederick J. Taussig, leading authority on this subject, in a White House Conference Report on Child Health Protection, estimates the total annual figure for the United States at six hundred and eighty-two thousand.

Doctor F. C. Holden has given the higher figure of one million crimes of this type each year in the United States.

S. Dana Hubbard, former Health Commissioner of New York City, regards one hundred thousand abortions per year as a conservative estimate for New York City.

Doctor I. W. Kahn, a Medical Examiner for the New York Board of Health, has given an estimate of two hundred and fifty thousand abortions annually in New York City. The latter opinion is surely too high an estimate.

Contrary to popular belief, ninety per cent of those who
have abortions performed are married women. Only ten per
cent of the total is found among the unmarried.

Even if we accept the most conservative of the above estimates, it is evident that the annual number of abortions is a
matter of the gravest concern. In fact, the number of destroyed
lives seems to be almost equivalent to the annual natural increase in the population of our country. (By "natural increase"
we mean the annual number of births minus the annual number of deaths.)

There are about two million births each year in the United
States. For the year ending July 1, 1937, it was estimated that
there was an increase of about eight hundred and eighteen
thousand in our population. The number of lives destroyed
each year through abortion would seem therefore to be about
equivalent to the annual natural increase in our population.

There are about four thousand deaths from abortion *recorded* each year; it is reasonable to assume that there is at
least an equal number of deaths from abortion that are not
recorded as occurring from this cause.

Excellent studies, based on the most painstaking investigation, have revealed that in the cities of New York and Philadelphia, twenty-five per cent of the deaths from abortion were
falsely entered on the records.

That deaths from abortion are not recorded is amply verified
by the records of 1933 for New York City. We recall the estimated annual number of abortions for that city, and that there
are 2.1 deaths per hundred abortions. In the light of the most
conservative statistics, there must be at least 2100 deaths from
abortion each year in New York City. Only twenty-two deaths
stand on the City's public health record for 1933 as resulting
from abortion. Incidentally, there was not a single civil prosecution in any of these twenty-two recorded deaths.

Doctor F. J. Taussig, the previously quoted authority on this
topic, estimates that there are 15,000 maternal deaths from
abortion each year in the United States. This figure would
lead to the conclusion that there are 2.1 deaths per hundred
abortions. This estimate does not, of course, include in any

way the high percentage of women who are seriously mutilated, rendered sterile, or made permanent invalids. (It is estimated that fifty thousand women are rendered sterile each year as the result of abortions.)

It is interesting to note that *abortion is the greatest single cause of maternal mortality in the United States.* According to the 1940 census, approximately one-fourth of all maternal deaths result from this cause. Of the abortions which caused this one-fourth of all maternal deaths, thirty-seven per cent were spontaneous abortions, thirteen per cent were so-called "therapeutic" abortions, fifty per cent were illegally induced abortions.

Dr. Thomas Parran, Surgeon General of the U. S. Public Health Service, states that 24 out of every 100 women who die in pregnancy perish from abortion. He states that three-fourths of these deaths are due to blood-poisoning; hemorrhage accounts for many others.

It is sometimes said that puerperal septicemia is the greatest cause of maternal mortality. This statement is quite accurate. The explanation of the apparent contradiction is that abortion is the cause of much of the disastrous puerperal septicemia.

Three-fourths of the deaths from abortion are due to puerperal septicemia; nearly half of the maternal deaths resulting from puerperal septicemia follow induced abortion. This wholesale destruction of both child life and maternal life is indeed a lamentable fact in our supposedly advanced civilization.

Moral Law and Abortion

Direct and voluntary abortion is a moral offense of the gravest nature, since it is the deliberate destruction of an innocent life. The very nature of direct abortion is such that it involves the deliberate and direct removal of the inviable fetus from its natural situs, the womb of its mother, to an environment in which it cannot possibly live. *Such an action is essentially murder.*

There is, of course, no possibility of profitably discussing the morality of direct abortion, particularly therapeutic abortion, with one who has a materialistic concept of life. The moral

truth herein involved is based upon very fundamental principles of Natural Law. It follows from an acceptance of the
spiritual nature of man, the spiritual and eternal objective of
human existence, the intrinsic morality of human actions, and
the supreme dominion of God over all creatures. One who
does not accept these truths cannot possibly have the same scale
of values as one who does.

To discuss the morality of direct abortion, especially therapeutic abortion, while differing on the underlying ethical basis
would be as fruitless as a discussion on the proper answer to a
calculus problem while differing on the essentials of arithmetic.
*The only recommendation in such cases is to try to establish
the basic ethical truths before discussing therapeutic abortion.*

We have said that before discussing the morality of direct
abortion, particularly therapeutic abortion, one must first
acknowledge *the intrinsic character of morality.*

Unless the truth is accepted that human actions are, *by their
very nature,* either morally good or morally evil, there is no
possibility of a stable moral code.

A human action is *by its very nature* morally good whenever
it is spiritually perfective of man, that is, whenever it helps
man to progress toward his final end.

A human action is spiritually perfective of man and helps
him to progress toward his final end whenever it fulfills a
moral obligation which rests upon his nature. Briefly, these
obligations are the duties which man owes to God, to himself,
to fellowman, to society, and, broadly speaking, to lower creation.

A human action is *by its very nature* morally evil whenever
it is spiritually injurious to man, that is, whenever it hinders
man in his progress toward his final end.

A human action is spiritually injurious to man and hinders
him in his progress toward his final end whenever it violates a
moral obligation arising from any of the above-mentioned
five sources.

The morality of an act is, therefore, determined by the very
nature of the act. It is by the performance of human actions
that our nature is brought to its final spiritual objective. *A*

human act is, therefore, measured in its morality by its intrinsic capacity to help or hinder man in the pursuit of the primary and final end of human existence."

To determine the *morality* of an act by the *temporal* benefits one might get out of it would be to set up an ethics of expediency. Countless acts which are universally acknowledged as immoral, such as stealing and lying, frequently produce much-needed *temporal* benefits. All of these acts would become permissible under such a principle."

To do away with the intrinsic character of morality is to do away with all ethics. No stable moral code would remain. Almost every conceivable action is capable of producing some temporal good and could therefore be justified. One can never make the end justify the means; that is, *one can never determine the morality of an act simply by a consideration of the physical and temporal benefits it can produce.* To adopt such a principle would be to destroy the foundations of both morality and social order.

The very nature of a direct abortion, criminal or therapeutic, is that it is an act of murder. *Murder is the direct and deliberate destruction of the life of a person, without proper authority.* Neither man nor the State has the authority to destroy the life of an innocent person, and certainly both criminal and therapeutic abortion involve a direct and deliberate destruction of an innocent life.

It would, indeed, be interesting to hear a proponent of therapeutic abortion define murder. If such a person defines "murder" accurately, he will not be able to justify therapeutic abortion. If some unique definition of murder is given, the path is opened immediately for the wholesale destruction of human life whenever notable temporal good would thereby be achieved.

Even in the case of those who agree on the intrinsic character of morality, the supreme dominion of God, and the spiritual nature and destiny of man, there may be some difficulty. It is not enough merely to know and accept these truths. One must *realize* the implications which follow from their acceptance.

As soon as the above truths are accepted, one must realize

that the all-important goal of human life is the achievement of eternal happiness.

Unquestionably, there are many important goods in this life. Wealth, reputation, friends, health, and life are very valuable. But, great as is their value, they are at best temporary goods. The greatest of them does not compare in value with any good or evil in the higher, the spiritual and eternal sphere.

For one who appreciates the above truths, there is an infinite gap between *any* temporal good and any spiritual good. The preservation of a physical or temporary good at the sacrifice of a spiritual and permanent good is certainly a most foolish act. It involves the deliberate throwing away of a higher and lasting good to preserve a lower and temporary one.

Centuries ago, and even up to modern times, it was believed by some that a distinction should be made between the fetus in its earliest stages of development and the fetus in its later stages when it has begun to take on a definitely human form. But today no such distinction is recognized. Both the science of Ethics and the science of Biology, as well as Church Law and Civil Law, regard the fetus as a human person from the very outset of pregnancy. NOT TODAY

The unborn child is, then, essentially a human being with all the rights of any other human person. The mere fact that the unborn child cannot defend its right to life does not in the least alter the gravely immoral character of the act. If anything, such a fact would render the action more despicable.

Neither does the fact that the life of the child is destroyed in the womb of its mother alter the grave immorality of direct abortion. The child is a human person whether it be in the womb of its mother, in the arms of its father, or playing in the street. The direct and deliberate destruction of that life is therefore sheer murder, regardless of the excuse which anyone might ever offer to justify it.

In the light of the moral law, the simplicity of the matter leaves little more to be said. Briefly, every living human fetus, regardless of its stage of development, is a human person and any act which is a deliberate and direct destruction of that innocent life is therefore an act of murder.

For these reasons, then, there is no moral basis whatever for any distinction between criminal abortion and so-called therapeutic abortion. Moral law unhesitatingly brands therapeutic abortion as murder in each and every case in which so-called medical "authorities" teach its indication.

Even the most serious complications of pregnancy offer no exception to this inviolable moral law. No mode of action, medicinal or operative, which is by its nature a direct attack on an inviable fetus, an innocent life, is ever morally justifiable. Regardless of the nobility or worthiness of an end or objective, man is never morally justified in acting immorally in order to attain such an end.

Briefly, no matter how readily and certainly direct abortion could preserve a mother's life or health, it is not morally permissible. Such an act is an obvious violation of the moral principle that the end does not justify the means. It is nothing more or less than the deliberate murder of an innocent life in order to preserve thereby the life or health of the mother.

Numerous pretexts are advanced in justification of abortion. Some are obviously mere excuses for the commission of this crime; others possess a certain amount of subtlety and convincing force.

Inadequate housing and poverty are sometimes suggested as causes justifying abortion. It should be clear from all that has preceded, that such a view is unquestionably immoral. People certainly deserve adequate housing and the necessities of life. But if these essentials of human living are lacking, the obligation to make them available rests upon the State and the citizen. It is the duty of the State to set up an environment in which man can earn a living for himself and his family. It is the duty of the citizen to work with industry within the social structure. Members of society are no more justified in procuring abortion in order to remedy poor economic conditions than they are justified in murdering a fellowman for the same reason.

More subtle and convincing is the demand for abortion in certain other difficult cases. Such cases are, for instance, those in which the continuance of the pregnancy will result in a serious danger to the health or life of the expectant mother.

Above all, there is the rare instance in which there is no possibility that the child can be born alive, and continuance of the pregnancy will certainly result in the loss of the woman's life.

Especially in this latter type of case, the advocate of therapeutic abortion invariably regards the attitude of sound Ethics as unreasonable and impractical. Why stand idly by and see two lives lost when one of these lives could easily be saved?

In response to this common and pressing question, we should like to offer four points of consideration, two from the scientific point of view, two on the moral basis on the problem.

First, from the *scientific* point of view, it is simply not true that we are confronted with cases involving a medical necessity to destroy the life of the fetus to safeguard the life of the mother. In earlier years, when the science of obstetrics was not as advanced as today, there were undoubtedly many baffling cases of this type. Today, there are still some cases of this type, but they are so infrequent that they are almost a medical rarity. The professor of Ethics will have this would-be dilemma proposed to him time and time again. Usually it is presented by a sincere layman who is almost wholly ignorant of the present-day medical facts; sometimes it is presented by an antagonistic mind as a sort of "bugaboo" which, it is expected, will make the defender of sound ethical principles appear quite unreasonable; more rarely, it will be presented by a doctor who has failed to keep himself informed on the progress of medical science.

The fact remains, however, that the top specialists in the nation unequivocally condemn any doctor who is "abortion-minded" and who looks to the cessation of pregnancy as the ready-made solution to his problems. These top-ranking specialists in obstetrics recognize that even from the physical or medical point of view, therapeutic abortions were needlessly performed in past years on a widespread scale. With recent advances in obstetrics available, they see no medical justification for therapeutic abortion and regard such a step as the product of either ignorance, laziness, or malice. Thus, in the September, 1944, issue of the *American Journal of Obstetrics and Gynecology,* Doctors Cosgrove and Carter showed very clearly that *even from a physical standpoint* there is rarely, if ever, a need of therapeutic abortion. In the Margaret Hague Maternity Hospital of Jersey City, N. J., only four therapeutic abortions were performed out of sixty-seven thousand deliveries in the thirteen year period from 1931 to 1943. For example, in a ten year period this hospital handled two hundred and ninety cases of *hyperemesis gravidarum* without a single maternal death and with only one therapeutic abortion performed. In sharp contrast to those startling figures, one learns that, between 1941 and 1942, for example, fifty-five therapeutic abortions out of nineteen hundred and three pregnancies were performed at Johns Hopkins. There is certainly food for thought in such statistics: the former hospital had recourse to therapeutic abortion in one case out of each 16,750 pregnancies; the latter institution resorted to the deliberate destruction of fetal life in one case out of each 35 pregnancies.

More recently, in November 1951, at the Convention of the American College of Surgeons, a Symposium on therapeutic abortion was presented. The members of the panel were: Samuel A. Cosgrove, M.D., of the Margaret Hague Maternity Hospital; Roy J. Heffernan, M.D., of Tufts College; Bernard J. Hanley, M.D., of the Los Angeles County Hospital; and John H. Morton, M.D., also of the Los Angeles County Hospital. All of the doctors unequivocally condemned therapeutic abortion.

Doctor Cosgrove stated: "I believe the negation of abortion on the strict grounds of moral law is good medicine." He reported that since 1944, more than 69,000 pregnancies have been handled at the Margaret Hague Maternity Hospital without a single therapeutic abortion. This hospital thus presents us with statistics from 1931-1951, totaling 136,467 pregnancies, with only four therapeutic abortions, and a maternal mortality rate as good or better than almost all of the other first-class hospitals of the nation.

Doctor Heffernan asserted that today there are no complications of pregnancy which cannot be successfully handled by proper medical care. In his own words: "Anyone who performs a therapeutic abortion is either ignorant of modern medical methods or is unwilling to take the time and the effort to apply them."

Doctor Frederick L. Good, Surgeon-in-Chief of the Gynecological and Obstetrical Service, Boston City Hospital, reported in 1951 that in more than sixty-six thousand pregnancies under his service, not one therapeutic abortion had been performed, and the maternal mortality rate from those conditions supposedly benefited by therapeutic abortion, has been zero. (Good-Kelly, *Marriage, Morals and Medical Ethics,* p. 149)

Even those specialists in obstetrics who are unwilling to admit that the advances in obstetrics have outlawed all need for therapeutic abortion do acknowledge unhesitatingly that today the so-called medical indications for it are few in number. Such is the general tenor of an article on "Changing Indications for Therapeutic Abortion" by Dr. Keith P. Russell, in the January 10, 1953, issue of the *Journal of the American Medical Association.* In this article he remarks:

"Until as recently as the past decade, therapeutic abortion was a relatively common procedure, well accepted by the majority of physicians as properly indicated for the preservation of the mother's life or immediate health in certain complicated pregnancies. All modern textbooks discuss the procedure, listing indications and incidences and describing methods of producing abortion. . . . During the past 10 years, however, there has been a growing appreciation of the fact that many indications for therapeutic abortion are no longer tenable in the light of continuing advances in medical and surgical knowledge. This realization has stimulated many institutions and organizations to study this procedure carefully and to re-evaluate their methods of managing the associated problems. The large decrease in the general maternal mortality rate to less than 1 per 1,000 live births has made it apparent that many of the complications formerly considered inimical to the mother's life can now be satisfactorily treated and the mother successfully carried through pregnancy."

Second, from the *scientific* point of view, in almost all of the cases in which there is a dangerous pregnancy, the difficulties could have been foreseen and pregnancy avoided either by refraining from marriage, by abstaining from the use of marital rights, or by a skilled supervision and application of the safe period method. (In this regard, the reader is referred to the opening pages of the next chapter which explain that the conditions which give rise to a demand for therapeutic abortion are almost always conditions which are not caused by pregnancy but which precede it and are independent of it.)

Even if pregnancy has occurred, practically all of the difficult cases can still be successfully handled. In nearly all cases, disastrous results are the product of the individual's own negligence and delay, failure to seek any prenatal care, failure to follow the advice of capable doctors, or a lack of necessary skill and care at the hands of others. It is a simple but cold fact that doctors, like all other men of science, vary in their knowledge, skill and experience. Common sense indicates, therefore, that an unusually difficult case may require the services of a specially skilled obstetrician. Patients should seek such aid when they need it; and less skilled doctors should be honest enough to refer a patient immediately to a capable specialist when they foresee that the woman will require the services of someone with more knowledge and skill than they themselves possess.

Third, from the *moral* point of view, one must again recall the basic ethical principle that the end does not justify the means. No one is more interested than the moralist in saving life. The innumerable Catholic hospitals operated by self-sacrificing men and women who have dedicated their lives to the alleviation of pain is abundant proof on this point. As much as the true Christian would like to save an endangered life, he knows that it would be immoral for him to deliberately and directly destroy an innocent life to achieve the desired objective. To effect direct abortion in order to save the mother's life is simply to murder the unborn child to save the mother. When man directly disposes of a human life, he is assuming a prerogative which belongs only to God Himself. The Creator alone is the supreme Master of life and death. The right, obligation and privilege of man is to do all in his power to conserve life. But the right to take innocent human life belongs to God alone.

Medical science deeply regrets its inability to save life in these comparatively rare and difficult cases. It knows that the true and best solution of the problem is to make available to prospective mothers good scientific prenatal clinics. Much commendable work has already been done in that direction. Men of science are, moreover, constantly and successfully devoting their knowledge and ingenuity to the discovery of morally good means of saving life in these difficult cases. Whatever is morally permissible to man, regardless of cost or labor, must be done by medical science in order to save life. But it must never descend to the destruction of an innocent life, to murder, in order to save another life.

Fourth, from the *moral* point of view, a proper appreciation of the position of sound Ethics on this difficult matter can be realized only by one who possesses a truly accurate concept of the nature and destiny of man. For such a person there is an infinite gap between moral evil (sin) and physical evil (suffering and death).

Moral evil is the only true and absolute evil. Physical suffering and death represent the loss of purely temporary goods of this life. Health and life are certain to be lost at some time. To effect an abortion to save a life is utterly opposed to a true scale of values. It is to commit a grave *moral* offense (murder) merely to preserve for a while longer a purely *physical* and temporal good (life). It is only a firm grasp of this concept of the purpose of life and the destiny of man which will enable one to understand this problem in its true light.

These thoughts were aptly expressed by Pius XII in his address on morality in marriage, delivered on October 29, 1951:

> "For this reason, those who approach the cradle wherein life is formed, assisting this activity in one way or other, must know the order that the Creator wishes to be preserved there and the laws that govern it. Hence it is not a question here of simple physical or biological laws which agents without reason and blind forces necessarily obey, but of laws whose execution and whose effects are entrusted to the free and voluntary cooperation of man.
>
> The order established by the Supreme Mind tends to

the object willed by the Creator. It embraces man's visible activities and the invisible participation of his free will; it implies both doing and not doing when duty so dictates. Nature puts at man's disposal the whole chain of causes giving rise to a new human life: it is man who has to release the living force, nature that must develop its course and bring it to completion. (Once man has performed his part and put into motion this wondrous evolution of life, his duty is to respect its progress religiously, and this is a duty that forbids his arresting the work of nature or hindering its natural development.)

Thus, the role of nature and that of man are clearly determined. Your professional training and experience fit you to know what man and nature do no less than the laws and rules to which both are subject. Your conscience, enlightened by reason and faith under the guidance of the Authority established by God, teaches you how far lawful action extends and where the obligation to abstain from action strictly imposes itself. . . .

Now the infant is 'man', even though it be not yet born, to the same degree and through the same title as the mother.

Every human being, even the infant in the mother's womb, has the right to life *immediately* from God, not from the parents or any human society or authority. Therefore there is no man, no human authority, no science, no medical, eugenic, social, economic or moral 'indication', that can show or give a valid juridical title for *direct* deliberate disposition concerning an innocent human life— which is to say, a disposition that aims at its destruction either as an end in itself or as the means of attaining another end that is perhaps in no way illicit in itself. Thus, for example, to save the life of the mother is a most noble end, but the direct killing of the child as a means to this end is not licit. . .

"The life of an innocent person is untouchable. Any direct attempt or aggression against it is a violation of one of the basic laws without which men cannot live together in safety. There is no need for us to go into details regarding the significance and weight of this basic law as far as your profession is concerned. But remember that the law

of God rises unshakable above all human laws, above all
'indications'."

The conscientious doctor and nurse will endeavor by word
and example to teach these truths to their patients. Certainly
they will teach the grave immorality of a deliberate and direct
attempt at abortion. But they should also instruct prospective
mothers to avoid all actions which might accidentally lead to
this same result. Good but uninstructed people will be encountered contantly. They should be taught how to conserve
and cherish the gift of God which is in their charge.

Prudent doctors and nurses will, for example, instruct them
on avoidance of violent forms of exercise and abstention from
strong purgatives. In these ways they will confer untold spiritual, physical, and social benefits upon those who come under
their care.

Certain contemporary writers would grant an abortion to
an innocent girl who has been the victim of a criminal attack.
Sound Ethics recognizes that such a person has been the victim
of unjust aggression. For this reason it assures her that she
may use any necessary means to eject or destroy the semen
provided this is done before conception takes place.

The reason for the permissibility of this act is that the semen
is present through an act of unjust aggression and is actually
still unjustly violating the girl's basic natural rights.

This situation is obviously different from any instance in
which the semen is present through the consent of a girl to the
act or through the exercise of marital rights by husband and
wife.

In these two latter instances, there is no basis for considering
the individual as the victim of unjust aggression and hence no
moral grounds for ejecting or destroying the semen.

Incidentally, on March 2, 1679, there was an official condemnation by the Church of any attempt to procure abortion
in order to save an unmarried mother from punishment or
loss of reputation.

It has been said that an innocent victim of unjust aggression
may eject or destroy the semen *provided it is done before con-*

*ception takes place. But once conception has taken place,
nothing may be done.*

A new and innocent life has then come into existence. This
new being is guilty of no offense, and its inalienable right to
life cannot be infringed upon in any way.

The application of this principle obviously involves an estimate on the probable time at which conception takes place. It
is possible that conception will occur within a quarter of an
hour after intercourse, but it is also possible that it will not
take place for some hours. Generous estimates hold that, even
in ordinary cases, conception may not take place for ten hours.
It is *possible, but not probable*, that conception would take
place even one or two days after intercourse.

For this reason, then, the victim of a criminal attack might
use all necessary means to eject or destroy the semen up to ten
hours after the offense took place. This is certainly a generous
estimate and provides a moral solution to the problem.

In most instances, one might well say that if a victim of a
criminal attack did nothing for ten hours, the unfortunate consequences would be largely the product of her own negligence
or ignorance.

The obvious implication in this matter for doctors and
nurses is that they may assist such an innocent victim, through
the administration of a douche, up to ten hours after the criminal attack. After that length of time has elapsed, it would be
immoral for them to do anything which could produce the
death or abortion of a fertilized ovum present in the uterus.

Church Law and Abortion

In view of the gravely immoral character of abortion, it is
not surprising to find that the Church takes a strict stand on
the matter.

In Canon 2350 of the Church's code of Canon Law, we read:
"Persons who procure abortion, the mother not excepted, auto-
matically incur excommunication reserved to the bishop of
the diocese at the moment the crime takes place."

The penalty of excommunication is incurred by all who
assist in procuring the abortion.

This includes (a) the mother; (b) all who knowingly and freely render necessary physical assistance in the commission of this crime; (c) anyone who commissions another to do the act (for example, any hospital authority who would delegate a doctor, interne, or nurse to carry out this action); (d) anyone who would order the action to be done (for example, parents who would force their daughter by threats to submit to an abortion); (e) anyone who formally coöperates in the crime (for example, those who advise, persuade, or instruct the mother in commission of the crime).

In an instance in which abortion is attempted but does not take place and the life of the unborn child *is not* destroyed, grave sin is committed, but the penalty of excommunication is not incurred.

Civil Law and Abortion

We have already seen that there is no moral basis for any distinction between criminal abortion and the so-called "therapeutic" abortion. The following chapter will give this matter further consideration. For the present, however, it must be stated that civil law does make such a distinction. *The condemnation of abortion found in civil law refers, therefore, only to criminal abortion.*

According to civil law, criminal abortion is a felony and subject to severe punishment. Civil law, moreover, regards as guilty of the crime, not only the principal perpetrator, but also those who are accessories either before or after the commission of the crime.

Doctors and nurses must realize that all crime is punishable by the State. They must understand that they, like all other members of society, are liable to civil prosecution for the commission of crime. Such criminal offenses may result either from doing an act which civil law regards as criminal or by failing to do an act which civil law obliges one to do.

This twofold division of crimes into acts of commission and omission is familiar to all. In these cases there is "evil intent" followed either by "a criminal act" or "criminal negligence."

In reference to "evil intent," one must not forget that a plea

of ignorance of the law will not be accepted as an excuse for
the committed crime.

The laws which govern society in general and the medical
or nursing profession in particular are formulated by the
proper legal authorities. These laws are then promulgated in
an established legal manner. After such publication, ignorance
of the law will not be accepted as an excuse for a crime committed against the law.

The obligation rests upon medical personnel to familiarize
themselves thoroughly with the laws which govern their profession in the specific State in which they happen to be working.

Usually we do not encounter the nurse as the principal perpetrator of the crime of criminal abortion. More frequently,
the nurse's rôle is that of an assistant to a doctor in this criminal offense. But the nurse cannot afford to forget that there are
laws, both moral and civil, which are far more basic than any
command a doctor may give.

Proper respect for superiors is a necessary virtue in a nurse.
Prompt obedience to commands is an ideal which should be
present in the character of every nurse. These virtues of the
medical profession are so frequently and strongly presented to
the nurse that, without realizing it, she frequently comes to
believe that blind obedience is always due her superiors.

Normally, this is a splendid attitude. *But the nurse must
never forget that Natural Law and Civil Law impose certain
limits on the type of action which any doctor may order or
suggest.* When the order or suggestion of a doctor is immoral
or illegal, no nurse may carry out that command without acting immorally and also leaving herself open to prosecution.

When there is any reasonable doubt as to the lawfulness or
unlawfulness of a doctor's order, with no immediate means of
discovering the true facts of the matter, the nurse should give
the doctor the benefit of the doubt and carry out the order
without question.

But there are certain cases, such as outright criminal abortion, which even the youngest nurse knows are both wholly
immoral and illegal. No nurse can carry out an order to assist
in such actions. Civil law admits that violent threats and

physical compulsion indicate a lack of evil intent. But it also emphasizes that the commission of a crime by a nurse will never be excused on the mere plea that she did it under the command of a superior. There is a vast difference between true coercion and command. The mere command of a doctor will never justify a nurse in carrying out an action which is immoral or illegal.

The nurse, moreover, should be well aware of the fact that even if she does a criminal act under physical coercion or grave threats she will have to present strong solid evidence to prove that point in court. It is known that she has committed a criminal act and the obligation will be placed on her to prove convincingly that she was not merely ordered but absolutely forced by grave threat or physical violence to carry out the criminal action. Very frequently it will be almost impossible to prove such a point even if it be true.

The prudent nurse will foresee and avoid situations in which she might be forced or commanded to perform a criminal act. She will invariably refuse to carry out any doctor's order which, in her judgment, endangers the life of her patients or which might be construed by civil law as a criminal act.

Civil law assumes the reasonable attitude that the graduate nurse is supposed to possess a definite amount of professional knowledge and skill. When she commits an act which such knowledge should indicate as immoral and illegal, civil law holds her responsible for that action. When she carries out any order which her training should indicate may endanger her patient, she leaves herself open to criminal prosecution. In some cases the charge against her may be nothing short of murder. Reflection on this fact should provide a nurse with much matter for serious thought.

In normal cases, the one who physically commits the criminal offense is regarded by civil law as the principal perpetrator of the crime.

If a person is present at the commission of a crime and aids in some way in its perpetration, civil law regards such a person as a principal in the second degree to the commission of the crime.

In instances in which a doctor or nurse is compelled to commit a criminal offense, civil law regards the instigator of the crime as its principal perpetrator. This thought should provide matter for serious thought for hospital authorities (chief of staff, hospital superintendent, superintendent of nurses) who compel their subordinates, through grave threats, to carry out or to participate in such actions as criminal abortion.

Doctors and nurses must remember that they may become enmeshed in the difficulties of civil law without even being present at the commission of a crime or even without being certain that the crime has actually occurred.

In another chapter, we speak of the implications which would follow if a doctor or nurse were to suggest to a woman a place or "doctor" where she might have an abortion performed. In such a case, even though they were not present at the commission of the crime, even though the woman never went to have the abortion performed, their words would be wholly sufficient for civil law to charge either of them with being an accessory before the fact in an attempt to procure a criminal abortion.

Similarly, civil law holds a person as an accessory to the crime of abortion if he or she conceals knowledge of the matter in court. This is true even though the person had nothing whatsoever to do with the commission of the crime.

Thus, a doctor or nurse might know that a certain doctor had performed a criminal abortion as the result of which the patient died. Even though they had nothing to do with this crime, civil law would hold them as accessories if it were discovered that they concealed knowledge of the crime when questioned about it in court.

Briefly, civil law regards anyone as an accessory to the crime if he or she possesses knowledge of the criminal abortion and uses his or her knowledge in such a manner as to obstruct justice.

Neither moral nor civil law could justify medical personnel in withholding the above information on the grounds of professional secrecy. Civil law does not recognize any right to maintain secrecy when the knowledge is relative to a crime.

Moral law does not recognize any right to withhold such information, because the good of society demands that the perpetrators of such crimes be punished. Moral law would, moreover, exempt doctors and nurses from any obligation of secrecy in such cases on the ground that retention of the knowledge would result in grave punishment coming to them.

Just as doctors and nurses can easily become accessories before the commission of the crime, so can they become accessories after its commission.

Civil law regards anyone as "an accessory after the fact" who shields the perpetrator of a criminal abortion in such a way as to enable the culprit or culprits to escape punishment. Any personal aid given by a doctor or nurse which the perpetrator of a criminal abortion uses to escape punishment makes the doctor or nurse a party to the crime.

Civil law takes the above rigid attitute toward all felonies. The legal duty rests upon every citizen to make known to the proper authorities the knowledge which he possesses of felonies which have been committed.

Murder, criminal abortion, and infanticide are regarded as felonies in practically every place. Members of the medical profession who possess knowledge of the commission of any of the above felonies are obliged by law to impart the information to the proper authorities. For them to conceal such information and thereby aid the criminal to escape punishment is to run the risk of being charged by civil law as accessories to the crime.

Moral law, then, brands abortion as a most grave moral offense. Church law inflicts the severe penalty of excommunication on all who particpate in this most heinous crime. Civil law takes the rigid stand that anyone who aids in the commission of this criminal act may be subjected to both heavy fine and imprisonment.

These thoughts should certainly be sufficient to make anyone refrain from even the most remote contact with this evil action.

Problems for Discussion

1. What steps must be taken by a woman guilty of abortion to regain her status in the Church after such a person has incurred excommunication?

2. A nurse casually discusses methods of committing abortion with two women friends. Later she discovers that one of these women has used this knowledge to procure abortion in her own case. Is the nurse responsible in this case? What lessons should she learn from this incident?

3. If the membrances accidentally rupture before the viability of the fetus, is it permissible to administer drugs to bring on an abortion?

4. A woman becomes pregnant and, after a few weeks, finds out that she has a venereal disease. Rather than having her child born in a deformed and diseased condition, she commits abortion. Evaluate the morality of her action.

5. A prospective mother has previously had two still-born children. Believing that her present child will eventually be born dead, she commits abortion. Do these circumstances alter the grievousness of her sin?

6. A woman in early pregnancy does not desire a child. She deliberately engages in strenuous athletics with the realization that abortion may result. Her attitude is that she would not directly destroy the life of the fetus but that she is certainly entitled to recreation. Comment on her attitude.

7. After reading the statistics on criminal abortion presented in the current chapter, how do you account for the almost complete failure to prosecute the guilty persons? What steps would you suggest for the enforcement of the law?

8. If you had a woman patient who has been habitually guilty of criminal abortion, would you attempt to point out to her the grave immorality of her actions?

9. A woman in the course of pregnancy falls down the stairs and suffers severe abdominal injuries. She cannot detect any fetal movements and is convinced that the unborn child has been killed. She then takes steps to procure abortion. Evaluate the morality of her action.

10. How do you account for the psychological fact that many persons who would destroy the life of an unborn child by abortion would shudder at the thought of murdering an innocent member of their own family?

References for Reading

BONNAR, A.: *The Catholic Doctor* (2nd ed.), pp. 72-81; 84-86, N. Y., 1939.

BURKE, E.: *Acute Cases in Moral Medicine*, pp. 1-47, N. Y., 1929.

DAVIS, H.: *Moral and Pastoral Theology* (4th ed.), Vol, 2, pp. 166-198, London, 1945.

FINNEY, P.: *Moral Problems in Hospital Practice*, pp. 5-95, St. Louis, 1930.

KELLY, G.: "Direct and Indirect Abortion," *Hospital Progress*, Oct., 1948.

MCCARTHY, J.: "Censure and the Crime of Abortion," *The Irish Ecclesiastical Record*, Nov., 1947, pp. 1007-1010.

MCHUGH, J.: "Canonical Penalties for Abortion," *Homiletic and Pastoral Review*, pp. 552-554, Feb., 1934.

MOORE, T.: *Principles of Ethics*, pp. 159-184, Phila., 1935.

ROCHELLE-FINK: *Handbook of Medical Ethics*, pp. 91-130, Westminster, Md., 1943.

SCHAAF, V.: "Canon Law and Abortion," *American Ecclesiastical Review*, pp. 623-624, Dec., 1935.

SCHEFFEL, C.: "The Criminal Responsibility of Nurses," *Jurisprudence for Nurses*, pp. 124-151, N. Y., 1938.

WOYWOD, S.: "Excommunication in Cases of Abortion," *Homiletic and Pastoral Review*, pp. 294-295, Dec., 1935.

CHAPTER 8

Therapeutic Abortion

In the preceding chapter, it was shown that direct abortion is gravely immoral and that there is absolutely no moral basis for any distinction between criminal and therapeutic abortion.

In the present chapter, we shall consider some of the more complex conditions which are frequently offered as a justification for a "therapeutic" abortion. We shall not repeat our explanation of the grave immorality of direct abortion. It shall be our task simply to show that the proposed procedure in these cases constitutes direct abortion. Having established that point, it will be clear, in the light of the previous chapter, that the proposed treatment would be gravely immoral.

The study of obstetrics should be a fascinating study for both doctor and nurse. It holds one in awe, as it were, watching the development of that gift of life which only God can create.

Along with the nursery, the prenatal clinic should be most interesting and inspirational. It is there that we have the priceless opportunity of watching the progress of that beautiful gift of God, the life of the unborn child. When need be, it is a truly noble task to pray and to fight for that life.

The normal cases as a rule are not difficult. The cases which are of grave concern are those involving the toxemias of pregnancy. The term "toxemias of pregnancy" is used to indicate a series of pathological conditions, specific in their nature, differing widely as to symptomatology, morbid anatomy and even as to the tissue attacked but having as a common factor the presence in a woman of a living embryo and its appendages. More than fifty per cent of all pregnant women become toxic

184

to some extent during the course of gestation, while about ten per cent are definitely affected.

Progress in accurate knowledge of the toxemias of pregnancy has been seriously hampered by a lack of uniformity in their classification. To overcome this difficulty, *The American Committee on Maternal Welfare* appointed a committee composed of seven of the nation's leading authorities on obstetrics to develop an acceptable classification of the toxemias of pregnancy based on available scientific and clinical knowledge of these diseases. The classification suggested by these specialists breaks down the toxemias into a fourfold division.

First, there are diseases with which a woman may be affected prior to pregnancy or which develop during but not as the result of a current pregnancy. This group includes preëxisting chronic vascular or renal disease and conditions such as acute glomerulonephritis and acute nephrosis which sometimes develop in the course of pregnancy but are not diseases peculiar to pregnancy.

The diseases in this first group are pseudotoxemias, rather than true toxemias of pregnancy. They are, however, classified among the true toxemias because the underlying pathologic lesion or lesions of each of these conditions tends to be aggravated by the increased physiologic demands of pregnancy and tends to produce symptoms which simulate either preëclamptic toxemia, eclampsia, or both.

The diseases in this first group may be either hypertensive or renal. The *hypertensive cardiovascular diseases* would be benign (essential), mild, severe, or malignant. The *renal* diseases would include chronic vascular nephritis or nephrosclerosis, acute or chronic glomerulonephritis, acute or chronic nephrosis, and other forms of severe renal disease.

Second, there are diseases dependent on or peculiar to pregnancy. This group would include mild and severe preëclampsia, as well as convulsive and nonconvulsive eclampsia.

Third, hyperemesis gravidarum is placed in this classification because of precedent. This condition is apparently not related to the hypertensive toxemias of pregnancy. It may or may not be a toxemia.

Fourth, some conditions are listed as "unclassified toxemias." This group is composed of cases which, because of insufficient or inconclusive data, cannot be classified in the course of pregnancy and the puerperium or during eight weeks of postpartum observation. The large majority of these cases can be classified ultimately under either the first or second group, during the course of a more or less prolonged period of observation or in consequence of subsequent findings at necropsy.

The above classification of the toxemias of pregnancy is most interesting to the moralist. It so happens that the severe moral problems are created by the first and third groups. The demand for therapeutic abortion is usually the result of pregnancy complicated by hypertensive disease and, to a lesser extent, by hyperemesis gravidarum. *These diseases which are not peculiar to pregnancy but which complicate it, and hyperemesis gravidarum, frequently create problems before the viability of the fetus has been reached.* Hence, the demand is made for therapeutic abortion.

In contrast, *the second group, which is made up of diseases dependent on or peculiar to pregnancy, does not usually produce a difficult situation until after the period of viability has been reached.* Under such circumstances, the moral problems which may arise are much easier to solve.

The above classification provides the moralist with an excellent division upon which he may base his treatment of direct and indirect abortion.

Since the conditions which create the most severe problems are not the result of pregnancy, and usually exist before it, one cannot help thinking that, whenever these conditions are remediable, adequate medical care before marriage would render many women more fit for the great privilege of motherhood.

Heart Conditions

Among the diseases of the blood and circulatory systems, certain heart conditions complicate pregnancy and occasionally offer a pretext for therapeutic abortion.

Some heart cases are looked upon as "bad obstetric risks."

These cases are women who have (a) congestive heart failure; (b) those who have a history of attacks of decompensation; (c) those who have or have had auricular fibrillation; (d) those who have an accompanying complication, such as profound anemia, notable obesity, nephritis, or equally serious conditions; (e) women over thirty-five years of age who have definite heart lesions, and (f) those who have had recent indications of acute rheumatic fever.

Many medical textbooks state that, in the above cases, pregnancy should be terminated by the vaginal route if the case is encountered before the third month, by abdominal hysterectomy with or without tubal sterilization whenever the case is met after the third month.

Pregnancy complicated by *leukemia* is a condition so rare that it hardly merits consideration. It is a fact, however, that medical textbooks frequently recommend therapeutic abortion when this condition accompanies pregnancy.

Rheumatic heart disease is said to furnish over ninety per cent of all difficult heart cases; congenital lesions account for about two per cent, while the remainder is made up of unusual heart conditions. Mitral stenosis is present in the vast majority of the rheumatic heart disease cases.

From the medical standpoint, it may be said that, as is the case with so many other conditions which complicate pregnancy, the trend of the best present-day obstetrics is away from therapeutic abortion in most heart cases. Wherever proper care is received, the maternal death rate should not exceed three per cent of the most serious cases.

At one time, mitral stenosis was so feared that women with this lesion were warned to remain single; if they married, contraception was urged; if they became pregnant, therapeutic abortion was advised. Today, very little concern is shown over the matter; almost ninety per cent of the pregnancies complicated by mitral stenosis terminate spontaneously without difficulty, while only about five per cent of the mothers die.

A survey of an eleven year period at the Cook County Hospital, Chicago, shows conclusively that, granted adequate antepartum care, there is little reason to fear that mothers with organic heart disease cannot carry a pregnancy to term. (*Journal of A.M.A.*, July 7, 1951, pp. 910-914.)

The Margaret Hague Maternity Hospital, in Jersey City, has done admirable work in this field. Various remedies, particularly confinement of the patient to bed, have proved most successful in arriving at a happy solution to cases in which serious heart conditions complicate pregnancy.

From the moral viewpoint, it need only be stated that it is never morally permissible to remove the living, inviable fetus from the uterus in order to alleviate the burden on the system created by pregnancy. In contrast, a premature delivery is surely allowable whenever sound medical judgment indicates this procedure to be in the best interests of mother and child.

Pulmonary Tuberculosis

Among the diseases of the respiratory system, pulmonary tuberculosis is the only one which presents a moral problem allied to pregnancy.

Women suffering from active tuberculosis often grow worse during the course of pregnancy and after the delivery of the child. The reason for this fact is not quite clear. Probably the increased respiratory rate due to compression of the lungs by the increase in the intraäbdominal mass, the added strain placed upon the system by pregnancy, and the exertion of labor, all combine to stimulate the growth of the tuberculous foci.

Medical textbooks do not suggest therapeutic abortion in the ordinary cases of pulmonary tuberculosis. In those cases, however, in which it is believed that the progress of the disease will be enhanced by gestation, an early therapeutic abortion is recommended. In his *Obstetrical Practice* (p. 434), Beck states that it seems justifiable to empty the uterus in active cases if the diagnosis can be made before the eighth week and if the patient's circumstances do not permit an adequate care of the tuberculosis. Schumann's *Textbook of Obstetrics* (p. 434) makes a similar recommendation.

From the medical standpoint, it must be emphasized that many recent studies, based on careful analyses of numerous cases, lead to the conclusion that the effect of pregnancy on pulmonary tuberculosis has been grossly exaggerated. The best obstetrical thought today holds that *more women would be saved if greater care were given to the treatment of the tuberculosis and less attention paid to the complicating pregnancy.*

From the moral standpoint, only two thoughts need be offered.

First, therapeutic abortion is always immoral and it would, therefore, never be permissible to remove the inviable fetus from the uterus for the supposed purpose of avoiding an intensification of the tuberculosis.

Second, a woman who is afflicted with this condition is obliged to do all within her reasonable power to preserve her own health and life as well as that of her unborn child. She should, therefore, be willing to subject herself to the rigorous discipline of tuberculosis therapeusis in the interest of this twofold objective.

Needless to say, in far-advanced cases, at or near term, in which it is foreseen that the woman may not be able to withstand the exertion of labor, cesarean section is morally permissible. Often, indeed, it is recommended, because cesarean section under local anesthesia frequently offers the best hope of a living child, while exposing the mother to the least danger.

Diseases of the Urinary System

Pyelitis complicates pregnancy about once in every one hundred cases. It is due to a hematogenous, lymphatic, or ascending infection of the upper urinary tract by colon bacilli and usually follows urinary and intestinal stasis. It may occur at any period of gestation but *it is most frequently noted at the beginning of the sixth month and also near term.* It may also develop during the puerperium, but this is less often encountered. Pyelitis usually responds well to treatment without any harmful effects being felt by mother or child. *In rare cases,* however, when the condition progresses in spite of all treatment, medical textbooks sometimes counsel the artificial termination of the pregnancy. Needless to say, *such an act would be direct abortion and never morally permissible.*

Renal tuberculosis is seldom encountered in pregnancy, but when a woman suffering from it becomes pregnant, the disease is aggravated. When only one kidney is involved, immediate nephrectomy is suggested, since pregnancy does not intensify the risk of the operation nor is there any notable danger of abortion. Whenever both kidneys are involved, various textbooks on obstetrics state that interruption of the pregnancy may sometimes be indicated. *Such an artificial termination of pregnancy would be direct abortion and gravely immoral.*

Pregnancy after nephrectomy is quite common, but the cases do not ordinarily present any great difficulty. However, if renal insufficiency or infection develops, or if symptoms of toxemia appear, many works on obstetrics counsel the emptying of the uterus. Once again, we must state that *this act would constitute direct abortion and would, therefore, never be morally permissible.*

Nephritis is regarded as a serious complication of pregnancy. It sometimes accompanies eclampsia in the late months of gestation; but it may either develop during pregnancy, or pregnancy may occur in a woman who already has nephritis. Maternal and fetal mortality rates are very high in nephritis. DeLee gives an estimate of thirty per cent maternal mortality and seventy per cent fetal mortality. Medical texts usually state that, if the disease is discovered early in pregnancy, prompt termination offers the best prognosis for the mother. *Such a procedure would constitute direct abortion and is, therefore, never morally permissible.*

It is true that fetal death frequently results in cases of nephritis. In these instances, there is, of course, no moral objection to the removal of the dead fetus at whatever time is in the best interests of the mother's health.

Similarly, after the fetus has reached viability and if the nephritis is being unfavorably affected by pregnancy, premature delivery of the child is often commendable. This may be done by the induction of labor or, if the occasion warrants, by cesarean section. It is better to have a premature child not yet profoundly saturated with toxins than an unhealthy full-term child which has been living for weeks in imminent danger of intrauterine death.

Hyperemesis Gravidarum

Hyperemesis gravidarum is frequently called "the toxemia of early pregnancy." Actually, it seems to be a hysterical exaggeration of the morning nausea and vomiting which is more or less common in early pregnancy. According to the classification of *The American Committee on Maternal Welfare,* hyperemesis gravidarum is considered under the toxemias only because precedent has placed it under that heading. It will be recalled that the demand for therapeutic abortion usually arises from complications created by conditions with which a woman may be affected prior to pregnancy or which develop during but not as the result of pregnancy. The best obstetrical thought today believes that hyperemesis gravidarum is no exception to this rule. It is not believed that it is a condition caused by pregnancy; rather, it is held that an unusual, abnormal, hysterical mental attitude toward pregnancy, especially toward the moderate nausea and vomiting common in early pregnancy, is creative of this condition. In philosophical language, one would say that pregnancy is more the *occasion* than the *cause* of this condition.

Long standing precedent has placed hyperemesis gravidarum among the toxemias of pregnancy. It is admitted that it is not proven beyond all doubt that the condition is almost always the product of hysteria. It is also true that many textbooks and obstetricians are not up-to-date on the matter and cling to the idea of therapeutic abortion as the solution to the difficulty. For these reasons, it is proper to consider the matter in the present chapter.

Hyperemesis gravidarum usually begins in the second month of pregnancy, more rarely in the fourth month, but it may appear as late as the sixth month. Many theories have been proposed throughout the years to account for this exaggerated and abnormal nausea and vomiting.

In former years, the condition was thought to have a physical basis, and the obstetrics of those days frequently called for therapeutic abortion as a means of relieving the condition. Other remedies were, of course, suggested as worthy of a brief trial; but prolonged delay in procuring abortion was regarded as useless and dangerous.

Recent advances in obstetrics lead to the conclusion that there is such a large psychic factor in severe nausea and vomiting of pregnancy that almost any therapy will remedy the condition. Thus, Sir Arthur Hurst, writing in the May 29, 1944, issue of the *Journal of the American Medical Association,* states that the pernicious vomiting of pregnancy is always hysterical. This outstanding authority reflects the best obstetrical thought of our age when he says that the division into "nervous" and "toxemic" cases is fallacious. All patients are "nervous," but the term "hysterical" should be substituted for "nervous," because the condition is primarily hysterical and remediable, particularly in its earlier stages, by psychotherapy. In the later stages of the condition, after the woman has lost a lot of weight, is dehydrated, has a rapid pulse, and evidences other well-known abnormalities, psychotherapy alone cannot effect a cure. Liquids and nourishment, especially glucose, are of inestimable value and must be given intravenously in large quantities. Sedatives must also be used. Vitamins (B complex and C) are of great value, but they are not specific remedies. Needless to say, it is most important and desirable to overcome the nausea and vomiting before the condition reaches the "pernicious" stage, and it is here that psychotherapy is the principal remedy.

These advances in obstetrics have practically eliminated the basis for the moral problem formerly created by hyperemesis gravidarum. It is true that many of the medical textbooks currently in use, as well as an inexcusably high percentage of obstetricians, still urge the termination of the pregnancy after various remedies have been given a short but unsuccessful trial. But such a procedure is not only immoral; it also represents an antiquated attitude toward this condition. *The American Committee on Maternal Welfare,* as well as many of the leading obstetricians in the nation, hold that there is no need for therapeutic abortion in cases of hyperemesis gravidarum nor does it represent the proper treatment of such cases.

Even before our present knowledge of the condition, and

before our knowledge of vitamins and other helps, hyperemesis gravidarum could be handled with almost complete success. Thus, in earlier years, in Misericordia Hospital, in Philadelphia, there was only one maternal death from hyperemesis gravidarum over a period of twelve years. More recently, the Margaret Hague Maternity Hospital in Jersey City, N. J., reported that over a ten year period it had handled two hundred and ninety cases of *hyperemesis gravidarum* without a single maternal death and with only one therapeutic abortion performed. A fact of this nature should make a conscientious person stand aghast at the thought of the countless lives needlessly and immorally destroyed as the result of the urging of medical textbooks to solve the problem readily by therapeutic abortion.

It does take great courage, skill, tact, and incessant labor to handle difficult cases of this type. This is especially true when the doctor or patient, or both, sincerely, though erroneously, believe in the moral justifiability, under certain conditions, of therapeutic abortion.

Doctors and nurses must pray constantly, work incessantly, use a great deal of tact in dealing with a patient, relative, or other doctors who are predisposed toward a therapeutic abortion. With both lives at stake, it is a hard fight to the finish. But it is worth all the effort that is expended, especially when both lives are saved.

In summary, in handling a case of hyperemesis gravidarum, moral problems are not created unless the doctor or patient insists upon a therapeutic abortion. The motive behind this demand will, of course, be the contention that this procedure is necessary in order to save the mother's life. Such termination of pregnancy would be direct abortion and gravely immoral. For no reason, therefore, may this act be done, even though it might be believed that continuance of pregnancy would result in the death of the mother.

In the comparatively rare cases in which hyperemesis gravidarum occurs after the fetus has reached viability, there is, of course, no moral objection to a premature delivery.

With implicit faith in the power of prayer and the grace of

God, with tact and diplomacy in handling difficult situations, doctors and nurses can usually convince a determined patient or relatives that the pregnancy should not be terminated. God has often rewarded such efforts by the preservation of the life and health of both mother and child.

When a case of this type occurs in a Catholic hospital, and the authorities cannot shake the determination of the doctor or patient to procure abortion, the authorities must order the patient removed to another institution.

Doctors and nurses employed in a secular hospital, who are asked to assist in this procedure must be guided by the moral principles governing assistance in immoral operations.

Hydramnion

Among the diseases of the decidua and fetal membranes, the only condition which creates a moral problem is that of hydramnion. According to the classification of *The American Committee on Maternal Welfare,* hydramnion would be placed under those conditions which are dependent on or peculiar to pregnancy. As previously explained, conditions of this type usually create a difficult problem *after* the viability of the fetus has been reached. This fact is generally verified in cases of hydramnion. By way of exception, however, about one-sixth of the cases of hydramnion reach a crucial point *before* viability. Since the demand for therapeutic abortion is sometimes made in these latter instances, we have seen fit to discuss hydramnion under the heading of "therapeutic abortion."

Hydramnion is the condition in which an excessive amount of the amniotic fluid collects within the membranes. Minor degrees of hydramnion are quite common, but occasionally large accumulations of the fluid occur.

Mild hydramnion, involving two or three liters of fluid, occurs about once in every two hundred pregnancies.

The really severe forms of hydramnion, involving ten to thirty liters of fluid, are very rare. Kustner has observed a case of fifteen liters at the end of the fifth month, while Schneider encountered an instance in which thirty liters had accumulated by the end of the sixth month.

The frequency of hydramnion is variously estimated. The difference of opinion as to what amount of fluid is truly excessive is the principal reason for the different estimates on the frequency of the condition.

Burstal records 54 cases in 8308 pregnancies; Sion encountered 623 cases in 10,977 pregnancies; Lay records only 75. cases in 14,650 pregnancies.

Under the sponsorship of Villanova College Summer School, Sister M. Dolores, C.S.J., of the Holy Name Hospital, Teaneck, New Jersey, made a detailed study of this subject. Her research revealed that there were 94 cases recorded as hydramnion in 102,000 pregnancies at the famous Margaret Hague Maternity Hospital of Jersey City, New Jersey. These statistics covered the five-year period of 1934-1939.

Hydramnion is obviously of comparative rarity, probably occurring about once in each thousand pregnancies.

The prognosis for the mother in hydramnion is said to be very good. In the above ninety-four cases at the Margaret Hague Maternity Hospital, for example, not one maternal death occurred. In contrast, *the prognosis for the fetus is extremely poor.* In the same ninety-four cases, no fetus survived; twenty-three were stillborn, while the others died at varying times.

Hydramnion occurs principally in the second half of pregnancy. Usually the fetus has reached viability, but in about one-sixth of the cases the fetus is not yet viable.

Considerable attention was given to hydramnion by the moralists of past years. Spirited debate concerned itself with the permissibility of rupturing the amniotic membrane and allowing abortion to result.

It appears that some well-known moralists, such as Antonelli, defended the view that, even though the fetus was inviable, a rupture of the membranes was indirect but not direct abortion. The vast majority of moralists held that such a rupture constituted direct abortion and was therefore never permissible in cases in which the fetus was still inviable.

The older moralists also searched the writings of their contemporaries for studies on comparable types of conditions, and an effort was made to apply their conclusions in these latter cases to the problem involved in hydramnion. Father Slater and Doctor Capellmann, for example, had considered the case of a retroflexed pregnant uterus incarcerated in the pelvic cavity. They held that, if all other methods of turning or replacing the uterus failed, it was allowable to induce abortion indirectly by perforating the amniotic membrane and effecting the discharge of the fluid.

Before continuing with hydramnion, we might state that the retroflexed pregnant uterus incarcerated in the pelvic cavity (considered by Slater and Capellmann) presents no serious problem today. Many such conditions correct themselves spontaneously; the knee-chest position remedies others; some are able to be replaced manually; gas and reflexing with a ring takes care of others; and finally, recourse to surgery (laparotomy) solves the problem in the remainder of the cases. There is never any need to rupture the membranes and procure abortion, though it is true that there is a high percentage of spontaneous abortion resulting from this condition.

To return to our consideration of hydramnion, this condition creates no moral problem except when the fetus is inviable and, as previously stated, the fetus is usually viable in cases of hydramnion.

If the fetus is inviable, it is the opinion of the present writer that it is direct abortion and, therefore, never permissible to release the amniotic fluid and thereby effect the death of an inviable fetus. This conclusion is also held by the vast majority of reputable moralists: Noldin, Prümmer, Aertnys-Damen, Wouters, Davis, Lehmkuhl, and Vermeersch. Other writers, whose works are written more directly for popular use, such as Fathers Burke, Klarmann, and Finney, concur in this opinion. This list of names is indeed a formidable one, for here we have some of the most outstanding moralists of modern times.

While it may not be strictly accurate to say that the amniotic membrane and fluid are part of the fetus, it does seem that they belong more properly to the fetus than to the mother. It would seem that Nature has created them specifically for the temporary vital needs of the fetus. Furthermore, there is no absolute guarantee that labor will follow the puncturing of the amniotic membrane. If labor does not supervene, a very severe risk to the mother's life may be created.

This writer therefore regards a perforation of the amniotic membrane and a release of the fluid, with the resulting death of the *inviable* fetus, as an act of direct abortion and never morally permissible.

The same moral conclusion would be applied to the similar release of the fluid in the case of the retroflexed pregnant uterus incarcerated in the pelvic cavity.

Generally speaking, the amniotic fluid is needed for the continued life of the fetus, just as truly as air is needed for the life of man. To deprive the fetus of the amniotic fluid is just as truly a direct attack on its life as is depriving a person, by smothering, of the air necessary for life. Both acts are direct attacks upon life, even though neither the amniotic fluid nor the air are part of the human person.

. .Unless further analysis by authorities in Ethics gives much more weight to the contrary view, it would not seem morally permissible to rupture the amniotic membrane and release the fluid in the case of the inviable fetus.

The writers who would allow the act are few in number and, for the most part, are of comparatively slight authoritative value. The moralists who declare that the act is immoral are very numerous and among the most outstanding of modern times.

Doctors and nurses must, therefore, regard as immoral the perforation of the amniotic membrane and the release of the fluid in the case of the *inviable* fetus. They must be guided by the principles governing assistance in immoral operations should they be requested or ordered to participate in such a procedure.

It is not usual for the membranes to rupture before the fetus is viable. But in infrequent cases in which this accident occurs, it is not morally permissible to use drugs or to adopt any other means directed toward the procuring of an abortion if the fetus is still living and inviable. Such an action would constitute direct abortion and be gravely immoral. (To clarify this point, it might be helpful to note that there is a case on record of a woman whose membranes ruptured in India and who made the trip to the United States and was delivered of a living fetus after her arrival in this country.)

Should medical science advance to the point wherein it could release *only the excess fluid,* such an action would be morally permissible.

Before a doctor would be justified in attempting such a procedure with an inviable fetus, he would have to be reasonably certain that he possessed the medical knowledge and technical skill which would enable him to release *only the excess fluid.* He would have to be reasonably certain that his action would not cause an expulsion of the inviable fetus from the uterus.

Vermeersch calls attention to the permissibility of releasing *only the excess fluid* in the case of an inviable fetus. But the practical value of this procedure is questionable, since it appears that the fluid would quickly build up again.

In his *Moral and Pastoral Theology* (4th edition, 1945, p. 190), Father Davis mentions the technique of piercing the womb below the sternum, the woman being seated or standing, and drawing off excess fluid. This practice is not favorably regarded by the best obstetricians in this country and it is not in use.

The frank attitude of obstetrics is that the prognosis for the mother in cases of hydramnion is excellent, whereas it is almost hopeless for the fetus. In practically all cases, the fetus is stillborn or so seriously deformed that, even if it is viable, it dies soon after birth.

As previously stated, *hydramnion is usually encountered after the viability of the fetus has been reached.* If sound medical judgment in a particular case indicates that a rupture of the membranes and a premature delivery is in the best interests of mother and child, this action is morally permissible. But once again it must be said that this procedure is, in general, not in conformity with good obstetrical practice. Rupture of the membranes creates the danger of serious infection, and there is also the possibility that labor may not follow the release of the amniotic fluid. (Of course, if the woman goes into labor and the membranes do not spontaneously rupture, good obstetrics frequently suggests that the doctor rupture the membranes at that time.) Since the fetus is almost always stillborn, or so seriously deformed that it dies soon after birth, it appears to be bad morals, as well as bad obstetrics, to rupture the membranes and thus create definite dangers to the mother's life.

Curettage of the Uterus

It is never lawful in cases of threatened or inevitable abortion to perform a curettage of the pregnant uterus before the viability of the fetus. To have recourse to currettage as a means of emptying the uterus is to change the threatened or inevitable abortion into a direct abortion, and direct abortion is never morally permissible.

Curettage of the uterus containing an inviable fetus is not only an immoral act—it is also regarded as very bad obstetrics. After the placenta and fetus have formed, present-day obstetrics almost always condemns curettage of the uterus.

In cases of incomplete abortion, where the ovum has been expelled, curettage is morally permissible because it does not involve the removal of a living and inviable fetus from the uterus.

Whenever a surgeon is convinced that a hemorrhage in the decidua has already killed the fetus, it is morally permissible to empty the uterus if the obstetrician believes that this is the best way to safeguard the woman's life. The best present day obstetrics, however, frequently urges delay, to avoid sepsis, as the safest course of action.

Embryotomy

Under this heading are grouped the various destructive operations of craniotomy, decapitation, and evisceration. These destructive operations are usually performed on a dead fetus when necessity demands this extreme procedure.

Unfortunately, this deliberate destruction of the unborn child is still occasionally performed on the living fetus. It is true that those who perform embryotomy on a living child do so infrequently and only when they feel that no other procedure will deliver the child and save the mother's life.

All forms of embryotomy on the living fetus obviously involve the direct and deliberate destruction of the unborn. The advocates of the procedure may bestow technical and pleasant sounding terms on the act, but it remains sheer, cold murder. Needless to say, the Church has repeatedly condemned these gravely immoral operations; for example, on May 28, 1884; August 19, 1889; July 24, 1895; May 4, 1898; and March 5, 1902.

Even in the case of an already dead fetus, an appreciation of the inherent dignity of the human being should cause the surgeon to have recourse to embryotomy only when truly necessary.

When the fetus is alive, there is no possibility of discussion from the moral viewpoint. Embryotomy of the living fetus is an act of murder and involves all of the immorality of this most heinous of all crimes.

The Rh Factor

In 1937, Drs. Karl Landsteiner and Alexander Wiener of the Rockefeller Institute detected a new agglutinogen capable of causing serious complication in blood transfusions and also in some way related to the health of pregnant women and unborn or newly born babies. This "factor" was discovered in the red blood corpuscles and was designated "Rh" because it was also found in the red blood cells of the *Rh*esus monkey.

Another pioneer in the study of the Rh factor was Dr. Philip Levine of Linden, N. J., who studied erythroblastosis (destruction of red blood cells) and associated it with the Rh factor.

In their experiments of 1937, Landsteiner and Wiener produced an antibody in rabbits by the injection of monkey blood as an antigen. This new antibody not only produced an agglutination (that is, a clumping rather than a proper mixture) of the red blood cells of monkeys but also agglutinated those of certain white humans. These results showed conclusively the presence of a hitherto unknown factor in the red blood cells of some human beings.

Persons whose blood contains this factor are called *Rh-positive,* while those who lack this factor in their blood are known as *Rh-negative*.

At first it was thought that this factor had no practical or clinical importance. However, it was demonstrated in 1939 by Levine and Wiener that Rh-negative individuals (persons lacking this Rh agglutinogen) might, under certain circumstances, develop immune antibodies against the Rh factor and suffer serious consequences from the action of such anti-Rh agglutinins.

Further studies revealed that approximately eighty-five per cent of white humans, ninety per cent of Negroes, and ninety-nine per cent of Chinese possessed this Rh agglutinogen in their red blood cells.

The Rh factor was therefore known to be a blood agglutinogen, comparable to the factors A, B, AB, and O, which determine the well-known four major blood groups. Medical science had long known that certain blood types will mix only with certain others and that when two types are fused which will not mix a clumping of the blood results. It had now become evident that medical science could no longer be content with the mere classification of blood into the four standard types. *The Rh factor would have to be considered seriously in all cases involving the transfusion of blood from one person to another.*

There is no need to offer a detailed scientific presentation of the Rh factor in this text. A brief exposition will, however, provide an adequate background for the treatment of the moral problems which arise from Rh incompatibility.

Extensive medical experience has shown that a *certain* percentage of Rh-negative individuals who receive blood from Rh-positive persons develop a sensitivity to any future Rh-positive blood that may be given to them.

The sensitizing of an Rh-negative person by the reception of Rh-positive blood can occur from one of two mechanisms: (a) *blood transfusions* given to an Rh-negative individual from an Rh-positive donor; and (b) when red blood cells from an Rh-positive unborn infant pass into the Rh-negative mother's blood stream.

In reference to sensitization resulting from blood transfusions, the most complete statistics resulted from medical experiences during the war. It appears that as many as fifty per cent of Rh-negative males may have developed sensitivity by this process. The explanation of this unusually high percentage is possibly to be found in two facts: first, multiple transfusions to a single patient were a much more common occurrence in military medicine than in civilian practice; second, evidence is accumulating to show that erythroblastosis occurs in the male in about three times the frequency that it occurs in the female and that it is fatal in about five times as many male infants as in female infants. These latter facts may be secondary in importance but they do emphasize the possibility that we may be dealing with some kind of modification of a sex-linked characteristic or possibly with some kind of secondary consequence of the male constitution.

Extreme care should certainly be exercised in the matter of blood transfusions. Dr. Neva Abelson, who is in charge of the Philadelphia Serum Exchange and who is one of the nation's leading authorities on the Rh factor, states that one-third of the present cases of sensitization have a history of transfusion of Rh incompatible blood. It seems reasonable to assume that in most of these cases accurate Rh typing of the donor and recipient would have prevented the resultant hemolytic disease in the newborn. Administration of intramuscular blood has also led to severe cases of sensitization which in turn have resulted in fetal or neonatal death.

The question is sometimes asked: will plasma sensitize, or lay a basis for sensitization of, Rh-negative individuals. In response, one might call attention to the fact that some of the larger blood banks report that they are no longer pooling plasma indiscriminately, but are storing it more or less according to types, reserving plasma from Rh-negative blood for Rh-negative patients. If plasma is not carefully separated, there is often a sediment of red cells at the bottom of the flask, and under sterile conditions these cells remain intact for some time. Moreover, blood banks often store plasma at temperatures above freezing. There is, therefore, at least a theoretical danger of introducting Rh antigen by use of such plasma.

In contrast, it does not appear probable that there is danger of sensitization by gamma globulin, but the fact remains that

we know very little about the chemical nature of the Rh anti-
gens and one must remember that at least part of the Rh antibodies have been shown to be present in this fraction of the
serum proteins. Whether or not sensitizing amounts of Rh
antigen may be associated with these antibodies is open to
future investigation.

In reference to sensitization produced in an Rh-negative
woman by an Rh-positive pregnancy, the percentages are comparatively low. It appears that *only one Rh-negative woman
out of every twenty-five to fifty is affected by the reception of
Rh-positive blood in pregnancy.* These percentages are based
on the fact that approximately twelve per cent of all marriages
are between Rh-positive men and Rh-negative women—and
yet the frequency of *erythroblastosis fetalis* (the infantile disease resulting from Rh incompatibility) is not over one case
out of every two hundred and fifty pregnancies.

Regardless of which mechanism has brought it about, once
Rh-positive red blood cells have entered the circulation of a
susceptible Rh-negative person, anti-Rh antibodies appear in
the Rh-negative individual's plasma and make this person
sensitive to any future reception of Rh-positive blood.

Note carefully that the first time a *susceptible* Rh-negative
person receives Rh-positive blood there is no *apparent* effect.
There will ordinarily be no ill effects on the first child born to
such a couple. The *first* reception of Rh-positive blood by a
susceptible Rh-negative person simply *sensitizes* that person to
a second, third, or any future receptions of Rh-positive blood.
Erythroblastosis fetalis could, of course, show up in the first
child if the Rh-negative mother had previously been "sensitized" by receiving Rh-positive blood in a transfusion.

As explained above, once a *susceptible* Rh-negative person
receives Rh-positive blood, he or she is sensitized to further
reception of Rh-positive blood, that is, anti-Rh antibodies are
formed in the person's plasma. The presence of antibodies to
the Rh factor in a person's plasma is not in itself, so far as
current science can detect, detrimental to the person's health.
Danger arises only when the already sensitized person receives
a further addition of Rh-positive blood by transfusion, injec-

tion, or pregnancy. If there should be a second reception of Rh-positive blood by an already sensitized Rh-negative person, the result is a hemolytic transfusion reaction in which the transfused Rh-positive cells are destroyed by the anti-Rh antibodies. (By way of contrast, the transfusion of compatible Rh-negative blood into a *sensitized* Rh-negative person is without danger because in this case the transfused red cells lack the factor against which the anti-Rh antibodies work.)

We have mentioned that the blood-destroying disease process is known as *erythroblastosis fetalis*. This process results in far-reaching and profound changes in the infant, often with severe damage to the liver, brain, and many other tissues. These changes may result in the death of the fetus in the uterus or, if the fetus is born alive, in severe neonatal jaundice, anemia, and brain injury. Many of these infants are born alive and seemingly normal, but they frequently become severely jaundiced in the first six to seventy-two hours after a hemolytic crisis which sometimes results in death.

Erythroblastosis fetalis actually takes one of three forms: (a) hemolytic anemia, (b) icterus gravis, or (c) hydrops fetalis. The two last-mentioned forms are the most severe, and fetal death in utero or shortly after birth is almost always the result. The first form mentioned (hemolytic anemia) is much less severe and, fortunately, much more common than either of the other types.

Much good has been accomplished of late in the diagnosis and treatment of infants affected with hemolytic anemia. Through the use of replacement transfusions soon after birth, a great number of these infants are being saved and protected from the permanent damage the disease may impart. The replacement transfusion is performed by transfusing the affected infant, preferably through the umbilical cord, with Rh-negative blood as soon after birth as possible. (Evidence, however, seems to be accumulating that in many instances transfusion of Rh-positive blood should be the procedure of preference.) At any rate, the blood of the infant is withdrawn so as to remove as much as possible of both its own Rh-positive blood and the anti-Rh antibodies which its blood contains as received from the mother.

An interesting discovery has been the presence of anti-Rh antibodies in the breast milk of *sensitized* Rh-negative mothers. It has been established that these anti-Rh antibodies are capable of being passed on to the infant by breast feeding. Naturally, these facts preclude breast feeding by the mother of any infant affected with erythroblastosis.

In the light of all that has been said above, the following advice is offered:

First, remember that negative knowledge, knowledge of what we do *not* know, is often very helpful. Hence, the following points should be kept in mind:

(a) We do *not* know the precise percentage of Rh-negative women that are sensitized by an Rh-positive pregnancy, but it seems to be one out of every twenty-five to fifty persons.

(b) We do *not* know the precise percentage of women that are sensitized by receiving Rh-positive blood in injection or transfusion. War records, however, show that nearly fifty per cent of Rh-negative males were sensitized by receiving Rh-positive blood in injections of transfusions. (Many of these soldiers had severe hemolytic reactions following a later transfusion of Rh-positive, but otherwise compatible, blood. These patients apparently had been immunized, or better "iso-immunized," to the Rh factor.)

(c) We do *not* have any test that will tell us whether a specific Rh-negative person will be sensitized by the reception of Rh-positive blood.

Second, we do have positive knowledge which is of great value:

(a) Every pregnant woman should have her Rh type determined by a competent laboratory. This should be done on the occasion of her first or second prenatal visit.

(b) If the woman is Rh-positive, there is but a very remote chance of her having any difficulty on this score.

There is one exception to this, as has been shown by Wiener and Diamond, in cases where we have subtypes of Rh, Rh_1, or Rh_2; here the mother, although Rh-positive, may develop agglutinins against the Rh fraction which is foreign to her, and later under a similar set of conditions may develop transfusion reaction or may give birth to erythroblastolic infants. These cases are extremely rare.

(c) If she is Rh-negative, an Rh determination should be made of her husband's blood.

If tests show that the husband is also Rh-negative, there can be no compatibility, and no further tests need be performed.

If tests show that the husband is Rh-positive, we have the factors for possible hemolytic anemia or erythroblastosis. There is, of course, no need for alarm. The chances are better than twenty-five to one that the woman will not be sensitized by the reception of Rh-positive blood. Furthermore, it is generally agreed that erythroblasosis in the first-born of Rh-negative women usually does not occur, that is, one or more pregnancies with an Rh-positive fetus are necessary to produce isoimmunization of a sufficient intensity to bring about hemolytic anemia in the next Rh-positive infant. The exceptions to this general rule are found in cases of Rh-negative women who have been previously immunized by transfusions of Rh-positive blood. At any rate, it is suggested in these cases that the mother's blood be tested for anti-Rh agglutinins at the seventh month. If no appreciable agglutinins are found at this time, we may assume that there will be no trouble and may allow the patient to go to term. After delivery, however, the baby's blood should be examined for anemia and the Rh factor.

If the baby is Rh-negative, we are able to conclude that the father is a *heterozygous* Rh-positive (that is, one of the husband's parents was an Rh-positive and the other was an Rh-negative), and his offspring, according to the Mendelian laws of heredity, may be either Rh-positive or Rh-negative. In other words, even if an Rh-negative woman with a *heterozygous* Rh-positive husband has been unfortunate enough to become sensitized, there is still an even chance that the fetus will be Rh-negative and no difficulty be encountered.

If the baby is Rh-positive, the husband may be either a *homozygous* or *heterozygous* Rh-positive. (When both parents of the husband were Rh-positive, he is classified as a *homozygous* genotype and all of his offspring are necessarily Rh-positive). When the baby is Rh-positive, a further test of the husband's blood is required to determine whether he is homozygous or heterozygous. If the Rh-negative wife has already been sensitized by the reception of Rh-positive blood from a *homozygous* husband, any future reception of blood from the husband will necessarily result in an affected infant.

(d) When tests reveal the presence of anti-Rh agglutinins in the mother's blood at the seventh month, her titer should be checked every two weeks and, if there is no increase in the anti-Rh agglutinins, the patient may be allowed to complete at least eight full months of pregnancy. If the baby is large enough to have a good chance for survival, some medical specialists induce labor at this time. If tests reval a marked increase in titer, the various possibilities in the case are considered and labor is sometimes induced one week before eight full months of pregnancy. It is not advisable to induce labor earlier than that, because the baby is usually too premature to survive.

(e) When certainly or probably affected babies are delivered, the baby should be examined thoroughly for evidence of erythroblastosis, and an Rh factor test and complete blood examination should be made. If the baby shows evidence of hemolytic anemia, it should receive a transfusion with Rh-negative compatible blood. A complete blood examination should be performed daily and, if hemolysis is still going on, more transfusions should be administered until the baby's blood is normal or the hemolysis has ceased. When these steps are taken, many of the erythroblastotic babies are saved.

These recommendations emphasize the prudence of having type O Rh-negative blood donors available at the time of delivery whenever tests have revealed the presence of anti-Rh antibodies in the blood of an expectant mother.

It should be stated, however, that there is as yet little proof that exchange transfusion reduces mortality. If properly done, the procedure may reduce the length of hospitalization and the number of manipulations necessary in treatment. Indications for exchange transfusion are not clear, but criteria include maternal obstetric history and Rh antibody titer, antibody and bilirubin content of the cord blood, and size of the infant's liver and spleen. Transfusion is frequently overdone. Some of the best authorities in the field who have performed a number of exchange transfusions report evidence of increased venous pressure in critically ill infants, and in these cases there is a growing tendency to leave the infant with a red cell deficit rather than with a normal count.

When exchange transfusion is not used, not more than 5 cc. per pound is administered to severe cases at one transfusion within the first five days of life. After this period, transfusion may be increased to 10 cc. per pound. In mild cases, where anemia seems to be the only problem, transfusions of 10 cc. per pound are given.

(f) Breast nursing of erythroblastotic infants should not be permitted because anti-Rh agglutinins may be secreted in the milk and, after absorption through the stomach, may produce further hemolysis of the infant's Rh-positive cells.

(g) Finally, where erythroblastosis fetalis is suspected, analgesics and anesthetics, particularly morphine and nitrous oxide, should be used only with caution during labor.

The Moral Aspects of the Rh Factor:

(a) *Rh incompatibility never constitutes a moral justification for the practice of contraception.* The immorality of contraception was treated at length in an earlier chapter. It was shown that the practice is contrary to Natural Law, Divine Law, and is clearly condemned in both the Jewish and Christian Revelation. There is no need for further discussion of that topic in this place. It is, however, our duty to state that no matter how deeply sympathetic we may be towards an unfortunate married couple we may never sanction their having recourse to contraception to solve marital problems occasioned by Rh incompatibility. No one can minimize the almost superhuman effort which is required of some married couples in order that they may live in accordance with moral ideals.

With reference to Rh incompatibility, the writer cannot help recalling a young married couple of his own acquaintance: after having a first healthy child, the young wife lost five babies, including a set of twins, and in the last pregnancy almost forfeited her own life, several months of hospitalization being required for her. This young woman, it might be added, had the service of some of the best specialists in Chicago and Philadelphia, as well as the interest and coöperation of one of the nation's leading medical schools. This picture will serve to indicate the present helplessness of medical science in the face of a severe case of Rh sensitization. It requires little imagination to appreciate the mental and physical strain that a situation of this type places on a married couple, the crushed hopes of the expectant parents, the realization that they are bringing souls into the world that are usually dying without baptism, the apparent uselessness of the constant risks to the health of the wife, the inability of medical science to help them, the open or implied encouragement of a doctor and friends to have recourse to contraception, the insistence of their Church that any usage of their marital rights must always be in a morally permissible form, the anticipated years of loneliness and frustration resulting from the fear of participating in those experiences to which the sacrament of Matrimony has given them a full right of enjoyment.

Three recommendations are offered to married couples who find that an unusually severe condition is present in their own case:

First, these couples must remember that they will find true happiness only in moral living. Recourse to immorality may seem to provide a ready solution to their problem, but in the end it will prove to have been a delusion. A married couple must be at peace with God and their own consciences before real and lasting happiness can be found in their home. Whatever be the sacrifice needed to hold on to moral ideals, Christian spouses should keep the image of their suffering Saviour before them.

It is only a materialistic philosophy of life which sees in physical suffering "the deepest and greatest of all human misfortunes and which would neglect for such a misfortune the sublime teachings of Christ, Who, by word and example, taught the inexhaustible sublimity of human suffering, the ennobling character of agony endured for His sake and Who upon the Cross gave us the significant example of His three hours of

loneliness in the midst of the hootings and cries of the as-
sembled multitude."

Second, these couples may feel morally justified in having recourse to some Safe Period Method. In the rare cases which are
so severe that pregnancy may constitute a real danger to the permanent health or life of the wife, the degree of unreliability
which characterizes most Safe Period Methods should be taken
into consideration. If such couples are unwilling to practice
permanent continence, it is suggested that they should submit
to the inconvenience and expense involved in the Farris
Method and carefully follow the guidance of the medical specialist in its application. Finally, these couples should keep in
touch with the progress of medical science on Rh incompatibility. It is not unlikely that some solution to this vexing
problem will develop from the extensive research work which
is now being conducted along these lines.

(b) *Rh sensitization never constitutes a moral justification
for the termination of pregnancy by abortion to prevent the
live birth of an erythroblastic child.*

In reference to therapeutic abortion in cases of Rh incompatibility, one must state emphatically that *the measure is medically and morally indefensible.*

On the medical side, there is absolutely no way of determining prior to birth the precise hematological condition of the
fetus. Even the most careful study of the mother's blood during
the course of pregnancy does not give us very precise information. If clear evidence of sensitization of an Rh-negative
expectant mother is at hand, there is admittedly a sound probability that the child will be erythroblastic. Even clear evidence
of sensitization of the mother's blood, however, does not make
it possible to determine the precise nature of the pathology
present in the infant. Moreover, even when definite increases
in the mother's sensitization are demonstrated, experience
shows that healthy Rh-positive births may result.

On the moral side, therapeutic abortion is never permissible.
This topic has already been treated at length in the text and
requires no further comment in this place.

(c) *Under due conditions, Rh sensitization may provide a*

*moral justification for radical obstetrics in the form of cesarean
section or premature delivery.*

It must be stated immediately, however, that the best scientific thought on this subject has undergone a notable change during the past several years. Up until a few years ago, it was very commonly believed that babies could and should be protected from the action of Rh antibodies by premature induction or cesarean section. This view is no longer held by the best authorities in this field.

As a matter of fact, *The Journal of the American Medical Association* stated as early as November 9, 1946, that "there is little to recommend cesarean section as a means of saving babies with erythroblastosis. Too many disappointments have been experienced. The handicap of prematurity is rarely outweighed by the alleged shortening of exposure to the damaging action of maternal Rh antibodies."

A fine presentation of the latest knowledge on this phase of the subject was given by Dr. Neva Abelson in a paper entitled "Preventable Factors in Erythroblastosis Fetalis," which was read at a meeting in the Philadelphia County Medical Society Building on February 4, 1949.

Doctor Abelson stated that in a detailed analysis of neonatal deaths involving the Rh factor, the majority were delivered by cesarean section or after induction at the thirty-sixth or thirty-seventh week. Doctor Abelson went on to state that these methods are of very questionable value and would appear to be rarely indicated.

At any rate, certain steps should be taken before premature induction or cesarean section is attempted.

First, the husband should be proved homozygous. It is obvious that unnecessary harm may be done an Rh-negative baby by premature delivery.

Second, the previous obstetric and transfusion history should be studied. If the mother has an antibody titer, but no history of transfusion or of erythroblastotic children, the over-all chances of survival of a full-term infant are probably between sixty and seventy per cent. If the antibody titer is low, the chance of survival may be as high as ninety-five per cent. Before premature delivery is undertaken in these cases, all of these factors must be weighed carefully. If there is a history of previous stillbirth or blood transfusion, the infant's chances of survival are not so great, and this may constitute an argument in favor of interference with the pregnancy.

In any recommendation of early delivery, one must keep in mind a danger to the infant which is not often mentioned. The premature child is said to be the only one in whom kernicterus occurs without other evidence (clinical or serologic) of ery-throblastosis fetalis. This complication would appear to be one of the greatest hazards associated with delivery at the thirty-sixth or thirty-seventh week.

The moral justification of cesarean section or premature in-duction therefore depends upon the verification of a medical fact: does sound scientific evidence indicate that this obstetrical procedure provides, without undue risk to the mother, the most likely method of obtaining a healthy baby?

As sometimes happens, in the absence of conclusive scientific evidence on some points and in the face of strong disagreement among the medical authorities on other points, the moralist is prevented from offering an iron-clad verdict. In the present state of our knowledge, however, it would appear morally per-missible for a doctor to have recourse to cesarean section when-ever expert medical judgment regards it as the best means of protecting the child from erythroblastosis without undue risk to the mother. On the other hand, the doctor must keep in con-tact with the progress of medical science and, if research shows that cesarean section does not confer a benefit on the child which is proportionate to the risk which it inflicts on mother and child, this radical obstetrical procedure would not be morally permissible.

(d) Finally, our present knowledge of the Rh factor is so unsettled that it should not be used as a determining factor in the selection of a spouse. Neither should disturbing fears be allowed to arise in the minds of an engaged couple when it is discovered that the young man is Rh-positive and the young lady Rh-negative. Such couples should take heart from the percentages that are in their favor. As we have previously mentioned, only one in from twenty-five to fifty Rh-negative wives of Rh-positive husbands become sensitized to the Rh factor and give birth to babies with erythroblastosis. Moreover, even the unusual Rh-negative wife who does become sensitized will be able to have a first child without any difficulty on this score, while in her second or later pregnancies the greater probability is that the pathology in the baby will not be too severe. In these latter cases, proper medical care will usually safeguard her baby's life and health. From all that has been said, it should be evident that from both the medical and moral viewpoint, Rh incompatibility should not be set up either as a partial determinant in the selection of a spouse or as a basis for judging the problems which are to be anticipated in married life.

Problems for Discussion

1. Does a small pelvis offer a plausible excuse for therapeutic abortion? Comment on the value of cesarean section or premature induction of labor.

2. Does pernicious anemia ever necessitate therapeutic abortion? Comment on the value of liver and blood transfusions.

3. It appears that the metallic poisons (lead, arsenic, phosphorus and mercury) are responsible for many interruptions of pregnancy in women subjected to their action. What do you think of an expectant mother holding employment in a match or paint factory, or even doing extensive painting at home?

4. When a pregnant woman is subjected to prolonged irradiation (roentgen rays and radium), what is the probable effect on her unborn child?

5. Severe nervous shock, such as the sudden tragic death of a husband or child, may and does bring about abortion, especially in women of a highly sensitive temperament. Comment on the obligations of an expectant mother with reference to the type and intensity of her recreational and social life.

6. What are the *legal* requirements in your State for the procuring of a therapeutic abortion? Do you think there is always a clear-cut line between criminal and therapeutic abortion? Is there any *moral* difference between the two?

7. Would you say that *Catholic Ethics* places a preference on the life of the child over the life of the mother?

8. Comment on this statement: "I think it is irrational to stand idly by and allow mother and child to die in those rare cases in which at least the life of the mother could be saved by a forfeiture of the life of the fetus."

9. Does the possibility of an increase in *criminal* abortion arise from the State's action of authorizing doctors to determine when *therapeutic* abortions are necessary?

10. What would you do if a married woman questioned you about possible ways of inducing abortion? You have some reason to suspect that the woman desires this knowledge for personal application and yet you do not want to offend her by even implying that she has such malicious intentions.

11. Comment on this statement: "A doctor has the professional obligation to save human life by all possible means."

12. Comment on this statement: "Necessity knows no law; therefore, whenever therapeutic abortion is necessary to save a woman's life, it is permissible."

13. Does the Church's penalty of excommunication refer to therapeutic, as well as to criminal abortion?

References for Reading

BONNAR, A.: *The Catholic Doctor* (2nd ed.), pp. 72-81; 84-86, 1939.

BOURKE, M.: "Some Medical Ethical Problems Solved," *Graduate Nurses*, pp. 198-220, N. Y., 1939.

BURKE, E.: *Acute Cases in Moral Medicine*, pp. 54-59, N. Y., 1929.

CONNELL, F.: "Curettage of the Pregnant Uterus During Severe Hemorrhage," *American Ecclesiastical Review*, p. 224, March, 1944.

————: "The Rh Factor and Rhythm," *American Ecclesiastical Review*, April, 1952, p. 309.

COSGROVE-CARTER: "A Consideration of Therapeutic Abortion," *American Journal of Obstetrics and Gynecology*, Sept., 1944, pp. 299-309.

DANNREUTHER, W.: "Therapeutic Abortion in a General Hospital," *American Journal of Obstetrics and Gynecology*, July, 1946, pp. 54-65.

DAVIS, H.: *Moral and Pastoral Theology* (4th ed.), Vol. 2, pp. 166-198, London, 1945.

FINNEY, P.: *Moral Problems in Hospital Practice*, pp. 1-95, St. Louis, 1930.

KAUMP, D.: "The Rh Factor in Hemolytic Disease of the Newborn," *The Linacre Quarterly*, Jan., 1947, pp. 1-8.

LUMBRERAS, P.: "Embryotomy," *Homiletic and Pastoral Review*, Aug., 1947, pp. 901-904.

MAHONEY, E.: "Therapeutic Abortion," *The Clergy Review*, London, June, 1938; also contained in *The Catholic Mind*, pp. 297-404, Oct. 22, 1938.

MOORE, T.: *The Principles of Ethics*, pp. 159-184, Phila., 1935.

QUINLAN, J.: *Whither Ethics in Medicine* (pamphlet), Paulist Press, N. Y.

ROCHELLE-FINK: *Handbook of Medical Ethics*, pp. 91-130, Westminster, Md., 1943.

SACKS-KUHNS-JAHN: "Studies in Rh-Isoimmunization in Pregnancy," *American Journal of Obstetrics and Gynecology*, Sept., 1947, pp. 400-414.

SCHWITALLA, A.: "The Moral Aspects of the Rh Factor," *The Linacre Quarterly*, Jan., 1947, pp. 9-18.

"The Druggist and a Prescription for Abortion," *Homiletic and Pastoral Review*, p. 136, Nov., 1943.

"Cooperation by a Nurse in Direct Abortion," *American Ecclesiastical Review*, pp. 58-59, Jan., 1944.

CHAPTER 9

Indirect Abortion

The subject of direct abortion has been treated at length in the two previous chapters.

The essence of direct abortion, as we have seen, lies in the direct and deliberate attempt to remove an inviable fetus from the uterus. In direct abortion, the fetus is the immediate object of attack. In direct abortion, the means employed tend by their very nature to destroy the life of the inviable fetus; the loss of life to the unborn child is the natural and necessary result of the means employed. In direct abortion, the primary motive underlying the performance of the action is a desire to terminate the life of the inviable fetus. In direct abortion, the termination of the pregnancy is always directly willed either as an end in itself or as a means to an end. Direct abortion is always gravely immoral.

The present chapter is concerned with the topic of indirect abortion. Too great an emphasis cannot be placed on the importance of this subject.

Indirect abortion is that which takes place when the fetus is in no way the direct object of attack. In indirect abortion, the loss of fetal life results as a secondary and unintentional objective. In indirect abortion, the means used tend by their very nature to effect the cure of the mother, and the motive underlying their use is to secure this good for the mother. In indirect abortion, the means used are directly productive of the cure of the mother; they do *not* cure the mother through the medium of destroying fetal life.

An ability to solve the complex problems of indirect abortion necessitates a thorough undersanding of the twofold effect principle. For, in cases of indirect abortion, a remedy is used

216

to effect a cure of the mother but incidentally it causes the death of the unborn child. Herein we have a clear example of an act producing a double effect, one effect good (the cure of the mother) and one effect bad (the loss of life to the fetus).

A review of this key principle should certainly precede the study of the difficult problems of indirect abortion. The successful application of the twofold effect principle hinges upon the verification of four conditions. First, *the act which produces the two effects must be in itself a morally indifferent act.* Second, *the indifferent act must directly produce the good effect;* that is, the occurrence of the evil must not be the means whereby the good is attained. Third, *the motive prompting the performance of the indifferent act must be a desire to bring about the good effect.* The bad effect may be foreseen and it may necessarily result from the indifferent act, but the desire to secure the bad effect must not be in any way the motive prompting the act. Fourth, *the good to be attained must be at least equivalent in value to the evil which is also going to result.*

In the present chapter, this complex moral principle will be applied to the most outstanding problems of indirect abortion.

Doctors and nurses should thoroughly familiarize themselves with the manner in which the principle is used in these cases.

Operations During Pregnancy

It is never morally permissible to perform any operation or give any medical treatment *for a disease not likely to be fatal to the mother when such operation or treatment is likely to cause an abortion or result in the death of the fetus.* In such instances, there is no proportion between the benefit conferred upon the mother and the loss of life suffered by the unborn child. The fourth condition of the twofold effect principle is unable to be verified in these circumstances.

In contrast, it is morally justifiable to perform an operation or use remedies which involve some slight danger to the fetus when the disease threatening the mother is truly serious, even though not necessarily fatal.

Thus, an operation for the removal of an appendix might well be necessary to save an expectant mother's life and at the same time involve a risk to the fetus. Under such circumstances, it would be morally permissible to go through with the operation even though the life of the fetus would thereby be seriously endangered. The operation is not directed toward the destruction of fetal life, and it is an operation which is necessary to preserve the life of the mother.

All possible precautions are to be taken to preserve the life of the unborn. If the loss of the life of the fetus should occur, it is only the indirect and incidental result of the operation. The good attained by the performance of the operation, the preservation of the mother's life, is proportionate to the risk of life to the unborn child.

In this latter type of case, one has no difficulty in verifying the four conditions of the twofold effect principle.

In passing, one should pay tribute to the excellent work being done on this score at the Margaret Hague Maternity Hospital in Jersey City. Major abdominal operations, such as the removal of an infected appendix, are being steadily performed during all periods of pregnancy with such a small loss of fetal life that it has elicited the admiration of the rest of the medical profession.

Cancer of the Cervix

The moral problems created by the occurrence of carcinoma and myoma during pregnancy were discussed briefly in Chapter Two, in our treatment of the twofold effect principle. The student may review that section with profit.

Carcinoma of the cervix is a rare complication of pregnancy. The exact frequency of the condition is not known; Werther has given an estimate of 1 case in 2000 obstetric patients, while Glockner gives the rather extreme figure of only 1 case in 15,000 pregnancies.

When pregnancy does supervene upon a cervical carcinoma, the growth of the latter is notably hastened by the general increase in pelvic vascularity. Resulting hemorrhage may be fatal even during the early months of pregnancy.

Briefly, the pregnant cancerous uterus may be excised even before the viability of the fetus. The manner in which the twofold effect principle serves as the basis for this conclusion was explained in the second chapter which dealt with that moral principle.

In addition, the following reflections on carcinoma are pertinent:

Cancer of the uterine cervix is always malignant and causes death if not removed before it has gone on to metastasis. This type of cancer usually appears *after* the child-bearing age. When it occurs in earlier years, the woman is usually sterile, unless the lesion is in its incipiency at the time of conception.

In cancer, when an operation may preserve the mother's life and the fetus is inviable, it is morally permissible to remove the uterus and its adnexa. We assume that immediate operation is essential if the mother's life is to be saved. The twofold effect principle can be successfully applied in this instance.

In cancer, when an operation may preserve the mother's life and the child is viable, the moral problem is not at all difficult. The child should be delivered immediately by cesarean section and then the uterus and its adnexa entirely excised.

When the cancer is inoperable in the sense that an operation cannot possibly preserve the woman's life, and the child is viable, an immediate cesarean section is the best procedure. The cesarean section would have to be done eventually if the child were allowed to go to term. The mother is better able to endure immediate operation and it may even be safer for the child. The immediate operation does not risk the life of the mother, but it is a risk which she is justified in taking in the interests of her child's life.

Although it is theoretically true that in some cases the mother is morally obliged to undergo the risk involved in an immediate operation, in practice, prudent counsel may be given to her, but coercive argumentation is not proper. Insistence could lead to a refusal which might place the dying mother in a state of grave sin. The final decision should be a product of her own free choice in the matter.

The Use of Drugs During Pregnancy

The use of drugs during the course of pregnancy and at parturition is a source of several moral problems worthy of consideration.

In cases of threatened abortion, the cautious administration of morphine is a practical means of quieting the woman, reducing uterine irritability, and thereby averting the threatened abortion. The use of the drug under such circumstances is morally permissible, if it is the only drug which will prevent the threatened abortion, even though its administration may involve a real danger to the fetus. This danger will arise from the fact that the use of the drug may cause the fetus to become narcotized. But, serious as this danger may be, it is a lesser risk to the life of the unborn than that which would be present if the mother did not receive the drug.

This conclusion is based upon the verification of the four conditions proper to the twofold effect principle: first, the use of the drug to avoid abortion is an indifferent act; second, the good effect of averting abortion proceeds directly from the use of the drug; third, the motive prompting the use of the drug is the desire to avert the threatened abortion; fourth, the good effect of averting abortion and thereby preserving fetal life outweighs any harm that the use of the drug may bring to the fetus.

In this case there is the obvious moral obligation to avoid an unnecessarily excessive use of the drug, as well as the moral obligation to take all possible precautions to preserve the life of the fetus. In such cases the fetus is often born narcotized and one should be previously prepared to do all that is possible to preserve its life as long as possible.

The administration of large doses of morphine during pregnancy to counteract physical pain arising from any cause is not morally permissible when such pain does not involve a true danger to the life of the mother or her unborn child. Large doses of morphine risk the life of the unborn child. One is not justified in so risking the child's life except for a proportionate cause. The mere relief of physical pain which does not risk the life of the mother or fetus is therefore no justification for the administration of large doses of morphine. It is the fourth condition of the twofold effect principle that is unable to be verified in this case.

The same principles apply to the proposed use of quinine during pregnancy.

Until recent years, quinine was the only drug known to be of value in cases of malaria. Even under such circumstances, however, the use of quinine in malaria cases during pregnancy did not constitute a serious moral problem. First, there is some evidence to the effect that the usual oxytocic properties of quinine are neutralized by the malarial condition. And, secondly, since it was the only known drug for the cure of malaria, the twofold effect principle was readily verified in any instance wherein the malaria threatened the life of the woman.

Recent advances in medical science have produced at least one synthetic antimalarial drug (atabrine). Science will probably produce others as time goes on. Hence, it is safe to say that there is no such thing as a serious moral problem created by malaria occurring during pregnancy. The drug which will have the least harmful effect upon the fetus and at the same time suffice to counteract the malaria of the mother is the drug to be used.

It is *not* morally permissible, in the absence of malaria, to administer large doses of quinine during pregnancy before the viability of the fetus. Where malaria is not present, the oxytocic properties of quinine are not neutralized and large doses of the drug are liable to harm the child or effect abortion. Since malaria is not present, there is no need to use quinine and, therefore, no justification for unnecessarily risking the life of the unborn child. The fourth condition of the twofold effect principle is unable to be verified under such circumstances.

The use of drugs at parturition to lessen the pains of labor is a practice which dates back to ancient civilizations. Unfortunately, the drugs used throughout these centuries were harmful either to the mother or child or to both. The search for an absolutely harmless analgesia has long been sought by medical science. This research has resulted in the discovery of various drugs and combinations of drugs which, when used by a skilled operator, involve very little risk to mother or child.

The old method of twilight sleep (scopolamine-morphine) need not be discussed here. It has been discarded by practically all hospitals as involving too great a risk to the child. With newer and safer methods available, there is certainly no moral justification for the use of the dangerous twilight sleep.

Some analgesia is used in approximately eighty per cent of all hospital deliveries and to a lesser extent in home deliveries. The barbituric acid combinations, particularly nembutal alone, or in combination with scopolamine and paraldehyde, rectal ether and caudal analgesia are probably the most widely used at the present time. Modern obstetrical specialists have thus developed drugs which have very little, if any, harmful effects on the mother and negligible effects on the full-term child.

Modern followers of the Good Samaritan, who spent so much of His life relieving pain and suffering, are certainly interested in alleviating unnecessary pain. But it is morally indefensible to use any drug which would risk the life of mother or child to relieve the pains of labor.

This moral conclusion outlaws many of the drugs and methods formerly used, such as twilight sleep. But the prudent use of various recently discovered drugs by a skilled operator involves no noticeable risk to mother or to a full-term child. The administration of such drugs, when deemed necessary, can meet with no moral objection.

Conditions in the mother will occasionally be encountered which will not tolerate the administration of certain drugs. Frequently it is known that these drugs will relieve intense physical pain, but will seriously endanger the woman's life. A drug may never be used simply to relieve pain, regardless of its intensity, if it is clear that the drug would seriously risk the life of the patient.

Conditions in the unborn child will likewise be encountered which will not tolerate the use of drugs to alleviate the pains of labor. One is not justified in using a drug to lessen the pains of labor when it is evident that the use of the drug will probably endanger the life of the unborn child.

Placenta Praevia

Placenta praevia is present when all or a portion of the placenta is imbedded in the lower uterine segment in the zone of dilatation below the fetus, either partially or completely covering the internal "os" of the cervix. In this condition, the placenta is implanted so low that it encroaches upon the internal "os" and is, for this reason, called "praevia."

True placenta praevia is relatively rare and occurs about once in each five hundred obstetric patients. It is, however, one of the more serious complications of pregnancy. Maternal mortality has been estimated as ranging between five and eighteen per cent, while fetal mortality is approximately fifty per cent.

The reason for the importance of placenta praevia as a complication of pregnancy is that dilatation of the cervix and uterine contraction results in the detachment of the placenta from its site. This separation of the placenta occurs, in varying degrees, either because it is pushed off by the descending head of the fetus or because the cervix is pulled away from the placenta by the contraction of the upper segment. Inasmuch as the fetus is not yet born and the uterus therefore incapable of contracting sufficiently to obliterate this blood space, free hemorrhage occurs. It becomes more profuse as more and more placenta is detached, and it will continue until the uterus is emptied and strong contraction of the organ may occlude the blood vessels. Even then the danger of hemorrhage persists because the lower uterine segment does not contract strongly and bleeding may continue despite the fact that the fetus has been delivered and the upper segment firmly contracted. It is for these reasons that the hemorrhage resulting from placenta praevia is also called *unavoidable hemorrhage*.

This condition creates a moral problem in so far as the emptying of the uterus brings about its contraction and thus provides an obvious way to stop the hemorrhage.

An important characteristic of hemorrhage resulting from placenta praevia is that *it almost always occurs after fetal viability has been reached*. There are, of course, some infrequent exceptions to this rule. But the fact that the condition is more or less peculiar to late pregnancy generally eliminates difficult moral problems.

The following moral principles should provide an adequate basis for the solution of any problems which this condition may create:

A viable fetus may be removed from the uterus whenever

*sound medical judgment believes such a procedure to be in
the best interests of mother and child.*

Even an *inviable* fetus may be removed from the uterus
after a *complete* separation of the placenta. The basis for this
conclusion is the fact that the fetus dies within ten minutes
of a *complete* separation of the placenta. Consequent emptying
of the uterus therefore involves only an already-deceased fetus.

Since the dilatation which causes the separation of the placenta usually takes place at term, the fetus is almost always
viable. But it is to be admitted that there are some rare cases
of dilatation, with resulting unavoidable hemorrhage, while
the fetus is still inviable. It would not be morally permissible
in such instances to remove the living inviable fetus from the
uterus as a means of stopping the hemorrhage. This would
be an act of direct abortion. If the hemorrhage is not too
severe, the doctor may treat the case expectantly and endeavor
to bring about a cessation of the hemorrhage by such measures
as rest in bed. But if the hemorrhage is so severe as to threaten
the life of the woman, vaginal tamponade may be used as a
method of curtailing the bleeding, even though its use may
cause a complete separation of the placenta and thus *indirectly*
bring about the death of the inviable fetus. The best present-
day obstetrics usually frowns upon vaginal tamponade, because
it is frequently incapable of stopping the hemorrhage and is a
source of possible infection. But it does not appear that any
other morally permissible solution is at hand to cover the
infrequent case of a *partially* separated placenta, causing a life-
threatening hemorrhage before the fetus is viable.

Abruptio Placentae

Abruptio placentae is the term used to describe the bleeding which results from the premature *detachment of a normally implanted placenta*. This condition is also known as
accidental hemorrhage, in contrast to *unavoidable hemorrhage*
(which results from the detachment of the *abnormally implanted placenta* in cases of placenta praevia).

Abruptio placentae occurs approximately once in five hundred pregnancies. Many of these cases, however, involve only

mild hemorrhage. Severe hemorrhage from abruptio placentae probably occurs about once in eight hundred pregnancies.

Premature separation of the placenta in its more severe phase is probably the most dangerous complication of pregnancy. In cases of complete separation, maternal mortality is approximately fifty per cent and fetal mortality is about ninety per cent.

There are, of course, many mild cases which involve the separation of the lower pole of the placenta only. These cases are either wholly unrecognized clinically or the symptoms are so trifling that they do not cause alarm. Many other cases in which the loss of blood is notable and the symptoms acute are saved from a fatal termination by prompt and thoughtful treatment.

The serious danger of abruptio placentae, however, can never be minimized. It is a grave accident in which both mother and child stand in deadly peril of losing their lives.

From the moral viewpoint, the one fortunate characteristic of abruptio placentae is that *it is an accident of late pregnancy*. In fact, it usually occurs at the onset of labor or during its progress.

Whenever the hemorrhage is not so severe as to endanger the woman's life, no remedial measure may be taken which would probably result even in the indirect loss of life to the unborn child.

In severe cases in which the hemorrhage endangers the mother's life, it is morally permissible to remove the *viable fetus* from the uterus by whatever means sound medical judgment indicates to be in the best interests of mother and child.

Whenever the fetus is *inviable* and the hemorrhage endangers the mother's life, it is morally permissible to use a vaginal tamponade to stop the bleeding. Even though fetal death may *indirectly* result from the use of this remedial measure, the act is morally permissible.

It is, moreover, lawful to empty the uterus of the inviable fetus whenever there has been a *complete* separation of the placenta. For reasons previously given, this act would involve only a deceased fetus and would therefore be allowable.

A *partial* separation of the normally implanted placenta, however, does not necessarily imply the death of the fetus. Hence partial separation of the normally implanted placenta can never morally justify the emptying of the uterus before the fetus has reached viability.

Fibromyomata of the Uterus

Fibromyomata of the uterus are occasionally a source of real danger during pregnancy, labor and the puerperium. Small tumors are quite common but have no clinical significance. Fibroids are present in possibly thirty per cent of all pregnancies. Those which are large enough to be regarded as a potential menace occur about once in every one hundred and fifty obstetric patients.

Early in pregnancy, abortion is the chief danger created by uterine fibroids. It occurs in about one-fourth of the cases in which these tumors complicate early pregnancy. At later periods, spontaneous abortion is less common but is nevertheless always a possibility. Premature labor is rather frequent and is responsible for a considerable part of the fetal mortality which is encountered whenever fibroids complicate pregnancy.

The majority of these cases can be handled without having recourse to surgery during pregnancy. The tumors will complicate the birth of the child but the delivery will not usually exceed the skill of a good obstetrician.

In some of the more severe cases, however, recourse to surgery during pregnancy will be necessary. Some medical textbooks, such as Beck's *Obstetrical Practice,* state that, whenever operative intervention is necessary, removal of the entire uterus is preferable to the removal of the tumors in the uterus. It is also held that, whenever a cesarean section is done in these cases, removal of the uterus is preferable to myomectomy. This authority on obstetrics states that the surgeon can be content to remove only the tumors "if it seems desirable to avoid sacrificing the uterus."

Regarding the foregoing views, it must be emphasized that *it is morally permissible to remove the uterus only as a last resort.* If the health or life of the woman can surely be safeguarded by the removal of the tumors, it is not allowable to remove the entire uterus.

Whenever the fetus is inviable and surgical intervention during pregnancy is necessary, operative procedures must be postponed until after the fetus reaches viability, if this can be done without risking the life of the woman.

In those comparatively rare cases of fibromyomata in which the fetus is inviable and in which it is necessary to excise the entire pregnant uterus immediately in order to safeguard the mother's life, it is morally permissible to do so.

Preëclampsia and Eclampsia

Preëclampsia is a term used to indicate those cases of sudden toxemia, *developing generally during the last two months of pregnancy*, presenting all the evidences of renal insufficiency, often terminating in true eclampsia but sometimes improving rapidly after treatment.

Preëclampsia and eclampsia differ from each other only in that the latter has reached fully developed pathological lesions and has culminated in convulsions.

The symptoms of preëclampsia are well known to medical science and the diagnosis is not difficult. In general, the prognosis in cases of preëclampsia might be called favorable. Due to ever-increasing prenatal care, the serious stage of preëclampsia is being avoided. We are told, however, that if the condition, once recognized, does not respond favorably to treatment, and the pregnancy is not then terminated, the prognosis for both mother and child is grave.

It must be emphasized that the most successful method of handling preëclampsia lies in its prevention.

This fact brings us back to the thought which cannot be repeated too often: proper and extensive prenatal care will prevent the occurrence of many of these difficult conditions which give rise to our most serious moral problems.

In the average case of preëclampsia, recommended medical treatments usually prove effective.

Many medical authorities, however, insist that if, in spite of such measures, a patient does not favorably respond, the possibility of an oncoming eclampsia should be kept in mind. These authorities admit that hasty or urgent means of artificial termination of pregnancy are neither justified nor necessary; such toxic patients do not withstand operative procedure well, and they are very susceptible to infection. But these specialists urge that if, after a trial of several days, the disease does not show clears signs of amelioration the pregnancy should be terminated.

Two motives lie behind this suggestion: first, a desire to avoid the tragic stage of the disease and, second, the hope of obtaining a healthy child.

In comment, we need only repeat that it is not morally permissible to terminate the pregnancy before the viability of the fetus. By implication at least, the medical authorities suggest artificial termination of the pregnancy *after* the fetus has reached viability. This is clear from the thought that the desire of obtaining a healthy child is a partial motive for the suggested procedure.

In such a case there is no moral objection to the procedure, and doctors and nurses are free to participate in it. The twofold motive of avoiding the tragic stage of the disease and obtaining a healthy child are certainly causes which morally justify a premature delivery.

Eclampsia may be defined as a toxic disease of late pregnancy, characterized by intermittent convulsions, which are followed by a steadily deepening coma. The convulsions are generally spasms of succeeding tension and relaxation; in fewer instances, rigidity is constant.

Not included under the term "eclampsia" are convulsions caused by epilepsy, hysteria, apoplexy, uremia, meningitis, syphilis, and poisonings. Eclampsia might likewise be defined as that unknown state of the constitution in late pregnancy, produced by physiochemical changes in the blood (or causing them), in which state the pregnant woman is liable to convulsions or coma.

Eclampsia is said to occur about once in five hundred pregnancies. If the preconvulsive stage be included in the statistics, it is probable that at least two pregnancies out of every hundred disclose some evidence of its presence.

The average maternal mortality in eclampsia is nearly twenty per cent, while fetal mortality is at least thirty per cent. Under the best hospital conditions, the maternal mortality does not exceed ten per cent. Death in eclampsia is usually the result of cardiac failure, respiratory failure during a convulsion, apoplexy, or overwhelming toxemia.

Fortunately, *eclampsia is a condition which occurs in the late period of pregnancy*. It has been observed that about ninety per cent of the cases occur after the sixth month, and about fifty-five per cent of this number take place during the last four weeks of gestation. In practically all cases of eclampsia the fetus has therefore reached viability.

When medical opinion indicates that a premature delivery of the viable fetus is advisable, there is no moral objection to the procedure. Every possible effort should be made to safeguard the life of mother and child.

In the comparatively rare cases in which eclampsia sets in before the viability of the fetus, there can be no possible moral justification for effecting a termination of the pregnancy. Such an act would be direct abortion and gravely immoral.

In the exceptional instances in which eclampsia is encountered before the seventh month of pregnancy, the fetus is frequently already dead. Whenever sound medical judgment believes the fetus to be dead, it is morally permissible to remove it from the uterus. The best present-day obstetrics, however, usually cautions delay in this matter. The danger of infection involved in removal is great, and the grave concern that older writers showed over the presence of a dead fetus in the uterus is generally without foundation. Medical literature abounds with instances in which a deceased fetus was carried for many months without any harm to the mother. In view of these facts, it should be stated as a moral principle that the dead fetus should be removed at whatever time medical science believes it to be in the best interests of the mother. If a capable doctor believed that it would be safest to delay the artificial induction of labor and to rely upon nature to expel the fetus, this course of action should be followed.

Adequate prenatal care is of a twofold value in this matter. First, it is a known fact that eclampsia is rarely encountered in those who have had proper prenatal supervision. Second, proper prenatal care makes possible an early diagnosis of the condition, and medical science is then capable of retarding the progress of the disease until the viability of the fetus has been reached.

The necessity of an early diagnosis brings us back to our constant thought that widespread, skilled prenatal care is most important. If attained, it will prevent innumerable moral problems from ever arising.

Interest in community welfare is here applied to a truly noble and necessary field of endeavor. All hospitals can make clinical prenatal service available to deserving people. Those who are blessed with the goods of this life can financially sponsor such a clinic, or at least aid in its support. Doctors and nurses can work incessantly to foster and to aid this type of clinical work. Prominent men and women can exercise their influence to obtain proper civic support, publicity and coöperation for the clinic. Organizations of women can aid in innumerable ways, for instance, by bringing a knowledge of the need and availability of such prenatal care to prospective mothers. A Committee of the local Girls' High School or College could provide help in various ways: members might take care of a mother's children while she attended the clinic or was confined to the hospital; others might exercise their skill to make or procure innumerable articles which young babies need and which poor parents cannot afford to buy.

Hydrocephalus

In certain pregnancies an excessive amount of cerebro-spinal fluid accumulates and results in an appreciable increase of every diameter of the fetal head. In fact, the various diameters of the head of the fetus become so much larger than the diameters of the mother's pelvis that a normal delivery becomes impossible. Fortunately, this condition is rather rare. Many of the standard texts on obstetrics state or imply the desirability of delivering a dead fetus and concern themselves only with adopting the method of delivery which is safest for the mother. Such an attitude usually results in obstetrical procedures which are directly aimed at destroying the fetus, such as the use of instruments to crush the head of the child.

We must insist always that safety for the expectant mother may never be our sole concern in evaluating a surgical or obstetrical procedure. *A direct attack on the living fetus is never permissible.* Hence, we may never use any technique which is intentionally aimed at destroying the fetal life, nor may any direct action be taken on the fetus which will be certainly destructive of its life.

Modern obstetrical science has, however, invented procedures whereby drainage of the hydrocephalic head is accomplished in such a way that the delivery of a living child is possible. Granted, the chance of the child living, or being normal, is not very good; but it has at least a better chance than if nothing at all were done to save it. Such drainage, whether called aspiration or intraventricular tap, whether a needle, a trocar, or any other instrument is used, has for its objective the preservation of the child's life, not its destruction. Such a technique is exactly the same operation that would be performed in favor of the child if it were already born and gave hope of survival. Such a procedure is therefore permitted by the ethical code for Catholic hospitals contained in the Appendix of this work and should not be forbidden in our hospitals. (Kelly G., *Medico-Moral Problems*, III, pp. 17-21.)

A type of problem quite similar to that involved in hydrocephalus is the case in which the child's head is so lodged in the mother's body that a forceful application of forceps will be required in order to deliver the child and this process is likely to injure the child seriously or even to kill it. On the other hand, if the child is left in its position, the sincere medical judgment is that it will surely die soon.

As previously stated, any *direct* attack on the life of the unborn child is opposed to Natural Law. For this reason, craniotomy and embryotomy were condemned in the previous chapter. Hence, even if the presence of the undelivered child within the mother constitutes a serious danger to her life, no direct action that would surely cause death can be taken against the infant so long as there is probability that it is still alive.

"However, it can happen that there is a slight probability that a procedure, such as the use of forceps, will succeed in delivering the child alive, though it will surely die if this procedure is not attempted. In such a case, the doctor may have recourse to this process, even though its use may actually accelerate the death of the child. For in such a case the direct purpose of the doctor's action is the delivery of a living child; the death of the infant, if it occurs, is only an indirect effect, permitted for a sufficient reason (*viz.*, the fact that this is the only procedure that offers a chance of life to the little one.) Injuries inflicted on the child in the course of such a procedure are justifiable on the principle that it is lawful to mutilate the body for the preservation of life—the same principle that justifies the excision of a limb that is diseased. It should be added that, according to reliable medical testimony, a case such as that described will rarely occur if a pregnant woman has recourse to the services of a competent obstetrician in the course of her pregnancy." (Connell, F. J., *Am. Ecc. Rev.*, April, 1951, 308-309.)

Premature Delivery

Premature delivery differs essentially from abortion. Premature delivery is the birth of a child before the normal and natural time but after the period of viability has been reached. In contrast, abortion is the expulsion of the inviable fetus from the womb of its mother.

Premature delivery of a child is morally justifiable whenever there is a sufficient reason for this procedure. Such a moral principle, however, necessitates consideration of two points: When does a fetus become viable? What conditions are considered as justifying a premature delivery?

The point of time at which a fetus is viable is essentially a scientific problem, not an ethical problem. Frequently, teachers of Ethics are asked by doctors and nurses: "After how many weeks may we attempt a premature delivery?"

The authority in Ethics can safely answer only: "After you are reasonably certain that the fetus is viable, you may effect a premature delivery, provided there is a sufficient reason for such procedure."

It must be remembered that whether or not a fetus can live outside the womb of its mother will depend on a number of variable factors. Under ordinary conditions, the normal fetus would appear to be viable at the end of the twenty-eighth week of gestation. In a scientifically equipped hospital, under constant skilled care, a normal fetus may be considered viable at a slightly earlier time. Under adverse conditions, a fetus would not be viable until a somewhat later date.

The above standards are at best general guides to action. The problem remains essentially a scientific one. In each particular instance, the doctor will have to estimate the age, health, and strength of the fetus, the conditions under which it will be born, as well as the amount and quality of the knowledge, skill, and equipment which will be available for its care. If, after considering these various factors, a doctor feels reasonably certain that a fetus is viable, he is morally justified in effecting a premature delivery for a sufficient reason.

Should later events prove that his judgment was wrong, there is no moral fault on his part. If his judgment is the product of a sincere and careful consideration of available facts, he is not morally at fault if the child should die. Prudence, however, would dictate that in borderline cases of viability, a doctor obtain from one or more specialists in obstetrics, a verification of his own judgment.

Obviously, the longer the premature delivery can be delayed without notable injury to the expectant mother, the longer it should be delayed. The reason for this conclusion is clear. Each additional day or week within the womb of its mother increases the chances of life for the unborn child. So long as this greater chance can be given the unborn child without notably injuring the expectant mother, it is evident that such delay is reasonable and moral.

In reference to the reasons which justify premature delivery, it must be admitted that these are very numerous. Generally speaking, any condition in which a continuance of pregnancy would endanger the life or permanent health of the mother would justify a premature delivery.

The sincere doctor will be able to determine whether there

is sufficient reason for a premature delivery. He will appreciate the risk to the child's life which is involved in a premature delivery and he will not cause the child to run that risk unless the condition of the expectant mother truly necessitates it.

Problems for Discussion

1. In a particular case of threatened spontaneous abortion, there is a hemorrhage which must be stopped. If a certain drug (ergot) is used, it will contract the uterus, the blood vessels will thereby be restricted and bleeding lessened. The contraction of the uterus, however, also tends to force the inviable fetus out of the uterus. May the drug be given? (Reference: *American Ecclesiastical Review,* Vol. 93, July, 1935, pp. 83-84.)

2. The husband of a woman in early pregnancy has recently died. The woman is forced to take a position in order to earn her living. This employment involves lifting heavy articles and there is therefore some danger of an abortion. May the woman continue in this position?

3. A young woman has always been athletically inclined. She derives particular enjoyment out of swimming, diving, and horseback riding. After her marriage, she becomes pregnant and realizes that these strenuous sports create hazards to the life of an unborn child. She does not wish to injure her unborn child nor does she wish to give up her pleasures. She convinces herself that certain precautions in her athletics will probably eliminate any dangers to the fetus. An abortion results. What is her guilt? Does she incur the excommunication attached to direct abortion?

4. A pregnant woman comes to her doctor in mid-November. Her child will probably be born around Christmas. She states that she would like to have her baby delivered prematurely, so that she will be out of the hospital and able to go to Florida for the Christmas season. Comment on this case.

5. Suppose a doctor on a maternity case ordered a medication to hasten the delivery of the child: In the light of your training and limited experience, you believe that this drug may injure the infant. Would you give the drug or report the order to the head of the obstetrical department in the hospital?

6. Comment on the taking of strong purgatives by a woman during the course of pregnancy. It is presumed that she is using these medicines in the interest of personal health.

References for Reading

BONNAR, A.: *The Catholic Doctor* (2nd ed.), pp. 72-81; 84-86, London, 1939.

BURKE, E.: *Acute Cases in Moral Medicine,* pp. 54-59, N. Y., 1929.

DAVIS, H.: *Moral and Pastoral Theology* (4th ed.), Vol. 2, pp. 166-198, London, 1945.

FINNEY, P.: *Moral Problems in Hospital Practice,* pp. 96-129, St. Louis, 1930.

MOORE, T.: *The Principles of Ethics,* pp. 159-184, Phila., 1935.

———: "The Morality of Certain Operations," *American Ecclesiastical Review,* pp. 136-154, Feb., 1935.

ROCHELLE-FINK: *Handbook of Medical Ethics,* pp. 91-130, Westminster, Md., 1943.

WOYWOD, S.: "The Use of Morphine and Other Opiates in Childbirth." *Homiletic and Pastoral Review,* pp. 1199-1201, August, 1937.

"Removal of the Pregnant Uterus," *American Ecclesiastical Review,* pp. 530-533, May, 1934.

CHAPTER 10

Ectopic Gestation

The word "ectopic" means "out of place," that is, not in its normal location. An ectopic gestation is, therefore, a fertilized ovum developing outside the uterus, an extrauterine pregnancy.

The site of implantation determines the variety. Extrauterine pregnancies, accordingly, are classified as *tubal, ovarian,* and *abdominal.*

Statistical estimates on ectopic gestation are necessarily only approximate. But in one thousand consecutive obstetrical and gynecological patients, approximately six cases of ectopic gestation are usually to be found. In practically all instances, the cases are of the tubal variety.

The causes of ectopic pregnancy are many and varied. It is usually a very difficult task to determine the specific causes in any individual case. Many pathological conditions of the tube, present before conception, are known to be instrumental in causing an ectopic gestation. But for the most part, these are conditions which *in themselves* would not constitute any serious danger.

Such conditions are, for example, a slight infection of the tube, a lack of vigor in peristalsis, a small nonmalignant tumor, an adhesion.

Frequently, however, there is no evidence of any abnormality in the tube anterior to the pregnancy. From all indications, ectopic gestation can occur in a tube which, before conception, was normal in all known respects.

Two pertinent observations can be drawn from these facts. First, it is not certain that the cause of ectopic gestation is in every case a pathological one. Second, even where the cause of the ectopic gestation is pathological in character, the cause is frequently of such a nature that *in itself* it would not constitute a serious threat to the life of the woman.

The consensus among medical specialists is that it is quite difficult to diagnose an ectopic pregnancy in its earliest stages. Great progress has been made in this regard in the past fifty years, but a certain diagnosis still remains a difficult matter. In more advanced cases, a certain diagnosis is, of course, not so difficult.

In all cases of ectopic pregnancy, it is naturally of supreme importance to determine whether or not the fetus is still alive. Fetal movements and fetal heartbeats are still the surest indications of life. Should any signs lead us to a positive probability of present fetal life, no medical or surgical procedure may be pursued, even for diagnostic purposes, which would *directly* destroy the life of the child. The *direct* destruction of fetal life is always gravely immoral.

An ectopic pregnancy may terminate in several ways. Tubal abortion, complete or incomplete, is probably the most frequent form of termination. It usually occurs between the sixth and twelfth week. Tubal rupture is the most serious and the second most frequent termination of ectopic pregnancy. It may occur at a very early time but usually takes place between the sixth and twelfth week.

The outcomes of tubal pregnancy are, in the order of their frequency: (1) tubal abortion; (2) rupture of the pregnant tube; (3) transit to secondary abdominal pregnancy; (4) uninterrupted development to term in the tube.

The last two terminations are exceptionally rare. Either tubal abortion or tubal rupture occurs in about ninety-nine per cent of all ectopic pregnancies.

The important implication of these facts, from the moral viewpoint, is that it is a very rare instance in which an ectopic fetus reaches viability.

The preceding explanation of ectopic pregnancy brings us face to face with one of the most difficult moral problems in the medical field: *Is it morally lawful to excise a pregnant fallopian tube?*

Doctors and nurses should possess a thorough understanding of the nature of the moral problem here involved. Such an understanding will bring with it not merely a solution to this particular difficulty, but also the ability to apply accurately a whole series of complex moral principles.

The moral problem involved in the proposed excision of a pregnant fallopian tube is primarily a problem as to whether this procedure is direct or indirect abortion.

Doctors and nurses may have encountered varied answers to this moral problem.

Perhaps they have read Father Edward Burke's *Acute Cases in Moral Medicine,* in which he apparently regards as immoral the excision of a fallopian tube bearing an inviable fetus.

In Father Finney's *Moral Problems in Hospital Practice,* they have possibly noticed the explicit condemnation of the removal of a tube bearing an inviable fetus.

In Father Bourke's chapter on "Medical Ethical Problems" in the symposium *Graduate Nurses,* one encounters another emphatic declaration on the immorality of excising a pregnant fallopian tube.

In the light of these manifold statements doctors and nurses are rightfully puzzled today when they read other authors upholding the moral lawfulness of excising a fallopian tube bearing an inviable fetus. Quite reasonably, they ask: Has our Ethics changed? Have we cast aside ethical principles which we formerly held?

The immediate answer is that ethical principles have not changed. The newer solution to the moral problem involved in ectopic gestation results from a more accurate knowledge of the pertinent medical facts.

The moral problem under discussion has undergone a wholly new orientation in the past decade. Doctors and nurses will notice upon investigation that, with the exception of Father Bourke's chapter, all of the above-mentioned writings antedate the year 1931. Since that time, the attainment of clearer medical knowledge has caused the current of ethical thought to follow another course.

In 1927-1928 Father Henry Davis, S.J., of England, published two articles on ectopic pregnancy in the *American Ecclesiastical Review*. In these articles the author upheld the moral lawfulness, under certain conditions, of excising a follopian tube bearing an inviable fetus.

In 1933, the most detailed and scholarly work on the moral aspects of ectopic gestation was published by Father T. L. Bouscaren, S.J.

This treatise was originally presented in Latin to the Faculty of Moral Theology of the Gregorian University, Rome, in June, 1928. One of the most notable characteristics of this work, along with its intrinsic merits, is that it was worked out under the guidance of Father Arthur Vermeersch, S.J. The latter is one of the most respected authorities in the field of contemporary moral theology. In the preface to this volume, Father Bouscaren assures the reader that both the reasoning and the conclusions of his treatise were approved by Father Vermeersch.

The conclusion of this scholarly work, entitled *The Ethics of Ectopic Operations*, is that, under certain conditions, it is morally lawful to excise a fallopian tube containing a living inviable fetus.

In 1935, Father T. V. Moore, O.S.B., published his work entitled *Principles of Ethics*. In this volume, the author upholds the views expressed in the above-mentioned treatise of Fr. Bouscaren.

In the same year, 1935, Father Henry Davis, S.J., first published his four-volume work on *Moral and Pastoral Theology*. In the second volume, the author repeats the thoughts which he previously expressed in his 1927-1928 articles in the *American Ecclesiastical Review*.

In 1937, Father A. Bonnar, O.F.M,. published his work entitled *The Catholic Doctor*. In this volume, the author unhesitatingly upholds the conclusion that it is morally permissible to excise a fallopian tube bearing a living inviable fetus.

The views expressed in these works mirror quite accurately the attitude taken by most moralists writing on ectopic gestation during the past twenty years.

The present writer also wishes to express the opinion that,

under certain specific conditions, it is morally lawful to excise
a fallopian tube containing a living inviable fetus.

The following argument for the legitimacy of this conclusion
is essentially the same as that employed by Fathers Vermeersch,
Bouscaren, Davis, Moore, and Bonnar, as well as by various
other authorities writing in several foreign languages during
the past ten years.

The Moral Argument

The moral lawfulness of excising a fallopian tube bearing a
living inviable fetus is dependent upon the successful application of the twofold effect principle. The four conditions of
that principle must be simultaneously verified if the operation
is to be one of indirect abortion, and morally permissible.

First Condition. The first point which must be established
is that the act which produces the two effects is at least a
morally indifferent act. At the very outset, it must be emphasized that this first condition is of vital importance in the consideration of the problem.

Formerly, moralists assumed that in cases of ectopic gestation
the fetus was developing in a normally healthy fallopian tube.
The ever-increasing size of the growing fetus, they contended,
naturally caused a distention of the tube, and eventually the
swelling terminated in the rupture of the tube, with resulting
hemorrhage. The surgeon was then counselled to stem the
hemorrhage and to do all possible to safeguard the life of both
mother and child.

In opposing the excision of the pregnant tube before imminent rupture, moralists formerly emphasized that the excision
was not a morally indifferent act. To excise a healthy tube is
mutilation and gravely immoral. To excise a healthy tube
bearing a living inviable fetus is an act of direct abortion and
gravely immoral. These advocates of the older view held,
moreover, that it is the growth of the fetus which endangers
the mother's life; and certainly one may not directly destroy
the life of a fetus to avert such a danger.

This attitude on the moral aspect of ectopic gestation was
influenced to some extent by certain surgical techniques used
in former years. It was not uncommon to have a surgeon slit

the tube and remove the fetus, or squeeze the fetus out of the tube. Others extinguished its life by piercing the amniotic sack and drawing off the fluid, or by an electric shock, or through the use of drugs.

These methods are now quite obsolete and could never be morally justified. They certainly involve a direct attack on the life of the fetus. In all of these methods the direct destruction of fetal life is a means used to safeguard the mother's life. Such methods are, from the moral viewpoint, unquestionably indefensible.

Obviously, the cardinal points here at issue are: first, whether the tube is healthy or diseased; second, whether the growing fetus or something else constitutes the danger to the mother. For, if the tube is diseased, its excision is not mutilation, and in itself it is a morally indifferent act. And if the danger to the mother results from the condition of the tube itself, and not from the presence of the fetus, the excision can be properly compared with the excision of the pregnant cancerous uterus.

The judgment as to the condition of the fallopian tube in ectopic gestation is one which belongs to the medical specialist, not to the moralist.

The expert testimony of present-day specialists in obstetrics appears to be unanimous in declaring that the tube in ectopic gestation is in a pathological condition. A reading of the most up-to-date volumes on obstetrics leaves no doubt that rupture of the tube is simply the climax of a gradual process of disintegration in the fallopian tube.

There is no need to quote here the unanimous testimony of these authorities. Father Bouscaren has presented abundant evidence of this type in his volume. More recent testimony on the severe disintegration of the tube may be found in any recent work on obstetrics, e. g., Bland-Montgomery's *Practical Obstetrics*.

From the viewpoint of medical science, therefore, there is no question about the character of the fallopian tube in cases of ectopic gestation; long before rupture a process of disintegration is in evident progress in the tube.

The present writer wishes to emphasize that he has *not* said

that all medical authorities hold that the tube is in a pathological condition *from the very beginning* of an ectopic pregnancy. Many medical authorities do hold this to be a fact, but
the unanimous agreement is on the point that *long before
rupture the tube is in a pathological condition.* As the fetus
develops, this disintegration of the tube becomes more marked
and dangerous. Finally, it culminates in tubal abortion or
tubal rupture attended by hemorrhage.

First Condition. The first condition of the twofold effect
principle therefore appears to be verified. The excision of the
fallopian tube in ectopic gestation is *in itself* a morally indifferent act; it is the excision of a diseased organ of the human
body. The decision as to the condition of the fallopian tube
belongs to medical science, and medical science today asserts
that the tube in ectopic gestation is in a pathological condition
long before its rupture. *The moralist who asserts that the
excision of the fallopian tube in ectopic gestation is the excision of a healthy organ up to the point of its imminent rupture
can find no support in medical science for his contention.*

Second Condition. The second condition which must be
verified is that the good effect (the preservation of the mother's
life) must result directly from the indifferent act.

Too great emphasis cannot be placed on the point that the
danger to the mother's life arises from hemorrhage resulting
from the disintegration of the fallopian tube. It is not the fetus
which endangers the mother's life, but the hemorrhage. In
tubal abortions and tubal rupture, the hemorrhage is very
dangerous; the loss of blood is considerable and may be fatal
even within a few hours.

Everyone realizes that the growth of the fetus has caused the
breakdown of the tube. Such an observation is true, but not
to the point. The present danger to the mother's life is the
danger of a fatal hemorrhage caused by the disintegration of
the fallopian tube.

The good effect (preservation of the mother's life) results
directly from the excision of the disintegrated tube. By excising the weakened and riddled tube, the hemorrhage is averted
and the mother's life is preserved. Hemorrhage is avoided and

the mother's life safeguarded, not because the fetus is killed, but because the diseased tube, which may at any time burst into a hemorrhage, is excised.

The destruction of fetal life is not the means of preserving the mother's life. The excision of a tube that is so diseased as to be prone to rupture is the means of safeguarding the mother's life.

The second principle is therefore fulfilled.

Third Condition. The third condition which must be verified is that the motive underlying the performance of the action is a desire to achieve the good effect.

No time need be spent on this point. The desire to preserve the mother's life is clearly the motive which prompts the excision of the pregnant fallopian tube. The loss of fetal life is simply a foreseen and permitted effect.

Obviously, the desire to destroy the fetus is not the motive prompting the operation.

Fourth Condition. The fourth condition which must be verified is that there must be a proportion between the good and evil effects. In order to justify a procedure which will result in the loss of fetal life, such procedure must preserve the life of the mother from a present grave threat against her life.

The decision as to whether or not a condition at any given time represents a present grave threat to the mother's life rests with skilled medical authority. It is not a decision which belongs to the moralist.

The fourth condition demands that the danger be an actual present one. It demands, moreover, that the danger to the mother be not merely present but actually grave. It is not sufficient that the condition will later develop into a grave danger to the mother's life.

It is well, however, to note that the necessity of the danger being a present one does *not* imply that it must be momentarily about to cause the death of the mother. The commonly-accepted interpretation of the fourth condition of the twofold effect principle does not demand that the danger be momentarily immediate but simply grave and actually present.

For instance, a woman might have cancer of the uterus and be one month pregnant; it might well be foreseen that the condition will probably not place her in imminent danger of death for some time; it would be equally clear that the condition would demand the excision of the uterus months before the possible viability of the fetus. Moralists would certainly regard the danger as grave and present and, under the circumstances, would authorize the present excision of the pregnant cancerous uterus.

The fourth condition revolves around a balancing of the good and evil which are to result from the indifferent act. *What good will an immediate operation produce which a later operation will not achieve? What evil will result from an immediate operation which will not attend a later operation?* These are the questions that must be answered in each particular case.

In the above-mentioned case of the cancerous uterus, death would probably not result for some time. The condition is, however, very unpredictable and the woman is certainly in a true, present, grave danger until the cancerous growth is excised. An immediate operation will remove the risk to her life which is constantly present as long as the cancer remains. An immediate operation will safeguard her life.

An immediate operation will bring only one evil which will not result from a postponed operation, namely, a shortening by some weeks of fetal life.

The good effect here is certainly greater than the evil effect. It would be unreasonable to force the woman to allow the cancer to develop and spread, to compel her to live in the danger that the condition might, without prediction, become suddenly so grave that her life might be lost, and to do this simply in order to prolong by some weeks the life of a fetus that could not possibly reach viability.

In ectopic gestation, the doctor encounters a grave and unpredictable condition. Some cases develop rapidly, others progress much more slowly. Tubal abortion generally occurs between the sixth and twelfth weeks, usually earlier than tubal rupture. But tubal rupture has occurred as early as the seventh day, and not infrequently in the early weeks. Ordinary and necessary human actions, not to speak of unusual activities, frequently bring on tubal abortion or rupture long before the estimated time of their occurrence. The medical judgment that throughout ectopic pregnancy there is a present grave danger to the mother appears to rest on a very solid basis.

We stress the point that the judgment of the presence and gravity of the danger belongs to the physician. No generalization should be made. Each case should be sincerely analyzed by the doctor. If he feels incapable of forming a judgment, he should consult one or more specialists in this field for their expert opinion.

Any doubt as to the gravity of the danger should be solved in favor of the mother; her life is at stake and it can be preserved, while the life of the fetus cannot be saved. The chances of an ectopic fetus ever reaching viability are so remote as to be practically negligible. It would not be proper to force the mother to run what may be a very grave risk to her life simply to prolong fetal life by a few weeks.

In the light of the above exposition, the following conclusions of Father Bouscaren appear quite accurate:

1. One should not make general and far-sweeping statements to the effect that whenever an ectopic pregnancy is discovered the tube should be excised immediately. One cannot take it for granted that every ectopic pregnancy constitutes a present danger which is sufficiently grave to justify the excision of the tube. With respect to both the pathological character of the tube and the gravity of the danger involved, each case must rest on its own merits. This twofold judgment should obviously be based on medical facts and thus belongs to the doctor.

2. Without questioning the testimony of obstetrical specialists to the effect that in unruptured tubal pregnancy immediate operation is *in general* the best procedure, it seems that there may be cases in which watchful delay will not endanger the mother. If a doctor's sincere and expert judgment is that there is as yet no pathological condition in the tube, that there is no present grave danger, the operation should be postponed. The woman should be kept under close observation and so situated

that an operation can be performed immediately in the event of a rupture which might occur sooner than expected.

3. When the sincere and expert judgment of the doctor is that the tube is pathologically affected and that the present danger is so grave that, all things considered, an immediate operation offers a notably greater probability of saving the woman's life, the operation may be performed. If the danger be present and grave, there can be little, if any, question on the fact that the tube is in a pathological condition.

4. In cases wherein the woman can be kept under close observation and constantly ready for an operation, there will not always be need for its immediate performance. Under such ideal conditions, immediate operation may not always offer a notably greater opportunity to save the woman's life, since the delay may not notably increase the danger to the woman. If such be the case, the mere fact that this period of observation will subject the woman to anxiety, inconvenience and expense does not appear in itself sufficient reason to justify an immediate operation. If competent medical authorities judge that the operation can be deferred without great danger, it should be deferred.

5. When circumstances make it impossible to keep the woman under observation, an immediate operation is morally justifiable when it confers upon the patient a notably greater probability of saving her life. It is assumed here that expert medical judgment believes that the tube is in a pathological condition and that it constitutes a present grave danger to the mother. The sense in which the danger must be "present and grave" has previously been explained.

Due to the difficulty of diagnosing an ectopic pregnancy, it is likely that the discovery of the condition in most cases has been made possible by some disturbance created by the pathological condition of the tube. In most cases, therefore, there is no question about the tube being in a definitely pathological condition.

The considered judgment of the doctor as to the gravity of the danger in each particular case will usually be the point of primary concern. His judgment on this matter must furnish the basis for action in each case. Briefly, if the woman cannot be kept under observation and if the doctor judges that a delay in operating would notably increase the already present danger to her life, the operation may be performed. In contrast, if competent medical authorities judge it prudent and safe to defer the operation, it should be postponed.

6. Further problems are created by the discovery of an ectopic gestation during the course of an abdominal operation. The above moral principles must be applied to these cases. In other words, if competent medical judgment holds that a present excision of the tube will confer a notably greater probability of saving the woman's life, the immediate excision of the tube is morally justifiable. *Such an opinion might frequently be based on the sound judgment that the woman would be incapable of sustaining another operation within a few weeks.*

It is here assumed that the medical authority handling the case judges the tube to be in a pathological condition. This point will probably be verified to the complete satisfaction of the doctor. Most medical authorities believe that a pathological condition is present almost from the very beginning of an ectopic pregnancy. Certainly, the tube is affected at a very early stage; we have seen that tubal rupture and abortion have occurred as early as the seventh day of pregnancy and frequently within a few weeks.

Once again, the twofold judgment to be made in each particular case must be made by competent medical authority: *Is this tube at this time in a pathological condition and will an immediate excision of the tube notably increase the woman's chances of preserving her life?*

If these two conditions are verified, the tube may be excised during the course of the operation for which the abdomen was originally opened.

7. In those comparatively rare cases in which the fetus has progressed to four or five months without rupture of the tube, the proximity of viability would seem to give some definite hope of its being reached. As compared with the previous cases treated, greater probability that any delay would result in

death for the woman would be required before one could perform the operation within a month of viability.

Even when the fetus has developed to four or five months, cases will be encountered, principally of the interstitial type, in which any delay in operating would mean almost certain death for the woman.

If the fetus is approaching viability as a secondary abdominal pregnancy, after the crisis of tubal rupture has passed, there is a still greater necessity of awaiting the viability of the fetus.

In brief, the closer the child is to viability, the more danger will a delayed operation have to involve for the mother before an immediate operation can be justified. When the child is very close to viability, a delay in operating would have to be almost equivalent to certain death for the mother before immediate operation could be permitted.

8. Needless to say, in all ectopic operations every effort should be made to baptize the fetus. The subject of Baptism is treated in a later chapter. For the present, however, it must be said that time is a most valuable element in the matter of baptizing an inviable fetus. Precious moments should not be lost. So long as life is *probably* present in the fetus, Baptism should be administered conditionally.

In the preceding exposition, the present writer does not wish to create the impression that the older opinion on ectopic operations is outmoded and untenable. The primary purpose of the exposition is to present the newer opinion as clearly as possible. The intrinsic value of the reasoning upon which it is based is evident. The extrinsic support which the opinion receives from so many reputable modern theologians gives it great strength. Any surgeon, nurse, or patient would seem justified at present in acting upon a moral conclusion which possesses such strong intrinsic and extrinsic support.

Problems for Discussion

1. One often meets people who hold that moral standards vary from time to time, from place to place. They believe that these standards are the product of the ever-changing culture,

education, and type of civilization in which man lives. What comments would you make on this opinion?

2. If you believe that moral ideals and moral laws are unchangeable, what do you regard as the basis of this absolute uniformity for all men of all times?

3. Do you think that there has been a change *in the moral principles* governing cases of ectopic pregnancy during the past twenty years?

4. Discuss the moral aspects of one or more cases of ectopic pregnancy which you encountered in your own experience.

References for Reading

BONNAR, A.: *The Catholic Doctor* (2nd ed.), pp. 86-88, N. Y., 1939.

BOUSCAREN, T.: *The Ethics of Ectopic Operations,* Chicago, 1933.

BURKE, E.: *Acute Cases in Moral Medicine,* pp. 48-53, N. Y., 1929.

DAVIS, H.: "A Medico-Moral Problem—Ectopic Gestation," *American Ecclesiastical Review,* pp. 275-291, Sept., 1927; pp. 405-414, Oct., 1927; pp. 413-416, April, 1928; pp. 122-126, Feb., 1942.

————: *Moral and Pastoral Theology* (4th ed.), Vol. 2, pp. 171-186, London, 1945.

FINK-BOURKE: "Some Medical Ethical Problems Solved," *Graduate Nurses,* p. 211, N. Y., 1938.

FINNEY, P.: "A Medico-Moral Problem—Ectopic Gestation," *American Ecclesiastical Review,* pp. 54-71, Jan., 1928.

————: *Moral Problems in Hospital Practice,* pp. 130-144, St. Louis, 1930.

KELLY, G.: "The Morality of Ectopic Operations," Hospital Progress, Jan., 1948.

MOORE, T.: *Principles of Ethics,* p. 174, Phila., 1935.

O'BRIEN, J.: "Moral Aspects of Ectopic Gestation," *American Ecclesiastical Review,* pp. 95-103, August, 1941.

————: "Ectopic Gestation," *American Ecclesiastical Review,* pp. 282-284, April, 1942.

ROCHELLE-FINK: *Handbook of Medical Ethics,* pp. 119-128, Westminster, Md., 1943.

SCHLUETER, E.: "Medical Aspects of Ectopic Gestation," *American Ecclesiastical Review,* pp. 81-94, August, 1941.

CHAPTER 11

The Sacrament of Baptism

Corresponding to man's physical birth into this temporal life, Christ established the sacrament of Baptism as the necessary means of spiritual birth into the supernatural life.

It was not long after the beginning of His public life that Christ told the inquiring Nicodemus that "unless a man be born again, he cannot enter the kingdom of heaven." Nicodemus thought that Christ referred to a second natural birth, and asked "How can a man be born again when he is old?" It was then that Christ explained that He was referring to a "birth" far more sublime than that of the body: "Amen, amen, I say to you, unless a man be born again of water and the Holy Ghost, he cannot enter the kingdom of heaven."

The teaching of Christ on the above occasion makes it crystal clear that baptism of water is required of man as the *ordinary* means of entrance into the life of grace. In contrast, Baptism of desire and Baptism of blood are *extraordinary* means.

The Church's teaching on the necessity of Baptism causes one question to arise frequently in the mind of every Christian: What will be the destiny of the child who dies without baptism?

The most accurate answer to this oft-repeated question is that God has not revealed the nature of such a child's future existence. We do know from the words of Christ that the unbaptized child can never enter the kingdom of heaven. For all eternity it will be deprived of that perfect and supernatural happiness which shall be the reward of those who enjoy the Beatific Vision. There are many who very justifiably believe that God, in His infinite Mercy and Goodness, may grant some

250

form of *natural* happiness to those unfortunate souls who have never had the opportunity to receive Baptism. Such a conclusion is, however, admittedly based more on hope and trust in God than upon any positive Divine assurance.

The reward of eternal happiness for the baptized infant is certain and definite. The lot of the child who dies without baptism is at best problematical. This truth alone should suffice for the Christian doctor and nurse. It should steel them in their determination never to allow a child, through their negligence, to die without baptism.

The Minister of Baptism

The priest is the *ordinary* minister of baptism, and he should be summoned whenever time and circumstances permit.

In cases of *necessity,* anyone—Catholic or non-Catholic—having the use of reason can and should baptize. A case of necessity is present whenever there is danger of a child or fetus dying without baptism. In this regard, the following rule which is followed in many Catholic hospitals merits high recommendation: baptism is administered immediately after birth to every premature baby and to every full term baby weighing less than five pounds. A case of necessity is also present whenever a properly disposed adult is dying and a priest is not available to administer the sacrament.

If an emergency baptism is properly administered, it is valid and final whether the person lives or dies. A properly administered baptism is not to be repeated. In view of the importance of baptism, however, it is recommended that priests administer conditional baptism to all infants baptized in cases of emergency by laymen. The conditional baptism would, of course, be administered when the infant would later be brought to the church for the supplying of the ceremonies omitted at emergency baptism. The only exception to this rule should be in cases of baptism administered by a person, such as a doctor or nurse, for whom the priest himself could personally vouch as to their accuracy in administering the sacrament.

After an emergency baptism has been performed by a doctor or nurse, the baptized person should be brought to the church as soon as possible. The priest will then complete the baptismal ceremonies by reading those beautiful and traditional prayers of the Church which ordinarily accompany baptism. These ceremonies include the bestowal of a Christian name and prayers for the spiritual security and progress of the already baptized person.

Though it be true that "the supplying of the ceremonies" should never be neglected, it is to be remembered that they are not essential to baptism. If a baptism is properly administered in a case of necessity, the person remains validly baptized whether the ceremonies are later completed or not.

Method of Baptizing

Baptism is to be conferred by pouring water on the head of the person and at the same time audibly saying the words: "I baptize thee in the name of the Father, and of the Son, and of the Holy Ghost."

In this regard, the following points should be kept clearly in mind:

(a) It must be *the same individual* who pours the water and pronounces the words of baptism. It is not permitted for one person to pour the water while another says the words. Furthermore, the words should be pronounced *during* the pouring of the water.

(b) The person administering the baptism must have the proper intention, that is, he or she must intend to administer the sacrament according to the mind of Holy Mother Church.

(c) It is permissible to dry the head of an infant immediately after the baptismal waters have flowed upon it. The temperature of the room or water, or the delicacy of the infant, may at times make this procedure desirable.

(d) The baptismal water should *flow* upon the head (or forehead) of the person being baptized. This sacrament "washes" away all stain of sin, and for this reason the sacrament should be administered in such a way as to symbolize its washing or cleansing effect.

(e) Care must be taken that the baptismal water flow

upon the *skin* of the person. Due to the presence of abundant hair on the heads of most adults, and even many infants, the safer course is to direct some of the baptismal water upon the forehead.

(f) If a new-born infant must be baptized, and if its body has been rubbed with oil, the baptismal waters must not be allowed merely to flow over the oil. It is advisable to remove the oil from the forehead of the infant until the baptism is completed.

(g) In the case of an emergency baptism by a doctor or nurse, a God-Father and God-Mother should be provided, if this can easily be done. Likewise, if the choice of the parents is known, a Christian name may be bestowed. In so far as possible, two witnesses, or at least one, should be present, in the event that the baptism is later called into question. (Canon 742.)

(h) All baptisms administered by doctors or nurses should be carefully and promptly recorded. This record should include the names of the parents of the child, the age of the child, whether the child lived, the date and place of baptism, the name of the one who administered the sacrament, and the names of the God-parents or witnesses. In instances where the baptism has been administered by one who has seldom or never baptized, it would be well to record also the precise manner in which the sacrament was given.

In hospitals, the authorities should set up a strict system whereby the records of emergency baptisms will be conveyed to the chaplain for placement in the baptismal register.

Regardless of whether an emergency baptism is administered in a hospital or a private home, some definite and effective procedure should be followed which will result in the baptism being recorded in the parish of the place of baptism and also in the parish to which the child's father belongs. Strong emphasis should be placed upon this point. Years later, the subject of an emergency baptism might find it impossible to prove that he was ever baptized, if his own parish has no record of such a baptism.

(i) Specially blessed water is used by the priest in the administration of baptism. In cases of necessity, however, any form of natural water will suffice: well water, lake, ocean or river water, rain water, mineral or distilled water. Even though water forms the greater part of certain antiseptic solutions, such solutions may *not* be used in administering baptism. A baptism administered with such a solution would be invalid.

On August 21, 1901, the Church stated that, in certain cases where there is danger of infection (such as the danger of infection to the mother in intrauterine baptism) it would be permissible to add one thousandth part of bichloride of mercury. In most cases, distilled water heated to body temperature would serve the purpose.

(j) One should add a final word to doctors, public health nurses and social workers who labor amongst the poor and in the crowded tenement sections of our large cities. They will find it prudent to inquire not only if a sick infant is baptized but also to ask the same question about the older children in the family. By following this suggestion they will frequently reap a rich harvest of souls for Christ.

Conditional Baptism

In cases in which it is doubtful that a person is *capable* of receiving the sacrament of baptism, the sacrament is administered conditionally.

Doubt as to the capability of receiving baptism arises:

(a) when we do not know with certitude that a person has been previously baptized;

(b) when we do not know with certitude that a person is still alive;

(c) when we do not know with certitude that an adult has the intention and desire to receive the sacrament;

(d) when we do not know with certitude that baptism can be validly received on the *only part* of the body which can be reached by the baptismal waters; (for example, in cases of intra-uterine baptism or baptism on a leg or thigh in cases of difficult presentation).

It is best for a doctor or nurse to use *the same conditional clause* for each of the above types of doubtful cases. It would be permissible, it is true, to formulate the proper condition for each precise type of case. Thus, one might use the conditions *"if you have not already been baptized,* I baptize you, etc."; *"if you are alive,* I baptize you, etc." But, it is much more simple and safe to use the one condition *"if you are capable of receiving baptism,* I baptize you in the name of the Father, and of the Son, and of the Holy Ghost." So far as the recipient of the sacrament is concerned, this one condition will serve adequately for all possible types of cases.

The words of the condition should be pronounced *before* the water is poured. The essential words of the baptismal form should be spoken *during* the actual pouring of the water.

Even though a doctor or nurse should find it difficult to formulate the proper condition, or should even forget to do so, it suffices that he or she have the intention of administering a conditional baptism. The most important thing is to pronounce audibly the essential words of the baptismal form while actually pouring the water on the head of the person.

Baptism of Conscious Dying Adults

For the valid reception of baptism by a conscious, dying adult, it is necessary that there be present the desire for the sacrament and the intention and desire to receive the sacrament.

An adult, unless he be knowing and willing and properly instructed, shall not be baptized; moreover, he must be admonished to be sorry for his sins.

In danger of death if the person cannot be completely instructed in the principal mysteries of the faith, it is sufficient for the administration of Baptism that the person show in some manner his belief in these truths and that he seriously promise that he will observe the commandments of the Christian religion. (Canon 752)

When there is ample time for proper religious instruction, a priest should be summoned for this purpose.

Some emergency cases will not admit of the delay which

would be involved in the summoning of a priest. The doctor or nurse should then briefly instruct the dying person in the most important doctrines of religion.

This basic religious instruction should explain the existence of God, that God rewards a good life and punishes an evil one, that in God there are Three Divine Persons, that the Second Person of this Trinity became Man and died for our sins.

The doctor or nurse should then endeavor to have the patient elicit *an act of faith,* in which the patient explicitly accepts the above truths, because God has revealed them, and implicitly accepts all other truths given by God to man; *an act of hope,* in which the patient expresses his confidence that God, in His goodness, mercy, and power, will give him the means necessary to attain his supernatural end; and *an act of contrition,* in which the patient expresses a true sorrow for his past offenses against God. Lastly, the dying man must seriously promise to live up to the commandments of the Christian religion.

After the doctor or nurse has completed the above religious instruction, a sincere effort should be made to arouse in the soul of the dying person the proper dispositions for the reception of the sacrament. Recollection of the goodness of God, the suffering and death of Christ, the loathsomeness of sin, the eternal reward bestowed upon a person who dies in union with God, the eternal punishment which is the lot of one who dies in the state of mortal sin—such are the spiritual thoughts which will be found most helpful in this noble task.

In extreme cases, it may be that there is not time even for the above brief instruction. The doctor or nurse should then have the dying person assent at least to the existence of God, indicate his desire to accept all that God has revealed, and make an act of sorrow for his sins.

Baptism of an Unconscious Dying Adult

For the valid reception of baptism, a person must have had at least the habitual intention or desire to receive the sacrament.

If an unconscious dying person has, in his past life or present illness, indicated in any positive way a desire for baptism, the sacrament should be conditionally administered. If possible, inquiry should be made of relatives and friends about this matter. Should inquiry reveal no evidence whatsoever of a past desire for baptism, the sacrament may *not* be administered. *The benefit of every doubt in this matter should, however, be given to the patient.*

In this regard, Father Gerald Kelly, S.J., (*Medico-Moral Problems*, Part 3) suggests that conditional baptism be administered to the following unconscious dying adults (unless it is certain that they are already validly baptized):

(a) in the case of the unconscious dying Protestant who has never shown any inclination to become a Catholic or who, in fact, has actually refused to become a Catholic. Most theologians agree that since the person is a Protestant it is likely that the person has already been baptized or at least desires the sacrament. However, unless it is known that the person has been validly baptized, it is advisable to baptize him conditionally when he is unconscious and dying.

(b) in the case of a man who belongs to no particular religion but whose wife and children are Catholics— the type of individual who has never openly declared his intention to join the Catholic Church but who has manifested such general good will towards the Church that all who know him well regard him as having 'leanings' toward the Church. The author has known a number of such persons who have faithfully attended Sunday Mass for years with their Catholic spouse, contributed financially to the Church, assisted in the social work of the Church and yet, for some inexplicable reason, never took the crucial step.

(c) in the case of a man who has never expressed any desire to become a Catholic but who had shown a disposition to be a 'Christian', that is, to belong to one of the sects which profess Christianity. Such a person has given indications of desiring to belong to "Christ's religion", whatever that is. There is, of course, only one true Church of Christ, and though this person has erred in his identification of that Church, it is his

evident desire to join Christ's Church. This would
obviously imply his willingness to receive baptism if
Christ imposed this obligation on all those who were
to join His Church.

(d) in the case of a man who belongs to no Christian body
but who has been regarded by his neighbors and
friends as a 'good man'. He has evidenced a desire to
do what is right, expressed a sorrow for his sins, and
shown a willingness to do whatever is required for his
salvation. Some theologians feel that these dispositions
are too general and too vague to imply a desire for
baptism. But other authorities emphasize that, since
baptism is one of the ordinary means of salvation instituted by God, the above dispositions are adequate.
In view of this diversity of opinion among authorities,
we would be justified in conferring conditional baptism when a person of this type is in danger of death
and unconscious.

When an unconscious dying adult is insane, *and has never
had the use of reason,* baptism is to be given in the absolute
form. The principles which govern such a case are identical
with those which pertain to infant baptism.

When an unconscious dying adult is insane, *but has had the
use of reason in his past life,* baptism should be given conditionally if there is any evidence whatsoever that, when a sane
person, he indicated a desire for baptism. If no such evidence
can be obtained from relatives, friends, or other sources, baptism may not be administered.

When an unconscious dying adult is insane, *but has occasional lucid intervals and is not in immediate danger of death,*
a rational interval should be awaited. At this time he should
be questioned and treated as an ordinary adult. If such a
person is in danger of death and it is not safe to await a lucid
interval, he should be baptized conditionally, if inquiry into
his past life indicates a desire for baptism. Should no such
evidence be found, baptism may not be administered.

The question has been asked: *Is it possible to administer
baptism to an unconscious dying person about whom we know
nothing?* This question presents one of the most difficult prob-

lems in moral theology. The traditional opinion is that a dying unconscious person may not be administered even conditional baptism unless he has previously given some positive sign that he wishes to be baptized. This opinion is backed by the majority of moralists and appears to be in conformity with the spirit of canon 752 (which does not expressly treat this matter).

A more lenient opinion, however, is supported by many highly-respected moralists of our day. They do not impose an obligation on the doctor or nurse to baptize such a person, but they praise them if they do so. In the light of the number and reputation of those who hold the more lenient opinion, it would appear morally permissible for a doctor or nurse to administer conditional baptism to a dying unconscious adult about whom nothing is known. But great care would have to be taken, not only to avoid scandal, but also to avoid acquiring and giving to others the impression that Baptism is a kind of infallible charm, which will surely bring salvation to anyone, regardless of his personal dispositions.

A final question on this matter may now be asked: *Is it permissible to baptize an unconscious dying person who is not unknown but, on the contrary, has been known in life to have never shown the slightest desire to receive baptism and who, in fact, has led a sinful life and even refused baptism?*

Most moralists would say that such a person is not a fit subject even for conditional baptism. A milder view, however, is approved by Father Henry Davis, S.J., (*Moral and Pastoral Theology,* vol. 3, pp. 54-55), by Father Edwin F. Healy, S.J., (*Christian Guidance,* p. 67), by Father Matthaeus Conte a Coronata O.M.C., (*Treatise on the Sacraments,* p. 95), and by Father Gerald Kelly, S.J., (*Medico-Moral Problems,* Part 3, pp. 42-44).

These authors do not say that we may baptize a person when it is evident that he does not desire the sacrament. They would readily grant that to attempt to baptize an adult, even conditionally, when it is clear that he does not desire the sacrament is a sacrilege. Their lenient opinion is therefore based on what they regard as some probability that the dying person has the necessary intention.

These authors admittedly do not hold much hope for the validity of the baptism in such a case. But they feel that it is probable that God has given the dying person powerful graces and that there is also at least a slight probability that emotional or other factors may have caused the person to adopt the attitude he took toward baptism during his past life. On the basis of these slight possibilities they believe it is permissible to administer a conditional baptism.

Finally, these authors acknowledge that the administration of conditional baptism in some of these extreme cases could cause scandal. The impression could easily be created that baptism is forced on unconscious persons who steadfastly rejected it during their conscious life. For this reason, they suggest that the conditional baptism be quietly and secretly administered.

Father Gerald Kelly, S.J., concludes his summary of this matter by quoting Father Arthur Vermeersch, S.J., professor of moral theology at the Gregorian University in Rome and one of the most eminent moralists of our age. After evaluating all of the arguments for and against the baptism of unconscious dying adults, Father Vermeersch concludes:

"If scandal is avoided, one may confer conditional baptism on any unconscious dying adult who is not known to be already baptized." (Vermeersch-Creusen, *Epitome Juris Canonici*, II, 35 (1940)).

Priests, doctors, nurses, and others are therefore justified in following the above directive in their spiritual ministrations to unconscious dying adults.

Baptism of the Non-Catholic Child

The indiscriminate baptizing of children of non-Catholic parents is certainly wrong. It is a basic principle that a Catholic baptism may be administered to a healthy child only if there is present reasonable assurance that the child will be raised as a Catholic. By baptism one becomes a member of the Church, and there is obviously no point in making a person a member of the Church unless its authority and means of salvation are to be accepted.

Even when the child of non-Catholic parents is seriously ill, but not in immediate danger of death, it should not be baptized by a Catholic doctor or nurse.

On the other hand, when the danger of death is real, certain, and proximate, the Catholic doctor or nurse should baptize such a child. This course of action is proper even against the will of the non-Catholic parents.

If a certain medicine were absolutely needed to save the physical life of a child, a doctor or nurse would give it, even though the parents were unwilling. The attitude of such parents would be unreasonable. To respect their unreasonable desire would be to deprive the child of its physical life at a time when it is wholly incapable of helping itself.

Similarly, baptism is absolutely essential for the dying child if it is to obtain supernatural life. All Christian parents should logically agree to this point, whereas non-Christian parents are in a state of ignorance on this truth revealed to man by God. The sincerity of parents who oppose baptism is not usually open to question, but one cannot acquiesce to wishes which would result in an eternal loss to the child.

There is no need, of course, to create antagonism. When the unreasonable attitude of the parents is evident, the doctor or nurse should quietly baptize the dying child without the knowledge of the parents.

One should repeat again the word of caution: the child of non-Catholic parents should not be baptized by a Catholic doctor or nurse unless there is a real, certain, and proximate danger of death.

In cases of this type a record of the baptism should be kept either by the hospital chaplain or preferably by the pastor of the place where the parents of the child reside. It is the duty of the doctor or nurse to inform either the hospital chaplain or the above pastor of the baptism. It has been suggested that a parish should keep the records of such baptisms in a private book, rather than in the regular baptismal register. If it is evident that the child's parents would not have objected to the baptism, or might even have been pleased by it, the hospital, doctor, nurse, or pastor should inform them of it. If it is known that the parents would have objected to the baptism, it would be well for the hospital to make a record of the fact and, in some instances, to assume the obligation of notifying the baptized person when the latter has reached a sufficient age to appreciate the nature of the sacrament.

In the case of a foundling, when there is no immediate danger of death, the doctor or nurse should consult a priest. If there is an immediate danger of death and no certain knowledge of a previous baptism of the child, the doctor or nurse should administer a conditional baptism. Even a note pinned to the infant stating that it has been baptized is not to be trusted; it is known that such notes have sometimes been written simply in the hope that the child would be more readily received by a Catholic family or orphanage. Unless the proof of baptism is clear, definite, and beyond any possible doubt, a conditional baptism should be administered.

Baptism in the Uterus

The law of the Church reads as follows: "An infant shall not be baptized in the mother's womb as long as there is probable hope that it can be baptized when born. If the fetus was baptized in the mother's womb, the child when born shall be baptized again conditionally." (Canon 746.)

Due to the difficulties encountered in uterine baptism, the validity of such a baptism is always open to some question. For this reason, the Church commands a *conditional* baptism after the birth of the child.

When there is a reasonable fear that the viable fetus will die before it can be delivered, it should, whenever possible, be baptized in the uterus—*provided the life of the mother is not thereby endangered.* This principle applies to premature labor as well as to labor at term.

Since the water should flow directly upon the fetus, baptism in the uterus is possible *only when the membranes are ruptured and the amniotic fluid discharged.* This should be done without undue haste and with special care not to cause injury to either mother or fetus.

In the case of an inviable fetus, most moralists hold that it is never morally permissible to rupture the membranes in order to confer baptism. They regard such an act as direct abortion and therefore never allowed.

If the "os uteri" is only partially dilated, it will be best to eject the water and audibly pronounce the words of baptism during "a pain." If the "os uteri" is undilated, a valid baptism is practically impossible.

Uterine baptism is usually accomplished with a sterile bulb syringe or other irrigating instrument. Sterile water of body temperature is to be preferred. The doctor or capable nurse, with one hand, directs the tube end of the instrument immediately through the "os uteri" against the fetus—not merely against the membranes—and with the other hand forces the water. As soon as the water begins to flow upon the fetus, the words of baptism should be audibly pronounced.

The suggestion has sometimes been made to attempt uterine baptism by wetting one's hand or fingers and rubbing the forehead of the undelivered child with the hand or finger while pronouncing the words of baptism. Such a suggestion is very impractical. Normally, one could have no confidence whatever in a baptism that depended on a hand or fingers retaining water from the time the vagina was entered until the head of the child was reached. Such a procedure would be possible only if the child's head were low down on the perineum, and in such cases it would still be far more reliable, and hence morally binding, to pour water on the child's head when it was presented externally during "a pain."

The umbilical cord is only a temporary part of the child, and baptism on it is certainly invalid.

It has been said that uterine baptism should be attempted when, in the prudent judgment of the doctor, the death of the child before delivery is to be feared. The conditions which most frequently create this necessity are: abnormally protracted labor, cases of difficult presentation, contracted pelvis, hydrocephalus, and eclampsia.

In cases of placenta praevia and uterine hemorrhage, it seems almost impossible to accomplish a uterine baptism. It is certainly impossible for the average nurse and she should not attempt it. A cesarean operation is often done in these cases, and an opportunity for baptism will thereby be presented.

Baptism in the uterus is always given conditionally: "If you are capable of receiving baptism, I baptize thee in the name of the Father, and of the Son and of the Holy Ghost." It may be found very helpful to hold a card bearing the above words before the doctor or nurse performing the baptism. Such a card should be available in every delivery room.

If a child has been baptized in the uterus and is later born alive, it must be again baptized conditionally.

Even though a priest be readily available, the Church regards it as more becoming for a doctor or nurse to administer baptism in the uterus.

In the case of an *inviable* fetus, most moralists hold that it is never morally permissible to rupture the membranes in order to confer baptism; they regard such an act as direct abortion and therefore never allowed. Some few moralists, including the respected Merkelbach, authorize intrauterine baptism for a fetus which is inviable and undoubtedly alive but rapidly growing weaker, and is very near its death.

The present writer regards the rupture of the membranes of a living inviable fetus as immoral. Several reasons underlie this conclusion. First, as discussed under the topic of hydramnion, it seems that the rupture of such membranes is not an indifferent act, but an act of direct abortion. The number and rank of the moralists who regard such an act as indifferent do not seem to be sufficient to constitute an opinion upon which one might safely act. Second, too little attention has been paid by these moralists to the fourth condition of the twofold effect principle in this case. *One may not hasten or seriously endanger the life of a mother to effect the baptism of the fetus.* For the most part, these writers have assumed that inevitable abortion will follow the rupturing of the membranes. Experienced obstetricians bear testimony to the fact that to rupture the membranes may be a hazardous venture. Labor may not follow, and if it does not, the risk to the woman's life from infection is severe. Third, expert obstetricians rarely feel that they could state that an inviable fetus is alive, rapidly growing weaker, and close to death. Finally, the chances of securing a valid baptism in the uterus of an inviable fetus are—for practical reasons—very slim. To attempt it would involve a grave risk to the life of the mother, and no one has the right to subject the mother to *a certain and grave* risk for the sake of a very doubtful spiritual effect on the child.

Baptism of the Premature Fetus

The law of the Church states that "care should be taken that every fetus born prematurely, no matter at what stage of pregnancy, be baptized *absolutely*, if life is certain; *conditionally*, if life is doubtful." (Canon 747.)

A fetus, even in the embryonic stage, if visible at all, should be baptized. Every product of human conception, no matter how immature, should be baptized. It is often difficult, it is true, to determine whether or not life is present. But, since an immortal soul came into existence at the moment of conception, it follows that every embryo or fetus prematurely expelled from the womb should be baptized absolutely if life is certain, baptized conditionally if life is uncertain, and left alone if certainly dead.

In cases of apparent death, an aborted fetus or newly-born child should be baptized *conditionally*—unless, of course, there is clear evidence of death, such as putrefaction.

When the presence of life in a fetus is doubtful, precious time should not be consumed in looking for signs of life. The fetus should be baptized *conditionally at once*.

If a fetus or embryo is delivered enclosed in the membranes, *the membranes must always be ruptured*. The ovum varies in size according to its age and is generally covered with its membranes when expelled. These membranes must be quickly opened and the baptismal waters allowed to flow directly upon the fetus.

If the expelled embryo is small, it may be baptized by immersion. Simply immerse the embryo in a small bowl of water, separate the membranes with the thumb and forefinger, then as the water contacts the embryo pronounce the words of baptism, and immediately withdraw the embryo from the water.

The advantage of this method is that no time is lost and there is no necessity of searching for the head.

Those attending a pregnant woman at the time of miscarriage or hemorrhage are cautioned to be on the alert to discover a fetus, if there be one in the contents expelled.

Baptism in Cases of Difficult Delivery

In certain cases of difficult delivery, the head of the child or some other part of its body protrudes and there is a reasonable doubt that the child will live until complete delivery has been achieved.

In case of *a head presentation,* baptism should be administered *absolutely* on the child's head, and the baptism should *not* be repeated when the child is fully born.

In any other type of presentation (such as hand, foot, buttock, shoulder, etc.), the child should be baptized *conditionally* on the part presented. When there are several such parts presented, baptism should be given on the part nearest the head of the child. When the child is fully born, it must again be *conditionally* baptized.

Baptism of the "Still-born" Child

When a child is apparently "still-born," that is, when a fullterm or nearly full-term child is apparently born dead, one should not quickly conclude that the child is *actually* dead. Experience has proven repeatedly that many children born after a protracted labor take on an appearance of death. Such an appearance may last for a considerable period of time and resuscitation may result only after prolonged artificial respiration.

When a child shows the slightest signs of life, it should be baptized *absolutely* in the ordinary manner.

If the child appears dead, there may still be some hope that life may be present. For while it is not permissible to baptize a dead child, the only true sign of death is putrefaction. When this indication of death is absent, there is the possibility of latent life, and the child can and should be *conditionally* baptized.

Baptism of Monstrosities

Emphasis must once again be placed on the point that any living product of human conception, regardless of its deformity, must always be baptized.

When a deformed fetus *clearly* represents more than one person, each should be baptized absolutely.

When it is *doubtful* whether the fetus is a single person or several persons, one should be baptized absolutely; the other (or others) should be baptized conditionally. (Canon 748.)

In the case of a fetus with two thorax sections and one head, the head should be baptized absolutely and *each* chest baptized conditionally.

When death is imminent in the case of multiple monstrosities, it is permissible to baptize them simultaneously by pouring water on the head of *each* and pronouncing the baptismal form in the plural: "I baptize *you* in the name of the Father, and of the Son, and of the Holy Ghost."

Baptism When Mother Is Dying

We refer here to cases in which the fetus is viable and a vaginal delivery is not possible without further increasing an already-present danger to the mother's life. What is to be said of performing a cesarean section in a case of this type in order that the fetus may be baptized?

When a cesarean section offers the only chance of saving the mother's life (as in some cases of difficult or prolonged parturition, eclampsia, etc.), the operation is *permitted*. It must be emphasized, however, that even though a cesarean operation be *permitted*, it is open to very serious doubt whether a dying mother is morally obliged, practically speaking, to undergo the operation. With caution and gentleness, the operation may be suggested to her, but any insistence on a moral obligation to provide by the operation for the baptism of the child is to be prudently avoided. A dying mother is in no condition to consider such a problem.

In the above case, the fetus should not be exposed to the danger of dying without baptism whenever baptism in the uterus is possible without increasing the danger to the mother's life.

When a cesarean operation does *not* offer any chance of saving the mother's life but, on the contrary, will directly contribute to her death (as in cases of pneumonia, fever, etc.), the operation should *not* be performed.

In cases of the above type, one should await the death of the mother and then observe the procedure outlined in the following section.

When a Mother Has Died

Church Law states that "Immediately after the death of a pregnant mother, a cesarean section should be done in order that the fetus may be baptized." (Canon 746.) This law holds whether uterine baptism was given or not, and when the fetus is viable there is the further obligation to do everything possible to safeguard the physical life of the child.

This cesarean section should be performed at the greatest inconvenience when the three following conditions are simultaneously verified:

(a) when it is *reasonably certain* that the mother has already died

(b) when it is *probable* that the fetus is still alive

(c) when there is a doctor present (or a nurse, in such places as civil law would permit) who is capable of properly performing the operation.

Practically speaking, there is no obligation to perform the operation if the sixteenth week of gestation has not been reached. From that point on, the cesarean section should be done, especially when the mother has died suddenly—unless, of course, there are weighty reasons pointing to the fact that the fetus died before or along with the mother.

The fetus will at best live only a short time after the death of the mother. The moments following the mother's death are precious. For this reason, prior to the mother's death, the consent of the proper relatives should be obtained if possible, the surgeon summoned, and everything required for the operation and the baptism, be set out. Due to the importance of the time element, it is recommended that these essentials be arranged in the sick room and the operation be performed there immediately upon the death of the mother.

Disposal of a Dead Fetus

A fetus which has been baptized either absolutely or conditionally should be buried in consecrated ground. A fetus which has died without baptism should be buried in unblessed ground.

It is advisable to bury a fetus in a cemetery, and not on the hospital grounds. A cemetery plot may be reserved for this purpose, and the gratuitous services of a responsible undertaker can usually be obtained for burials devolving upon the hospital.

If a fetus that has been taken from a dead mother dies *after receiving baptism*, the proper procedure is to replace it in the uterus, when this can be done conveniently, and to bury it with the mother.

A fetus should not be burned unless such action is necessary to prevent the spread of contagious disease.

Finally, when there is a sufficient reason for doing so, a fetus may be retained for laboratory study and observation. It is fitting, however, that a baptized fetus be retained only in exceptional cases.

The Disposal of Amputated Members

The Canon Law of the Church does not lay down specific directives concerning the disposal of excised organs and amputated parts of the body. Canon No. 1203 does, of course, specify that "the bodies of the faithful must be buried and their cremation is reprobated." It is evident, however, that this law refers to the whole body and is not directly concerned with the disposal of excised or amputated parts.

The mind of the Church on this matter is best reflected in a reply which was given more than fifty years ago by the Holy Office to a question proposed by a community of hospital Sisters. On that occasion, the Superior General of the Sisters of the Sorrowful Mother explained to the Holy Office that amputations were of frequent occurrence in their hospitals and that they desired some official guidance on the course of action which they should follow. The Sisters stated that they had frequently buried the amputated parts in unblessed ground on their own hospital property. At other times, upon the counsel of the doctors in charge of the patient, they had burned the excised organs and amputated parts. As might be expected, the patients who underwent these operations were Catholics, baptized non-Catholics, and unbaptized persons. In seeking the counsel of the Holy Office, the Superior General explained that burial of the amputated members in a cemetery would often be morally impossible and sometimes even physically impossible.

The reply of the Holy Office to this question was as follows: "With regard to the amputated members of non-Catholics, the Sisters may safely continue their present practice. They should try to have the amputated members of Catholics buried in blessed ground; but if serious difficulties stand in the way of such burial the Sisters need not be disturbed about their present practice. As for the burning of the members, if the physicians demand this, the Sisters may keep a tactful silence and carry out their orders. Moreover, it is the mind of the Sacred Congregation that, if it can be done, a small part of the hospital garden should be blessed and set aside for the burial of the amputated members of Catholics." This reply of the Holy Office was formulated on August 3, 1897, and received the official approval of Pope Leo XIII three days later.

This reply of the Holy Office is noteworthy in several respects:

First, the content of the response makes it quite clear that the Church does not insist upon the burial in consecrated ground of excised organs or amputated members with the same degree of rigidity that it does the bodies of the faithful. The lenient attitude of the Church towards the burial or even the cremation of the amputated members is a most reasonable one. Actually, excised organs and amputated members are frequently so diseased as to necessitate their burning. Furthermore, the cremation of parts of the body would rarely, if ever, have the anti-Christian connotation which is historically associated with cremation of the body.

The second notable characteristic of the reply of the Holy

Office is its mildness. While burial is held up as the most proper method of disposal, the Holy Office appears most willing to relax this regulation whenever its observance would entail undue hardship.

It must be acknowledged that some recommendations of the Holy Office are not always possible of fulfillment in this country. Thus, the Holy Office mentions that a small section in the hospital garden might be used for the burial of amputated members. Actually, many of our large city hospitals do not have any garden and, even if they did, it is likely that the sanitary codes of the state or community would not permit such a burial. Furthermore, in reference to burial in a cemetery, the extensive formalities which are usually required in the United States would make such a procedure a practical impossibility. In many, or possibly most, places in this country a burial permit must be obtained and a grave opened. It is also doubtful that a burial permit would be granted in some places except for the whole body of a deceased person. Collectively, these formalities would involve a serious financial burden for the patient; and in large hospitals, which would have to handle many of the burials themselves, the constant repetition of the formalities for numerous amputations would constitute an excessive drain on time and personnel.

It is well known that Catholic hospitals encounter different degrees of difficulty in conforming to the mind of the Church on the burial of amputated members. For this reason, it is not surprising to find that this problem is handled in a variety of ways in our Catholic hospitals. Thus, one diocesan hospital code says, "Every major portion of the body must be buried; arrangements must be made with the local Catholic cemetery." Another diocesan code states, "Notable parts should be buried in a cemetery, when it is reasonably possible to do so. Where health, sanitation, or direct prescription of the doctor demands it, then other means of suitable disposal can be tolerated."

In one Catholic hospital with which the author is familiar, the patients are urged to attend to the burial of both amputated members and the products of pregnancy. In a notable percentage of cases, the patients are unwilling to incur the expense and inconvenience which this would involve. The hospital then stores the amputated members under refrigerated conditions and preserves the products of pregnancy in formaldehyde in the laboratory. Once a year the hospital arranges with a Catholic undertaker for a burial of all of these parts.

In a second Catholic hospital with which the author is familiar, the authorities demand with an unrelenting insistence that the patients, or their families, arrange for the prompt burial of both amputated members and products of pregnancy.

In the light of the foregoing analysis of the reply of the Holy Office, the following recommendations are offered:

(a) Any Catholic hospital which is located in an area in which there are official diocesan directives governing the disposal of amputated members must diligently observe those regulations. Whenever such directives are offered to the hospitals they must be respected not only out of fitting obedience to proper authority but also because the suggested measures are undoubtedly the product of serious consideration, prudent judgment, extensive knowledge of moral law, and familiarity with local conditions.

(b) The law which orders the burial of bodies and prohibits cremation is, of course, an ecclesiastical law and as such applies only to the bodies and amputated members of Catholics. A fitting respect, however, is due to the bodies of *all* men; and it is therefore the apparent desire of the Church that, in the case of non-Catholics, the burial of amputated members (in unblessed ground) is preferable to cremation when the latter is not necessary.

(c) With regard to the amputated members of Catholics, the law applies only to such members as are reasonably considered notable or major parts of the body. It has been suggested that a part that retains its "human quality" after amputation should be regarded as a notable or major part of the body. According to this standard, arms, legs, and probably the female breast, would be construed as notable parts of the human body. In contrast, even very important internal organs usually lose their specifically human quality after excision and therefore are not considered as notable or major parts.

(d) Whenever major parts of the body are so crushed as to be simply a mass of flesh and bones, they may be burned without hesitation. The same may be said of members that are greatly distorted by disease.

(e) Some authors, relying upon the moderate tone of the reply of the Holy Office, hold the opinion that the Church is not opposed to the preservation of amputated parts for scientific purposes.

(f) The obligation to attend to the decent burial of major amputated parts rests primarily with the patient or his family. When the patient or his family is willing to fulfill this duty, the hospital has no further obligation in the case.

When the patient or his family is unwilling or unable to see to the decent burial of the amputated members, the hospital authorities should attend to the matter.

(g) When the prescribed legal formalities or the expense involved would constitute a grave hardship for the patient or his family, it is not necessary or advisable for the hospital to insist on their duty of burial of the amputated parts. Similarly, if insistence upon burial would arouse antagonism against the Catholic hospital, there is no need to press the issue. In this reference, one recalls that the reply of the Holy Office seems to imply that *even when doctors are not justified in their demand for cremation of amputated parts* Catholic hospitals may give in to the request without compromising their conscience.

It was stated above that, when the patient or the family, for any reason, fails to bury the amputated parts, the obligation falls on the hospital. The hospital, however, is freed from this duty whenever fulfillment would involve grave hardship. Thus, it could be possible that a hospital could not fulfill the obligation without notable expense, a great loss of time, drain on personnel, or involvement in technicalities of civil law. Where such serious difficulties prevail, the hospital would be justified in having recourse to cremation of the amputated members.

The Cremation of the Body

Lest there might be any misunderstanding in this matter, it should be stated immediately that cremation is *not* intrinsically wrong. In fact, when grave reasons necessitate this step in the interests of the public welfare there is no moral objection to it. Typical situations of this type might well be found during a devastating plague or when there has been a great loss of life in battle. In these exceptional cases, cremation could be necessary or at least very useful in the prevention of infection. (It is to be noted, however, that in the two recent great wars, military authorities did not have recourse to cremation; apparently it was not looked upon as an honorable way of disposing of the remains of soldiers who had died for their country.)

The Congregation of the Inquisition published decrees prohibiting cremation in 1886, 1892, and 1897. The most recent and complete decree of the Church, however, was issued by the Holy Office on June 19, 1926 (Acta Apostolicae Sedis XVIII, 1926, pp. 282-283).

This decree of the Holy Office severely rebukes those who hold up cremation as one of the outstanding achievements of so-called modern progress and of the science of health. The decree brands cremation as a barbarous practice which is contrary to Christian belief and to the natural respect due to the bodies of the dead.

A brief glance at religious history bears witness to the fact that cremation runs counter to the traditional practice of Christianity. In both the Old Testament and in the New we encounter references to the burial of the dead. It is one of the corporal works of mercy. We have, moreover, the burial of Christ and the metaphors of St. Paul which attach a definite dignity and symbolism to burial.

The decree of the Holy Office also recalls some of the historical background of cremation. It states that the enemies of the Church praise and propagate the practice of cremation with no other purpose in mind than that of gradually removing from people's minds the thought of death and the hope of the resurrection of the body, and of thereby paving the way for materialism. This was especially true of the advocates of cremation in the eighties of the last century, as the decrees of the Church clearly testify. At that time cremation and French Masonry were so closely linked together that advocacy of cremation was practically a declaration of membership in the Masonic Order. Thus, for historical reasons, the doctrinal associations and implications of cremation are gravely offensive. Moreover, in normal circumstances, cremation is opposed to a deeply-imbedded respect and reverence which men feel towards the bodies of their dead. In the Christian concept of human life these bodies should be reverently treated because of what they have been, the temples of the Holy Ghost, and because of what they are destined to be, the sharers with the soul for eternity in the Beatific Vision.

It is for these reasons that the Decree states that to adopt or to favor the practice of cremation regularly and as an ordinary rule is impious and scandalous and, for that reason, gravely sinful.

It is true that the rites and prayers of the Church are not forbidden in the case of those whose bodies are cremated, not at their own request, but at the insistence of other persons. But this rule applies only insofar as scandal can be effectively prevented by a timely and public declaration that the cremation took place, not at the request of the deceased, but because of the actions of other persons. And even in this latter case, the prohibition of ecclesiastical burial remains in full force if the circumstances do not afford sufficient grounds for the hope that scandal will be prevented by such a declaration.

Furthermore, the Decree states that in the case of a person who has left orders for the cremation of his body, no significance is to be attached to the fact that, while alive, he habitually practiced acts of religion, nor to the thought that he might perhaps have retracted his bad intention in the last moment of his life. Under no such specious pretexts could the funeral rites of the Church be performed and then the body cremated according to arrangements made by the deceased person himself.

It seems scarcely necessary to observe that in all cases in which it is forbidden to hold the funeral rites of the Church for the deceased, it is also forbidden to honor the ashes with ecclesiastical burial or in any way to preserve them in a blessed cemetery.

Autopsy

There is no ecclesiastical law which forbids an autopsy for the purpose of discovering the cause of death or to acquire medical knowledge. The Divine Law, however, demands reverence for the bodies of the dead, particularly the bodies of the faithful. For this reason, the dissection of a body for no adequate reason, for example, merely through curiosity, would not be morally permissible. On the other hand, if there were a suspicion that the deceased person had been murdered, there would certainly be sufficient reason to perform an autopsy. Similarly, the reasonable hope that medical science will profit from an autopsy and thus be better equipped to aid the sick in the future will certainly justify the dissection of a corpse. In fact, medical students must have recourse to this procedure if they are to possess an adequate knowledge of human anatomy. It should be emphasized, however, that when a sufficient examination of the body has taken place, what remains of it should be buried.

Embalming

In the United States, where embalming of the dead is a general practice, it is of importance to know how soon after apparent death the process of embalming may begin. The main principle is this: the process of embalming may not be commenced until it is certain that life is extinct. For, undoubtedly, if the person is still alive, the embalming process will directly cause death. Furthermore, mere probability, even very great probability, that death has already taken place will not justify the beginning of the process, for it is not morally permissible to do anything which even only probably will *directly* cause the death of an innocent person.

It would therefore seem best to have the testimony of a good doctor to the effect that the person is certainly dead before the undertaker is allowed to begin the process of embalming. Frequently, of course, it is not possible to obtain such testimony, and even when it is procured, a period of time should be allowed to elapse between the apparent moment of death and the beginning of embalming. Thus, even in our States wherein a doctor must pronounce the person dead before the undertaker can begin the embalming, this period of time should be allowed to elapse. It would seem that when a person has died after a long and wasting illness, embalming may not be commenced until one full hour after all signs of life have ceased. But in the case of one who has died suddenly after enjoying at least moderately good health (for example, from drowning, strangulation, electrocution, heart failure, apoplexy, etc.) three hours should be allowed to pass before the undertaker is allowed to make an incision on the body. Catholic undertakers should be instructed to this effect; and Catholic people should be informed of their duties in this matter towards members of their families who may die.

The same principles which govern the time at which embalming may begin also apply to the time at which an autopsy may be performed. The author is familiar with many instances in which an autopsy was performed shortly after the person was pronounced dead. This practice is morally unjustifiable and should not be tolerated.

Problems for Discussion

1. After an accidental abortion, a nurse is about to rupture the membrances and baptize the embryo when a doctor tells her not to do it. He desires to retain the embryo in its unbroken membranes as a specimen. What should she do?

2. A non-Catholic minister happens to be in the hospital when a non-Catholic baby is dying. He is going to administer emergency baptism and requests a nearby nurse, a Catholic, to act as god-mother or official witness. What should she do?

3. Do you think that a fetus should be baptized conditionally at delivery if it appears evident that it has been dead for several weeks? Nurses often say that it makes them "feel better" if they do this.

4. If a nurse acts as god-mother at an emergency baptism simply because no one else is available, does she acquire any obligations towards the child if it should live?

5. A woman who is two months pregnant is expected to abort. She is frequently passing blood clots. The nurse realizes that life will pass away quickly after the actual abortion,—so

she has little time to examine these blood clots. Is she supposed to administer conditional baptism to all of these "blood clots"?

6. If a fetus dies shortly before delivery and a craniotomy is done in order to effect delivery, should the fetus be baptized conditionally upon delivery?

7. A child dies before it can be delivered. Having foreseen the possibility of such an outcome, the mother "desired" baptism for her living, unborn child. Does this constitute baptism of desire?

8. A nurse working in the nursery secretly baptizes all of the babies under her care. Her attitude is that it will do them no harm; and, since some of them may never be given the opportunity of baptism and may die in their childhood, she is securing heaven for them. Comment on her actions and on her outlook on this matter.

9. A baby in the nursery is unexpectedly found dead. No pulse can be detected. Would you baptize it?

10. Since baptism removes all sins from the soul, why not delay baptism until death is imminent? This would enable the person receiving baptism to enter heaven immediately upon death.

11. The newly-born infant of Catholic parents is dying. A Methodist nurse administers an emergency baptism. The child survives. Is the child a Catholic or a Methodist?

12. Is an emergency baptism valid if the nurse who administers it is not in the state of grace?

13. How soon after birth should the normal infant be baptized?

14. A healthy premature baby is going to remain in the hospital for two months to build up weight. Should it be baptized in the hospital or may baptism be delayed until it goes home?

15. How long after an abortion should a conditional baptism be administered?

References for Reading

BECK, SR. BERNICE: *The Nurse: Handmaid of the Divine Physician,* pp. 26-55, Phila., 1945.

BONNAR, A.: *The Catholic Doctor* (2nd ed.), pp. 89-96, N. Y., 1939.

BOWEN, J.: *Baptism of the Infant and the Fetus*, Dubuque, 1939.

BURKE, E.: *Acute Cases in Moral Medicine*, pp. 65-100, N. Y., 1929.

CONNELL, F.: "Administration of Baptism to Unknown Dying Persons," *American Ecclesiastical Review*, pp. 389-392, May, 1945.

————: "Record of Private Baptism," *American Ecclesiastical Review*, p. 148, Aug., 1945.

CONWAY, W.: "Baptismal Registration of an Illegitimate Child," *Irish Ecclesiastical Record*, pp. 347-348, Nov., 1946.

"When Is a Person Said to be 'Baptized in the Catholic Church'?", *Irish Ecclesiastical Record*, pp. 1107-1109, Dec., 1948.

————: *Baptism* (pamphlet), Catholic Truth Society, Brooklyn, 1937.

————: *Rebirth of the Soul* (pamphlet), Paulist Press, 1939.

FLETCHER, J.: *Notes for Catholic Nurses*, pp. 21-37, Catholic Truth Society, London.

KELLY, G.: "Should We Baptize Unknown Dying Adults," *Review for Religious*, pp. 49-59, Jan. 15, 1945.

KELLY, G.: "An Instruction on Baptism," *Hospital Progress*, Feb., 1949.

McALLISTER, J.: *Emergency Baptism* (pamphlet), Milwaukee, 1944.

McCARTHY, J.: "Baptism of Foundlings," *Irish Ecclesiastical Record*, p. 1018, Nov., 1948.

O'CONNOR, W.: "The Lot of Infants Who Die Without Baptism," *American Ecclesiastical Review*, pp. 37-49, July, 1936; pp. 152-164, August, 1936.

OSTLER, D.: *A Nurse's Manual*, pp. 13-25, St. Anthony Guild Press, Paterson, N. J., 1936.

ROCHELLE-FINK: *Handbook of Medical Ethics*, pp. 202-234, Westminster, Md., 1943.

WOYWOD, S.: "Consent of Parents Required for Baptism of Children," *Homiletic and Pastoral Review*, pp. 430-431, Jan., 1941.

————: "Baptism of Infants in Hospitals," *Homiletic and Pastoral Review*, p. 635, March, 1936.

"Anyone Having the Use of Reason Can Baptize," *American Ecclesiastical Review*, p. 80, July, 1937.

"The Disposal of a Baptized Fetus," *American Ecclesiastical Review*, p. 80, Jan., 1931.

CHAPTER 12

Sterilization

Before taking up the study of sterilization, it is necessary to recall man's moral obligation to conserve his health and life.

The body and soul of man belong, in the most absolute sense, to God as their Creator. Man is simply the guardian and custodian of his life, and it is his solemn duty to adopt all reasonable means to protect and to cherish this great gift of God.

To forget for an instant that man's total being belongs to God is to sweep away the moral basis for the immorality of both suicide and euthanasia. If man's life were his own, he could destroy it, and suicide would not be immoral. If man's life were his own, the incurable patient, desiring relief from ceaseless agony, could legitimately designate someone to confer a painless death upon him.

Since the body of man truly belongs to the Creator, suicide is obviously a direct and grave infringement by man on the supreme dominion of God, and any unnecessary destruction or mutilation of any part of the human body is equally a violation of the absolute ownership of the Creator.

The Nature of Mutilation

A brief survey of some of the more important definitions of mutilation will help to clarify its precise nature.

In the *Dictionnaire de Theologie Catholique,* Michels defines mutilation in the following manner:

> Mutilation may be defined as the suppression of a member or of some part of the body. Surgical operations which have as their object the suppression of an organ are, then,

280

mutilations in the proper sense of the word; those which have as their object simply to open tissues in order to heal more efficaciously some interior malady are not, properly speaking, mutilations; however they are akin to it, since the body receives from them, even though only momentarily, some more or less grave deterioration.

In the first volume of his *Manual of Moral Theology,* Wouters presents his definition of mutilation:

Mutilation properly so-called, takes place when, by an excision, some organic function or use of members is suppressed.

A very precise definition is given by Vermeersch in the second volume of his *Moral Theology:*

Mutilation is a cutting off or equivalent action by which an organic function or the definite use of members is suppressed or directly diminished.

In the second volume of his classical work on *Moral Theology,* Noldin presents his analysis of mutilation:

Mutilation, properly, is the destruction (or the suppression of the function) of some member, i.e., of an organic part of the body, which has its own function, so that this member being removed, the body is no longer integral; if certain members exist in a twofold number, even the removal of only one of them would constitute mutilation, because the twofold number is not intended by nature without a grave reason; whence the cutting off of one hand, the destruction of one eye, the privation of only one sex gland—all are mutilations. However, mutilation is not present if, for example, a man is deprived of a part of the skin or of a portion of blood (for transplantation or transfusion into the body of another person who is ill) because the body remains integral and these parts are soon restored.

Finally, in his work on *Moral Theology,* Merkelbach states that "mutilation is the cutting off of a member, or an operation which suppresses its use or organic function."

Immoral forms of mutilation, therefore, involve the needless destruction of a healthy part of man's body. It is an act which

unnecessarily lessens the integrity of the body, and a body must
be regarded as "lessened in its integrity" when it is made less
capable of performing those vital functions which are proper
to it. (Throughout the remainder of this chapter, the term
"mutilation" is used in the sense of "immoral mutilation.")

Man, as we have said, does not have complete dominion over
his body or its members. Hence, he may use his body and its
members only in accordance with God's designs. But, as the
part must be subordinated to the whole, *it is morally permissible to sacrifice a part for the good of the whole, when the welfare of the whole body cannot be secured by any other means.*
Such is the reasoning of St. Thomas and of all moralists.

On the other hand, moralists maintain that mutilation is not
justified for any *extrinsic* end or good, such as sterilization performed in order to make impossible future pregnancy which
might create a danger to life or a burden on society. The
encyclical on *Christian Marriage* emphasizes this point:

> Christian doctrine establishes, and the light of reason
> makes it most clear, that private individuals have no other
> power over the members of their bodies than that which
> pertains to their natural ends; and they are not free to
> destroy or mutilate their members, or in any other way
> render themselves unfit for their natural functions, except
> when no other provision can be made for the good of the
> whole body.

In brief, man has only such dominion over his members as
is required for the good of the whole body. The excision of
any organ, the amputation of any member, or the destruction
of any of the vital functions of the body is an immoral act,
unless the welfare of the body as a unit is dependent upon this
sacrifice. No extrinsic good, such as the benefit which might
accrue to some other person or to society, would ever provide
a moral justification for mutilation.

Several illustrations will help to clarify the precise nature
of mutilation in the strict sense of the term:

A. *Excision of Pathological Organs.* The removal of a
diseased organ is not mutilation because such removal does
not lessen the integrity of the body. The organ is admittedly

diseased and its excision, therefore, cannot be construed as a loss. Moreover, its presence in the body threatens the integrity of the entire body. Its removal is an act which protects the health of the whole and represents an effort on man's part to preserve and safeguard his body to the best of his ability. Instead of such an excision being immoral, it is an act which man does in fulfillment of the moral obligation which rests on him to preserve health and life.

B. *Surgical Incision.* The opening of the abdomen to perform an operation, such as an appendectomy, involves the cutting of healthy abdominal tissue. Is this act one of mutilation? The answer is certainly in the negative. There is no permanent injury to the body, since nature quickly restores the severed tissue. It is an act done in the interests of the integrity of the body, not in violation of it.

C. *Blood Transfusions and Injections.* Any injury to healthy tissue which would be involved in intravenous injections, or the procuring of blood from one person to give to another, is not mutilation. Nature quickly provides new tissue and new blood.

D. *Plastic Surgery.* Alterations of the human body effected through modern plastic surgery cannot be construed as mutilation. Abuses could certainly take place, but plastic surgery work is ordinarily done in the interests of correcting natural defects or deformity resulting from accident. Plastic surgery work is usually performed to increase the integrity of the human body and is therefore morally permissible.

E. *Excessive Members.* At times one encounters children who are born with six fingers and toes. Even assuming that the extra members are perfectly sound, is the amputation of these members an act of mutilation? Again, the answer is in the negative. Even though the extra members are physically sound, it would appear that their removal actually increases or perfects the integrity of the body. An individual who had the extra members would suffer many handicaps in life. To mention only a few: certain articles of clothing would not fit properly, and standardized methods of operating various types of machines, such as typewriters, would not suit the person.

All things considered, it would appear that the removal of the excess members would make the body better able to do those things which a body must do for man throughout life. For this reason, the amputation of excess members is not an act of mutilation and is certainly permissible.

F. *Voronoff Operation.* A few years ago there was a great deal of publicity given to the Voronoff operation. This operation took two forms: in some cases, testicle grafting from one man to another was proposed; in other cases, the grafting of these reproductive organs to man from the monkey was suggested. Very briefly, both operations are immoral.

The first-mentioned operation is immoral because it would involve the mutilation of the person from whom the reproductive organs were taken. This mutilation would not be for the welfare of that person's body, but for an objective wholly extrinsic to that person.

The second Voronoff operation, whereby monkey glands are transplanted to man, cannot be condemned for the same intrinsic reason. There is ordinarily no deordination in using the lower animals for the benefit of man. Thus, we assimilate the flesh of animals through our digestive organs. We employ innumerable animal serums in our battles against diseases. But it does not appear that there is a parallel between these uses of lower creation and that which is involved in this Voronoff operation. This operation seems to be repugnant to human nature and offensive to the dignity of man. If the transplanted gland were assimilated into the human body as completely as animal foods or serums, the act would not be so repulsive. The unnatural character of the operation rests in the fact that the transplanted organ is said to continue to function in a non-human manner, effecting notable physical and psychical changes in the subject. If this be so, the operation is manifestly immoral, not only when performed on normal children for the suggested purpose of producing a more virile race, but also when performed for the purpose of saving life or health in an individual case. (In most instances, an immoral mutilation would also have been committed on the human being who was to receive the organs of the lower animal; only after such a mutilation would the person be capable of receiving the other organs.)

G. *Prefrontal Lobotomy.* Within the past few years a new operation has attracted widespread attention in the public press. This surgical procedure is known as prefrontal lobotomy and involves the opening of the brain and the severance of some of the projection or association fibers connecting the frontal lobes and the thalamus.

In the description of this operation to the reading public, the graphic accounts in the popular press have been characterized by sensationalism rather than by scientific accuracy. The most fantastic phrases are used to describe the effects of the surgery upon the patient. We are told, for example, that the operation destroys all sense of moral responsibility and reduces the patient to the mentality of a child.

Prefrontal lobotomy does admittedly bring about drastic changes in the personality of a patient. This fact is beyond all reasonable dispute. The behavior of the patient is usually characterized by inertia and lack of ambition. Nothing seems to excite, or even to interest him. He shows no concern over the opinions expressed by others. He does little or no work, and what work he does is poor in quality because of his indifference towards it. So little does he care about anyone or anything that selfconsciousness is almost completely absent. He can, in fact, be described as living in a state of complete listlessness and indifference to everything.

The noticeable mental and physical indifference which follows upon lobotomy is apparently due to a lessening of the usual effects of man's sensitive appetite. After the operation, the patient seems to be devoid of the passions or emotions which are so much a part of the human make-up.

In fact, the loss of the emotional factor which is normally a part of the patient's process of thinking is precisely what is sought by his doctors. For the time being at least, this relief from emotional tension is the principal good effect of the operation. The effective psychoses that result from abnormal emotional states are the very ones which are most helped by the patient's release from the emotional factor in thinking. The precise manner in which this relief is achieved is not certainly known. Some specialists explain that the operation brings about a divorce between cognition and emotional response; for example, a thought or situation which, before the operation, would have aroused intense anxiety in the patient, will be of little concern to him in the postoperative period. A return to a moderate degree of emotional response usually begins a few weeks after the operation and occupies a convalescence period of several years.

We mentioned above that in describing the aftermath of lobotomy, popular articles have emphasized the drastic effects of the operation upon the intellect and will of the patient. If this were even a probable result of the operation it would be of the greatest concern to the moralist. Any change which would be so deliberately brought about and which would so affect a person that he would no longer be capable of a human act, could not easily be justified. Actually, however, it does not seem that the operation has, or can have, any *direct* effect upon the inherent powers of man's rational faculties. Any diminution or loss of intellectual and volitional capacities which seemingly results can readily be explained in terms of the patient's almost complete lack of interest in everything which surrounds him.

The effect of lobotomy upon the specifically rational powers of man is, therefore, an *indirect* one. The dependence of the human intellect upon the sensitive powers is a fundamental thesis in Rational Psychology which undoubtedly finds a measure of confirmation in the effects of lobotomy. But the fact still remains that the patient is inherently capable of a human act, though his incentive to perform it may be almost completely absent and when the act is done it may be done very imperfectly because of the devastating effects of the operation upon the sensitive powers. One can hardly expect to find intellectual keenness and volitional determination in a person who is almost totally deprived of emotional response.

Any statement to the effect that lobotomy destroys all appreciation of responsibility in the patient cannot possibly refer to "moral responsibility." The operation does bring about notable changes by lessening the emotional powers of the person but the loss or diminution of these powers does not in itself render him incapable of a moral act or of an appreciation of moral responsibility. It is noteworthy in this regard that neither our Ethics nor our Moral Theology has ever regarded emotion as a formal or necessary component of a rational act. Any "irresponsibility" which characterizes the patient is therefore to be interpreted only in terms of carelessness and lack of interest on his part.

Any statement that the operation reduces the patient to the intellectual level of a child does not mean that the rational powers *in themselves* are damaged or destroyed. A statement of this nature is correct only to the extent that it emphasizes the serious need of the patient for constant care and training in the postoperative period. During his long period of convalescence the patient must be gradually brought back to a fuller use of the emotions by a constant stimulation of interest in various activities.

The description just presented of the nature and effects of prefrontal lobotomy should provide a sufficient basis for its moral evaluation. It is true, of course, that the operation is still in the experimental stage and, as so frequently happens, the moralist appeals to the medical profession for more complete and more accurate data on it. It is always difficult to evaluate an operation such as this one, especially when we read that "no *complete* cures have been effected in twenty brain lobotomy operations performed on mental patients at the Oregon State hospital," that there was nearly a three per cent mortality from the operation in 1947, and that the damage to the emotional factor in the life of the patient is deep and, to a certain extent, irreparable. However, despite these facts, prefrontal lobotomy would appear to be morally permissible *whenever all four of the following conditions are verified:*

First, *prefrontal lobotomy is morally permissible only if the patient is afflicted with a mental illness which leaves him in a truly handicapped condition.* Hence there can be no moral objection to the operation when it is performed on the hopeless psychotic patient who has failed to respond to the various shock therapies ordinarily indicated in such cases. A patient of this type has almost nothing to lose, and possibly much to gain, from the operation. It does not seem that the patient's condition need be so severe as to be accompanied by violent behavior or suicidal tendencies.

Second, *prefrontal lobotomy is morally permissible only if it is clear that no other known, applicable, and less drastic therapy can be of any value in the case.* Whenever there is any less drastic and more certainly effective therapy available it must be used.

It must be evident, therefore, that the patient has been afflicted with a true psychosis or other mental illness of sufficient duration that competent medical authority is convinced that environmental changes, or time alone, will not bring about a cure; delay in having recourse to prefrontal lobotomy, however, does not have to extend to the point that organic deterioration has set in.

In other instances, certain types of therapy, such as electroshock, may be available but contraindicated in a particular case. At still other times, less drastic measures may have already been tried and proved useless. Thus, in some cases of psychoneurosis and chronic schizophrenia, the operation has proved beneficial after all ordinary therapies had failed. Hence, whenever sound medical judgment indicates that no less drastic measure can render a comparable and needed benefit to the patient, the operation may be performed.

Third, *prefrontal lobotomy is morally permissible only if the hope of benefit exceeds the danger of harm.* This condition requires serious consideration: Precisely to what extent is the patient really handicapped in his present condition? Are there good reasons for believing that lobotomy holds out at least a probability of bettering the present condition? If so, is it expected that the relief will be permanent or merely temporary? Will the operation substantially better the patient's condition or merely alleviate it to a minor degree? Are there any grounds for believing that, even though the operation will probably benefit the patient in some respects, it may give rise to complications that will be as serious as the present illness? These questions place a serious responsibility in the hands of the surgeon. The fact remains, however, that the operation is permissible whenever sound and sincere medical judgment is to the effect that the hope of benefit outweighs the expectation of any harm that may result.

Fourth, *prefrontal lobotomy is morally permissible only if adequate postoperative care will be available for the patient.* This condition would seem to be implicitly contained in the preceding one in the sense that lack of retraining in the postoperative period will usually bring about failure of the operation to produce good results—hence the probability of harm in an unsupervised patient would most likely surpass any benefits which would be derived by him. The grave need of proper aftercare must, however, be emphasized because the period of convalescence will occupy several years and the restoration of the patient to a pattern of normal living hinges upon his receiving such care. It matters little whether the task is handled by sympathetic relatives and friends or trained personnel; but, for a long period of time, someone must aid the patient by constant suggestion and stimulation in the recovery of his emotional powers. Still further reasons for emphasizing the importance of this postoperative care and retraining are these: it is not unusual for these patients to be subject to occasional epileptic seizures after the operation; and it is not unusual to find that the operation leaves them more or less indifferent to pain and, therefore, in danger of neglecting some serious disease which may arise within the body and thereby endanger both their own life, and, if the disease be contagious, the lives of others.

In conclusion, as the new body of Ethical and Religious Directives for Catholic Hospitals expresses it:

> Lobotomy is morally justifiable as a last resort in attempting to cure those who suffer from serious mental illness. It is not allowed when less extreme measures are reasonably available or in cases in which the probability of harm outweighs the probability of benefit.

H. *Cornea Transplantation.* Another operation which merits treatment under the topic of mutilation is that of transplanting the cornea from the eye of one person to another. Science is now able to restore sight to persons whose blindness is due to a defective cornea. In fact, an "eye bank" for storing this vital part of the human eye was opened in the spring of 1945 in New York City.

As one would expect, this scientific discovery has resulted in much that borders on sensationalism: criminals condemned to death or to prison for life have offered the cornea of one of their eyes to blind persons; poverty stricken women have stated that a cornea from one of their eyes could be bought at prices ranging up to five thousand dollars.

The morality of this operation depends upon the precise source from which the healthy cornea is obtained. Since no extrinsic good that may be obtained will justify the mutilation of the human body, the cornea may never be taken from the healthy eye of a living human being.

The cornea may, however, be removed from the eye of a living person if that eye is already permanently blind due to a defect in some other part of the organ. A cornea derived from such a source could be transplanted to the eye of a person for whom it would mean a restoration of sight. The operation would not be one of mutilation because it would not involve a lessening of the integrity of the body of the donor.

Finally, the cornea may be removed from the eye of a person immediately after death and transplanted to the eye of a person who needed this vital part of the organ for sight. Experiment has proved that a cornea removed immediately after death is living tissue which can be successfully transplanted. Naturally, a proper permission should be obtained in order that the act will not be punishable by Civil Law.

Due recognition must be made at this point of an excellent dissertation on mutilation produced by Father B. J. Cunningham, C.M., in 1944, at the Catholic University of America. This work is entitled *The Morality of Organic Transplantation* and was written under the direction of Father Francis Connell, C.Ss.R.

The work of Father Cunningham is noteworthy for several reasons, but particularly because it advances certain conclusions which are contrary to the traditional teaching on mutilation. Father Cunningham points out that, whenever it is necessary for the good of the whole body, even a healthy part of the body may be sacrificed to achieve the worthy objective. He then advances the principle that it is morally permissible to do for another person, out of motives of Christian charity, whatever one may do for oneself. In a word, it is the contention of his work that direct mutilation of self for the good of one's neighbor is in itself a licit and commendable act. Such a conclusion would authorize the sacrifice of a healthy cornea by a living person, in order to bestow sight upon a neighbor; it would authorize the transplantation of an ovary or part of a healthy ovary to another person, in order to confer health or fertility upon that person.

This matter is now being widely debated by moralists. Father Francis Connell, of Catholic University, has several times expressed sympathy with this conclusion, as has Father John McCarthy, of Maynooth College, Ireland. Without becoming involved in all of the intracacies of the discussion, the author would simply like to state that, for the present at least, he is unwilling to admit the validity of such conclusions. Furthermore, such conclusions appear to run counter to the teaching of Pope Pius XI, in his encyclical on Christian Marriage:

> "Furthermore, Christian doctrine establishes, and the light of human reason makes it most clear, that private individuals have no other power over the members of their bodies than that which pertains to their natural ends; and they are not free to destroy or mutilate their members, or in any other way render themselves unfit for their natural functions, except when no other provision can be made for the good of the whole body."

I. Bone Bank. A new phenomenon in the medical world is what is called "a bone bank." This consists in preserving, by refrigeration, all useful bone removed at operations. The bone can be used as needed, even by other hospitals; and thus many patients are saved a secondary operation which would ordinarily be necessary when bone grafting is done. Reports from reliable authorities say that the use of the bone bank is safe and practical and that it produces no untoward results. Such being the case, there can be no moral objection to the procedure, for it simply consists in putting to advantageous use bone that would otherwise have been discarded.

J. *Elective Appendectomy.* It appears to be generally accepted today by medical science that the healthy appendix serves no worthwhile purpose in the present human digestive system. Its removal, therefore, does not constitute in itself an immoral form of mutilation. Its removal does not render the body less perfect; it does not interfere with the natural integrity of the body; it does not suppress any organic function; it does not bring about even a minor disfigurement of the body. Its removal, therefore, does not inflict any harm or loss on the human body; but, *before one can justify such an excision, there must be a sufficient reason for subjecting the patient to the medical risk involved in the removal.* It is an obvious fact that an abdominal operation always subjects the patient to some appreciable risk and is not to be lightly regarded. If, however, the abdomen has already been opened in the course of another operation, there can be no moral objection to what is now accepted surgical procedure, namely, the excision of the appendix before closing up the abdomen. It has been said that nearly twenty per cent of all Americans require an appendectomy some time during the course of their life—and it is a fact that these attacks often come at times and places where surgical aid is not immediately at hand. A very real danger to the life of the person is thereby frequently created. These points would certainly constitute a proportionate and sufficient reason for excising the healthy appendix in the course of another abdominal operation.

The further question has been asked: *would it be morally permissible for a healthy person to arrange to have his appendix removed? Ordinarily,* this would *not* be morally permissible. The possibility that a person might at some future date have appendicitis and that, if and when such an attack came, medical aid might not be available, is not sufficient to justify the deliberate exposure to the present and serious risk of an abdominal operation. In an *unusual* type of case where it is evident that surgical aid will not be available (for instance, missionaries going into primitive areas which are out of contact with advanced civilization) it would appear permissible for such persons to arrange for this operation, if they so desired, before their departure. (Connell F., "Surgery for the Healthy," *Am. Ecc. Rev.*, Feb., 1947, 143; Kelly G., *Medico-Moral Problems*, Part I, pp. 35-39).

K. Elective Tonsillectomy. In the light of the principles explained in the above section, it is evident that *ordinarily* there is no moral justification for the removal of healthy tonsils. It is true that, like the appendix, their removal does not lessen the perfection of the body; but their excision does involve some measure of risk, and usually there would be no sufficient reason for undergoing this risk. After all, the tonsils are easily reached and bodily conditions rarely necessitate their removal with the unpredictability and gravity that characterizes the removal of the appendix. On the other hand, tonsillectomy involves only minor risk and could be justified if a sufficient reason were present. It is a fact, for example, that the tonsils have to be removed from most children as sources of infection. Hence, if a poor family of four or five children were going to move to a new area, a surgeon-friend of the family might volunteer to remove the tonsils for all of the children before they left in order to save the family very probable, notable, and quite proximate surgical fees.

L. Ovarian Grafts. Modern surgery has engaged in the grafting of part of an ovary from one person to another. Such grafting is done for either of two reasons: (a) to correct, or balance—so to speak—complementary pathological conditions in the two parties, or (b) to remedy a pathological condition in only one of the patients.

The *first* type of case is encountered when one woman is afflicted with amenorrhea (abnormal absence of menstruation), while a second woman is afflicted with hypermenorrhea (excessive menstruation). All of the customary medical treatments are, of course, first attempted before this surgical procedure is contemplated. In the course of the operation about three-fourths of one ovary is excised from each of the women and grafted to the ovary stem of the other. After this operation it is usually found that the ovarian functions of both women approximate normality. It is the opinion of the author that this is a morally permissible operation because the organs of *both* women are in a pathological condition; the operation does not lessen the perfection of the body of either woman; rather, it perfects their respective bodies in a vital function and there is certainly a definite and sufficient reason for each of them undergoing the surgical risk involved in the procedure.

The *second* type of case visualizes the grafting of part of an ovary *from a healthy woman,* as the donor, to another woman who is afflicted with one of the above-mentioned pathological conditions. The moral problem involved here is the same as that treated earlier when we considered the transplantation of the cornea from the eye of a living, seeing person to one who is blind. As stated at that time, the author regards as immoral the mutilation of a person which is not done in the interests of that person's own body. This conclusion appears to be necessitated by the traditional principles on man's duties to his own health and life, as well as by the already-quoted encyclical of Pope Pius XI.

The foregoing considerations on the nature and morality of mutilation provide adequate background for the analysis of *therapeutic, eugenic,* and *punitive* sterilization.

Therapeutic Sterilization

Sterilization is called *therapeutic* when it is done in order to safeguard the personal health or life of an individual.

The reproductive organs sometimes have to be removed from the body because they have been attacked by a disease, such as cancer. In cases of this type, the primary objective is the removal of a diseased organ and the preservation of the health and life of the patient. Desire to effect sterilization is certainly not the motive prompting such an operation. Both moral law and civil law permit this type of sterilization. It is permitted because it is neither an act of mutilation nor an invasion of the supreme dominion of the Creator, but an act done in the interests of preserving the body as a whole.

In the light of the above principle, the following practical conclusions may be legitimately drawn: Whenever both fallopian tubes, or both ovaries, or the uterus, are so diseased as to endanger seriously the life or permanent health of a woman, they may be excised. Whenever only one fallopian tube, or only one ovary is diseased, the other tube or ovary may not be removed in order to prevent future conception. The remaining healthy tube or ovary is so important to a woman that the mere possibility of its later becoming diseased does not provide moral justification for such mutilation. If, however, the woman is beyond childbearing age and there is any reasonable basis for believing that the removal of the organs will help safeguard health against future disease, the organs may be excised. After a cesarean operation is performed on a woman, it is not morally permissible to sterilize the patient simply in order to prevent future conception. If fibroids or scars and adhesions in the uterus indicate that its presence in the body would constitute a real danger to the woman's life, it may be removed.

A further question on sterilization is created by the technique which is employed in performing a cesarean operation. Two methods are possible: in the first, the uterus is left in, and the woman can again become a mother; in the second, the uterus is removed (the so-called Porro operation), and the woman is thereby rendered permanently sterile. The moral question which arises is on the justifiability of the more radical operation.

In answer, it should be emphasized that the Porro operation is medically indicated only in frankly infected cases, in rupture of the uterus, in the presence of multiple or single large fibromata, and in abruptio placentae where the uterine muscle is infused with blood appearing as petechiae under the serosal surface. In such frankly infected cases, whenever sound medical judgment holds that the removal of the uterus must accompany cesarean section in order to safeguard the woman's life or permanent health, it is morally permissible to follow this procedure.

The Latzko Operation and the Gottschalk-Portes Operation, it is true, are designed to handle frankly infected cases without removing the uterus. But these operations involve technical knowledge and skill not possessed by most workers in the field. Morally speaking, our only recommendation would be that all obstetricians endeavor to develop the highly specialized skill required for these latter techniques.

Needless to say, cesarean section may not be followed by removal of the uterus, except in cases wherein the safeguarding of the woman's life or permanent health from above-mentioned causes necessitates this radical procedure.

Sterilization by Irradiation

Sterilization frequently results from the use of radium and x-rays. For this reason, special consideration must be given those cases in which the irradiation of the reproductive organs is proposed.

A. *Adolescent Menorrhagia.* It is sometimes suggested that irradiation by x-rays applied directly to the uterus is a sound treatment for adolescent menorrhagia (profuse menstrual periods).

When menorrhagia manifests itself in the adolescent, great care must be taken to determine its cause. In general, menorrhagia is due to inflammatory conditions of the pelvis, tumors, moles, blood dyscrasias, displacements, visceral and systemic diseases associated with the heart and kidneys, nervousness, and functional disturbances. If organic pathology can be ruled out, and in most adolescents it can, the cause is usually due to some endocrine disturbance.

The treament of uterine hemorrhage in young women is not a simple matter. Many young girls develop a severe menorrhagia and the condition becomes so severe that the patient's health is completely undermined. The treatment should consist of rest, change of environment, hormone therapy, and curettage. All of these treatments should ordinarily be tried before subjecting the adolescent to irradiation or hysterectomy.

Some moralists suggest that irradiation of the uterus is morally permissible only if the ovaries are shielded from the rays and sterilization thereby averted. Two comments are quite pertinent: first, medical authorities state that it is hardly possible to protect the ovaries from the rays directed on the uterus; and, second, competent medical authorities state that, since uterine bleeding is controlled by ovarian function, effective treatment by irradiation must extend to the ovaries as well as to the uterus.

The moral problem is, at times, eased considerably by the fact that mild irradiation is all that is required for effective treatment, and it rarely produces sterility. Medical science has produced conclusive proof that *mild* irradiation of the ovaries of young girls is not destructive of ovarian tissue or function. Mild doses are often sufficient to remedy the menorrhagia and practically never result in sterility. Doses too small to produce demonstrable organic changes have a definite and adequate effect on glandular function.

The chances of sterility resulting from mild irradiation, and the temporary or permanent character of the sterility, depend to a great extent on the age of the patient. Thus, in five hundred cases treated by Rubenfeld and Maggio at Bellevue Hospital, sterilization did not result in one case of girls between the ages of twelve and eighteen years. Sterilization occurred in only twenty to twenty-five per cent of the nineteen to thirty-two age group.

Assuming that all of the preliminary treatments recommended above have been tried and proved ineffective (rest, change of environment, hormone therapy, curettage, and mild irradiation), it would appear morally permissible, under certain conditions, to have recourse to full dosage irradiation or hysterectomy. *First,* the sterilizing procedure (irradiation of the ovaries, removal of the ovaries, or removal of the uterus) must not be contraceptive in intent. In most cases of this type, it is perfectly clear that the procedure is honestly needed to handle the pathological condition which is present. The best guarantee in this regard is, of course, the statement by a medically competent and morally conscientious doctor that the procedure is necessary. *Second,* there must be a proportionate reason for allowing a procedure which will result in sterility. *It would appear evident that there is sufficient reason to justify the action whenever the condition would constitute a danger to life or whenever the bleeding would be so prolonged and*

*heavy each month that the patient would be repeatedly sub-
jected to much pain or discomfort or be incapacitated during
a notable portion of each menstrual cycle.*

B. *Menopausal Menorrhagia.* It is known that a menorrhagia at the menopause may be checked by positive sterilization of the ovaries. If it is necessary to take such steps in order
to save the life of the woman or to prevent permanent
invalidism, then sterilization is morally permissible. (The
term "permanent invalidism" was used in an earlier edition of
Medical Ethics and was misunderstood in some quarters. In
Taber's *Cyclopedic Medical Dictionary,* an invalid is defined
as one who is not well, a sickly person. Hence, whenever the
bleeding would be so prolonged and heavy each month that
the patient would be repeatedly subjected to much pain or
discomfort or be incapacitated during a notable portion of each
menstrual cycle we would classify such a condition as
"permanent invalidism.") Naturally enough, if any measure
less drastic than sterilization will remedy the condition, that
method must be adopted. But whenever the life or permanent
health of a patient hinges on sterilization this step is morally
permissible. This conclusion is in conformity with the principle that our duty is to preserve the integrity of the body as
much as is possible. In the case under discussion, the welfare
of the whole is achieved through the sacrifice of a part. The
fact that the woman is at the end of the childbearing period
of her life adds further cogency to this conclusion.

C. *Carcinoma of Breast.* It is widely held today in medical
science that there is a definite relationship between the growth
of the tissue of the breast and the secretions of the ovaries. For
this reason, it has been suggested that, in cancer of the breast,
the cancerous tissue, as well as normal tissue, is stimulated to
growth of the ovarian secretion; the regrowth of cancer cells
which have not been removed by surgery can be prevented by
x-ray treatments of the ovaries, resulting in sterilization which
is sometimes temporary, sometimes permanent.

It was stated above that medical science has shown that mild
irradiation of the ovaries of young girls and young women will
not usually result in sterilization. Even with mild doses, however, sterilization will ordinarily occur in an older person.

When one combines the dosage required to decrease the ovarian secretions (folliculin and lutein) with the likely age of a patient who has cancer of the breast, it is reasonable to assume that sterilization will result.

The above statements give rise to a moral problem: *Is it morally permissible to treat the ovaries with x-rays (or to remove them surgically) in order to curtail ovarian secretions in cases of cancer of the breast?*

The answer to this moral problem depends upon the verification of a scientific fact. If medical science holds that cancer of the breast is likely to develop more slowly and to spread less rapidly if not affected by the ovarian secretions, the use of x-rays would appear to be morally permissible. Actually, there is still some dispute among medical authorities on the value of oöphorectomy or irradiation of the ovaries for the prevention of metastasis. It does seem, however, that the positive view is steadily gaining ground and is held today by many eminent physicians. This opinion would therefore appear to be based on good evidence and could be regarded today as solidly probable. It is undoubtedly on this basis that several diocesan Hospital Codes, published with ecclesiastical approval, permit oöphorectomy or irradiation of the ovaries for the prevention of metastasis. These Hospital Codes specify that the hospital may demand consultation. In other words, whenever prudent medical judgment considers removal or irradiation of the ovaries advisable, these Hospital Codes regard the procedure as morally permissible. It would seem clear therefore that, whenever there is no equally effective but less drastic measure available, a patient (or the patient's doctor) may in good conscience have recourse to removal or irradiation of the ovaries to prevent metastasis in cases of carcinoma of the breast.

D. Irradiation Therapy for Sterility. We have said that medical science now informs us that low dosage irradiation can be applied to the ovaries without producing sterilization. Medical science actually goes still further; it states that mild irradiation of the pituitary gland and ovaries will, in certain cases of sterility associated with various types of functional menstrual disorders, restore the childbearing capacity to a woman.

If a woman is presently sterile due to some functional menstrual disorder, it is certainly permissible to rely upon the therapeutic value of low dosage irradiation of the pituitary gland and ovaries in the reasonable hope of restoring her child-bearing capacity.

E. *Enlarged Prostate.* It is stated by reliable medical authorities that an enlarged prostate can sometimes be treated successfully (and without the danger that would be involved in prostatectomy) by the ligature or irradiation of both *vasa deferentia.* Since this treatment would result in sterilization, a moral problem is created. Once again, it must be answered that, if necessary for the welfare of the body as a whole, a part of the body may be sacrificed. Hence, such ligature or irradiation would be morally permissible in the case of patients, principally old men, who could scarcely stand the major operation of prostatectomy. The four conditions of the twofold effect principle would be verified in these cases. In particular, it might be noted that the fourth condition is quite crucial in this type of case; but, the good effect, the removal of the grave risk to life involved for old or very weak persons in prostatectomy, will outweigh the resulting evil of sterilization.

Whenever prostatectomy would not involve a truly grave risk for a patient, the fourth condition is not verified, and the above ligature or irradiation would be immoral.

F. *Carcinoma of Prostate.* Orchidectomy is frequently suggested as the most suitable remedy for treating cases of carcinoma of the prostate. Since this operation produces sterility, a moral problem is created.

A few facts pertinent to carcinoma of the prostate will help to clarify our discussion of this operation.

Carcinoma of the prostate is an extremely painful disease which is rarely discovered at a sufficiently early stage to admit of complete cure. The development and spread of the disease is fostered by androgens, which are supplied principally by the testes. For this reason, any procedure which lessens the supply of androgens or neutralizes their effects is of the greatest value. Hence, even when complete recovery is out of the question, it is often possible in this way to relieve the intense pain and to help the patient to lead a fairly normal life.

Three methods of lessening or neutralizing the effects of the androgens are commonly proposed: *hormone therapy* (which involves the administration of estrogens), *irradiation of the testes,* and *orchidectomy.* Each of these procedures induces sterility; but, in the case of the hormone therapy, this effect need not be permanent. In contrast, the sterility induced by irradiation and orchidectomy is truly permanent.

Estrogen treatment, however, involves disadvantages not connected with the other two procedures, viz., hypertrophy of the breast, gastric disorders, the need for a more careful supervision of the patient over a long period of time, and the fact that it is not always effective in treating the condition.

A second fact which is of moral significance is that, in practice, it seems to be nearly impossible to treat carcinoma of the prostate without inducing sterility. Even in the rare cases when a cure can be effected through the mere removal of the prostate gland, it appears to be extremely difficult to perform the operation without injuring the reproductive tract to a degree that impedes fertility. (Moreover, as we mentioned above, many competent physicians attach little value or hope of success to any procedure which does not eliminate the testicular output of androgens.) For these reasons, it appears that sterility is almost an inevitable result of any treatment of carcinoma of the prostate, whether curative or merely palliative.

A third factor of significance in cases of carcinoma of the prostate is the usual age of those who are afflicted with the condition. The condition *ordinarily* arises after middle age has been reached. This fact would provide an additional reason, if such were necessary, for the permissibility of orchidectomy. A less serious reason would be needed to justify a sterilizing operation on an older man than on a younger person.

Carcinoma of the prostate can, of course, occur in young men. But, regardless of the age at which it occurs, it is so gravely dangerous and so extremely painful that the age of the patient need not be considered in evaluating the morality of measures recommended for its alleviation or cure.

In the light of these facts, it is clear that orchidectomy is permissible under the following conditions:

First, the operation must not be contraceptive in purpose.

There can be little hesitation about the verification of this condition. It is perfectly true that sterilization inevitably results, but it is nevertheless an indirect effect of the operation. The objective of the whole procedure is to suppress the internal secretions of the testes and thereby to remove a factor which would foster the development of the cancerous condition.

Second, the operation must offer some hope of worthwhile benefit to a patient who is suffering from a serious condition. The medical facts involved in cases of carcinoma of the prostate clearly indicate that this condition is satisfied. This cancerous condition is admitted by all to be most serious; and it is well known that by preventing the flow of androgens from the testes the patient is greatly helped. Even when cure is out of the question, this operative procedure brings notable relief from pain to the patient, as well as an increase in bodily weight, appetite, and strength. Due to these combined benefits, the patient is often enabled to lead a fairly normal life for several years.

Third, the operation is permitted only if there is no less drastic procedure available which would secure equally good results. The thought behind this condition is that orchidectomy must not be needlessly performed. It must be, in a sense, a last resort. Whenever hormone therapy can be successfully used to suppress the effect of the androgens, it must be used. It is known, however, that in many cases the administration of estrogens is not an effective measure. On the other hand, sound medical science testifies to the fact that irradiation of the testes is frequently just as effective as orchidectomy.

Hence, if hormone therapy cannot be used or will not produce the desired effect, either irradiation of the testes or orchidectomy may be used. Whether estrogens should be tried first (in some cases, delay in having irradiation or orchidectomy could be dangerous) or whether these latter procedures should be used immediately is a judgment that should be left to sincere and competent physicians.

Eugenic Sterilization

Sterilization is called *eugenic* when it is performed on defective persons in the interests of social betterment. The emphasis of eugenic sterilization is primarily on the production of a more healthy race and the eradication of serious problems created by the presence of defective persons in society. The proponents of eugenic sterilization are secondarily interested in the benefits which they believe their program will bring to the mentally defective persons themselves.

A clear grasp of the spirit and objectives of eugenic sterilization depends upon an understanding of the factors which have aroused modern interest in a program of this type.

Background to Eugenic Sterilization

Possibly the most important factor in creating a demand for sterilization has been the development of the science of genetics. Ever since 1900, when the scientific world first became aware of the great value of the laws on heredity formulated by the Augustinian Abbot, Gregor Mendel, serious efforts have been made to apply them to man. In particular, much thought has been given to the possibility of eradicating defective traits through selective breeding.

Using the discoveries of Mendel as a basis, medical science has devoted much time and labor to studies on the transmission through heredity of physical and mental diseases. Some positive results have been achieved in this field, but speculations and probabilities are more common than established facts.

It has also been within our century that sociology has risen to the stature of a science. As a consequence, extensive investigations have been made on all conditions which produce social problems. It is no surprise, therefore, that great concern is shown over the vast number of mental defectives in society and the problems which their presence creates.

The eugenicist reminds us that there are now 1,500,000 mentally defective persons in the United States, of whom only 100,000 are under institutional care. The remainder shift for themselves and receive some sort of help outside of institutions.

There are, moreover, 500,000 insane persons in the United States, and their care costs more than that of the mental deficients. Society cannot continue, says the eugenicist, to support an ever-increasing number of socially inadequate persons; their presence in a highly-civilized community is an injustice both to themselves and to fellowman.

Among the more common conditions with which these unfortunates are afflicted are dementia praecox, manic-depressive insanity, mental deficiency, and epilepsy. A brief consideration of these mental states will be helpful in appreciating the attitude of those interested in fostering eugenic sterilization.

(a) *Dementia Praecox.* Of all mental illnesses, there is none at which selective sterilization is so directly aimed as *dementia praecox* (schizophrenia). It is one of the most serious of all known diseases and the most incurable of the more important types of psychosis. It fills more hospital beds in the United States than any other single disease, physical or mental; countless others are cared for in their homes or are free in society where, in a protected environment, they sometimes earn their living. Innumerable vagrants, beggars, prostitutes, and criminals are chronic sufferers from dementia praecox in a mild form.

Dementia praecox runs in families to a marked degree. If one parent is afflicted with dementia praecox, about one-half of the children will be abnormal in personality and at least one-tenth of them will eventually break down with the disease. The remaining children are likely to evidence peculiarities of behavior.

It is said that this one disease costs the United States one million dollars a day, and the largest number of psychotic persons who are sterilized are those afflicted with dementia praecox.

(b) *Manic-depressive Psychosis.* This condition progresses steadily from its onset to mental deterioration and final death. The condition tends to run in cycles and, for this reason, is sometimes called "cyclical psychosis." These cycles represent exaggerated swings to extreme moods of seriousness and gayety, joy and despair. For example, a patient may first be encountered in the high excitable, *manic* state; it is during this stage that he may commit some act of violence. A period of *normalcy* will follow and may last for weeks, months, or even years. The *depressed* stage will then set in; it is during this phase that suicide is common.

At the ages of fifteen to twenty-five years, men and women are about equally affected by this condition. Thereafter, the rate for women is about fifty per cent higher than that for men.

About twenty-one per cent of the persons who are sterilized are men afflicted with manic depressive psychosis. About thirty-seven per cent of those who are sterilized are women who are afflicted with this condition.

Manic-depressive psychosis develops out of a definite type of inherited constitution, and it runs in families just as does dementia praecox. If one parent has a manic-depressive psychosis, thirty per cent of the children who survive until adult life will have this same type of psychosis, and thirty per cent of the rest will be peculiar in personality and subject to emotional disturbances.

(c) *Mental Deficiency.* As has already been mentioned, only 100,000 out of 1,500,000 of the nation's mental defectives are in institutions. A large part of this 100,000 represents the lower grades—idiots and imbeciles—who are committed for their own protection and to take a burden off their parents.

The other feebleminded persons sent to state institutions are usually the delinquents, who are committed as much for their delinquency as for their mental deficiency. Yet, few of these delinquent defectives are ever committed to suitable institutions; the vast majority are to be found in our juvenile courts, reformatories, and at large in the community.

These facts make it clear that, outside of the delinquents, most of our high-grade mental defectives are living in society and propagating their kind. (It is said that if an I.Q. of 70 were insisted upon as normal intelligence, six and a half million persons in the United States would have to be classified as mentally deficient.) State institutions are crowded to capacity; some have waiting lists of two or three years. South Dakota and Nebraska have endeavored to curtail some of the inevitable evils arising from these conditions by prohibiting the issuance of marriage licenses to any defectives until it can be shown that at least one of the parties seeking to wed is sterile.

(d) *Epilepsy.* There is apparently a close connection between epilepsy and mental deterioration. In California, for example, about one hundred epileptics are admitted each year to the state institutions; nine-tenths of these patients are found to be mentally ill as well as epileptic.

The number of epileptics in the United States may be as high as half a million; but many of these have only light and sporadic attacks.

Among the sterilized patients in California state hospitals for the *mentally ill,* six per cent of the men and four per cent of the women were epileptics. Among the sterilized patients in California who are *feebleminded,* four per cent of the men and two per cent of the women were epileptics.

Epilepsy usually manifests itself at an early age and it places an individual under such handicaps, as well as being hereditary, that many such patients are said to welcome sterilization.

The Spread of Eugenic Sterilization. More than one hundred and fifty million people, including the people of twenty-eight of our states and Puerto Rico, are now living under sterilization laws. Apart from the United States, such laws were passed in the Canadian provinces of Alberta and British Columbia, Norway, Sweden, Denmark, Finland, Esthonia, Germany, the City of Danzig, the state of Vera Cruz in Mexico, and the canton of Vaud in Switzerland.

The table on page 307 will give the reader a bird's-eye view of eugenic sterilization as it stands today in the United States. This table lists the states which have enacted laws authorizing eugenic sterilization, the year in which the law was passed, and the total number of sterilizations performed by the state on each type of patient from the inception of its law until January 1, 1944.

The Case for Eugenic Sterilization

(a) The advocates of eugenic sterilization state that modern techniques make this operation simple and painless, that it certainly cannot be classified as mutilation.

Former centuries engaged in crude, bloody, and very dangerous methods of depriving man of his reproductive capacity.

In contrast, sterilization of the male by *vasectomy* is able to be done under a local anesthetic in fifteen minutes, and the patient, unless engaged in heavy work, could return to his

State	Year	PSYCHOTIC Male	PSYCHOTIC Female	FEEBLEMINDED Male	FEEBLEMINDED Female	OTHERS Male	OTHERS Female	Total
Alabama......	1919–1934	—	—	129	95	—	—	224
Arizona.......	1929	10	10	—	—	—	—	20
California.....	1909	5,905	5,414	3,173	3,783	767	—	19,042
Connecticut...	1909	21	391	10	83	—	—	505
Delaware......	1923	207	71	197	282	—	26	783
Georgia.......	1937	11	243	95	278	—	9	636
Idaho.........	1925	2	10	2	—	—	—	14
Indiana.......	1907	272	241	647	680	—	—	1,840
Iowa.........	1911	186	299	65	291	23	27	891
Kansas........	1913	1,205	850	500	333	42	71	3,001
Maine........	1925	6	14	18	127	—	70	235
Michigan......	1913	72	291	679	1,737	44	159	2,982
Minnesota.....	1925	117	279	385	1,430	—	—	2,211
Mississippi.....	1928	140	284	14	44	—	14	596
Montana......	1923	17	23	50	151	—	—	241
Nebraska......	1915	55	91	267	273	1	1	688
New Hampshire	1917	25	187	88	205	—	52	557
New York.....	1912–1918	—	41	—	—	1	—	42
North Carolina.	1919	137	318	260	1,193	69	175	2,152
North Dakota..	1913	126	226	132	268	13	19	784
Oklahoma.....	1931	71	232	51	199	—	—	553
Oregon.......	1917	322	394	361	638	30	76	1,821
South Carolina.	1935	—	—	8	73	—	—	81
South Dakota..	1917	5	11	264	448	6	11	745
Utah.........	1925	44	53	216	242	—	—	555
Vermont......	1931	1	12	73	137	9	19	251
Virginia.......	1924	1,223	1,780	902	1,437	10	14	5,366
Washington....	1909–1942	147	256	33	243	4	2	685
West Virginia..	1929	—	19	—	10	1	18	48
Wisconsin.....	1913	—	—	342	1,316	—	—	1,658
Puerto Rico....	1937	—	—	—	—	—	986	986
TOTALS.......		10,327	12,140	8,961	15,996	1,020	1,749	50,193

(a) This is the latest official report (up to January 1, 1949).

(b) The New York State Law was declared unconstitutional in 1918.

(c) Alabama's law was declared unconstitutional in 1934. Strong efforts are still being made to reinstate the law.

(d) Washington's law was declared unconstitutional in 1942 by the State Supreme Court.

(e) New Jersey and Nevada passed sterilization laws that were declared unconstitutional, in 1913 and 1915 respectively, before they were applied.

(f) The above figures for Puerto Rico are for 1948 only. The law has been in effect in Puerto Rico since 1937, but its statistics were not reported previous to 1948.

position on the next day. No disfigurement of the body would be involved.

Sterilization of women through *salpingectomy* is admittedly a more serious matter, since it involves the opening of the abdomen. The operation is about as serious as an ordinary appendectomy. The patient has to remain in bed for ten days or two weeks, but fatalities are almost unknown.

(b) Modern sterilization has one effect only: it prevents parenthood. It does not deprive the individual of the ability to perform the marital act; it does not affect the pleasure involved in the exercise of these rights; it does not affect the general health of the patient in any way.

(c) Eugenic sterilization enables many high-grade mental defectives to return to their families. It thus prevents the breakup of families. Often it is the fear of an illegitimate child being born to a mentally defective girl which ultimately forces parents to institutionalize their daughter. Less frequently, in the case of boys, parents confine their child because they fear the social problem that would be created if conception were to result from a sex crime committed by him.

When these dangers are removed by sterilization, the family is mentally relieved and welcomes back the child into its midst. The child, too, is more happy; it is free of the routine and discipline of an institution and is surrounded by the affection of the family and many of the pleasures of social life.

These mentally defective persons who return to their homes can usually perform some type of manual labor. By so doing, they support themselves and are not burdens on their families and on the state.

For these reasons, we are told that patients and their families are among the best friends of sterilization. They know by experience what its protection means to them.

(d) Eugenic sterilization enables many persons to marry who could not otherwise contemplate marriage. Many high-grade mentally defective persons or those who may later have a recurrence of mental illness are capable, says the eugenicist, of living in society. They may even marry, provided the possibility of their having children has been removed. In this way, they can have a life that is normal in most respects.

Marriage for such persons, without sterilization, would be unwise, if not disastrous. Their mental capacity is such that they could not care properly for children nor solve the many problems of a complex domestic situation. Their further mental deterioration is, moreover, a possibility and hence there is no guarantee that they might not have to be taken from their home and institutionalized at a later date.

(e) Eugenic sterilization decreases the tax burden on the state by reducing the number of persons who must be kept in institutions. Should the state be willing to spend the same amount of money as it does today on the care of the mentally defective, a program of selective sterilization will increase the extent and efficiency of the care for this class without increasing the cost to the taxpayer.

(f) Eugenic sterilization is a protection for the mentally defective person, not a punishment; therefore, it carries no stigma or humiliation. These persons are to be regarded as mentally ill. There is no fault on their part. To regard protective sterilization as a stigma upon such a person would be as crude and as cruel as to laugh at the physical deformity of some unfortunate cripple.

(g) Eugenic sterilization prevents the birth of children who would probably have a bad heredity, who could not be cared for properly by their parents, and who would be likely to become state charges. It is well known that *dementia praecox, manic-depressive psychosis,* and certain physical conditions associated with mental deficiency are able to be inherited. It is well known also that many illegitimate children are born to the vast number of mental defectives who are living in society. (One must recall that only 100,000 out of 1,500,000 mentally defective persons in the United States are confined to institutions.) Conservatively and sympathetically administered, selective sterilization is a practical, humane, and necessary step to prevent race deterioration.

(h) Eugenic sterilization has not increased sex offenses. Medical staffs, social workers, probation and parole officers who have come in contact with the patients before and after the operation are said to hold this opinion.

Particularly in the case of the mentally defective person, the fact that conception is not possible does not seem to result in greater moral laxity than existed previous to sterilization. There is, of course, no intention to sterilize the already evident sex delinquent and then allow a return into an unhealthy and unsupervised environment. The objective is to sterilize only the best type of person and allow a return into a morally sound family unit.

(i) Eugenic sterilization is not intended as a mass procedure. There is no intention or desire to sterilize everyone who is sent to a state institution. There are, for example, about 4500 patients admitted each year to California state hospitals for mental diseases. About forty-five per cent of these patients subsequently return to their homes. The remaining fifty-five per cent are incurable by present methods and will have to remain in institutions until death.

Of the above forty-five per cent who are discharged, some are classified as recovered, others as partly recovered. Many of this group will get along well in society for some years but will later break down and have to be readmitted to institutions. Studies made of patients discharged from New York state hospitals, for example, revealed that only one out of every four discharged cases turned out to be a permanent recovery.

Men and women have been sterilized at an average age of thirty years, usually only a few months after commitment. In California, the sterilizations are about evenly divided between men and women. Throughout the country as a whole, there have been 24,650 sterilization operations performed on women, as compared with 17,958 operations performed on men.

The Case Against Eugenic Sterilization

(a) Since the immoral character of eugenic sterilization is so clearly and so authoritatively set forth in the *Encyclical on Christian Marriage,* it merits quotation at the very outset of our criticism of this materialistic program.

> Finally, that pernicious practice must be condemned which closely touches upon the natural right of man to enter matrimony but affects also in a real way the welfare

of the offspring. For there are some, who over-solicitous
for the cause of eugenics, not only give salutary counsel for
more certainly procuring the strength and health of the
future child—which, indeed, is not contrary to right reason
—but put eugenics before aims of a higher order, and by
public authority wish to prevent from marrying, all those
who, even though naturally fit for marriage, they consider
according to the norms and conjectures of their investigations, would, through hereditary transmission, bring forth
defective offspring. And more, they wish to legislate to
deprive these of that natural faculty by medical action
despite their unwillingness; and this they do not propose as
an infliction of grave punishment under the authority of
the state for a crime committed, nor to prevent future
crimes by guilty persons, but against every right and good
they wish the civil authority to arrogate to itself a power
over a faculty which it never had and can never legitimately
possess.

Those who act in this way are at fault in losing sight of
the fact that the family is more sacred than the state, and
that men are begotten not for the earth and for time, but
for Heaven and eternity. Although often these individuals
are to be dissuaded from entering into matrimony, certainly it is wrong to brand them with the stigma of crime
because they contract marriage, on the ground that, despite
the fact that they are in every respect capable of matrimony, they will give birth only to defective children, even
though they use all care and diligence.

Public magistrates have no direct power over the bodies
of their subjects; therefore, where no crime has taken place
and there is no cause present for grave punishment, they
can never directly harm, or tamper with the integrity of
the body, either for the reasons of eugenics or for any other
reason. St. Thomas teaches this when, inquiring whether
human judges for the sake of preventing future evils can
inflict punishment, he admits that the power indeed exists
as regards certain other forms of evil, but justly and properly denies it as regards the maiming of the body. (No one
who is guiltless may be punished by a human tribunal,
either by flogging to death, or mutilation, or by beating.)

Furthermore, Christian doctrine establishes, and the

light of human reason makes it most clear, that private
individuals have no other power over the members of their
bodies than that which pertains to their natural ends;
and they are not free to destroy or mutilate their members,
or in any other way render themselves unfit for their
natural functions, except when no other provision can be
made for the good of the whole body.

These thoughts were also strongly expressed by Pius XII in
his address on morality in marriage, delivered on October
29, 1951:

"It would be very much more than a mere lack of readiness in the service of life if the man's attempt affected not
just a single act but the organism itself, in order to sterilize
and deprive it of the faculty of procreating a new life.
In this case, too, you have, in the teaching of the Church,
a clear rule for your inward and outward conduct. Direct
sterilization, that which aims at making procreation impossible as both means and end, is a grave violation of the
moral law, and therefore illicit. Even public authority has
no right to permit it under the pretext of any 'indication'
whatsoever, and still less to prescribe it or to have it
carried out to the harm of the innocent. . . . Therefore, ten
years ago, when sterilization came to be more widely
applied, the Holy See found itself in need of stating expressly and publicly that direct sterilization, either permanent or temporary, of man or of woman, is illegal by
virtue of the natural law from which, as you are aware,
the Church has no power to dispense."

(b) *Sterilization involves a grave mutilation of a human
being.*

The plea of the eugenicist that modern sterilization is not
mutilation because it is not a dangerous operation hardly
merits rebuttal. One does not judge whether or not an act is
mutilation by the quantity of blood shed, the amount of pain
suffered, or the length of time a person is incapacitated. It
would, for example, be quite simple to deaden the nerves of
the eye and stick a needle into a vital part of that organ. Yet,
even if this were a deliberate act done to produce total and

permanent blindness, the eugenicist could not logically call it mutilation; no pain would be felt, no blood shed, and no scars apparent.

An act is mutilation if it impairs an organ in its vital functions. As previously explained, such an act is morally permissible only if the organ be diseased or if the preservation of the body as a whole hinges upon the sacrifice of a part.

The program of eugenic sterilization ignores completely the supreme dominion of God over His creatures and the inherent dignity of a human being. Motivated by materialistic philosophy, it endeavors to transfer selective breeding from the animal to the human level. Its interests are completely centered around material and temporal objectives, such as a physically better race and a society with fewer problems. It sees no value in a defective person; it has no appreciation of the fact that such a person has an excellent chance of attaining eternal happiness, which is the all-important objective of human existence. It does not realize that the strong are spiritually better by virtue of having cared for the weak. It does not know how many healthy persons, witnessing the physical and mental handicaps of the less fortunate, have been made to turn to God in gratitude for their own blessings. There is a spiritualizing influence in life created by the presence of suffering among us, but it can never be perceived through the eyes of materialism.

We should like to emphasize that the remaining portion of our criticism of eugenic sterilization is quite secondary in importance. We will point out that the program is not practical, that it will not notably lessen the social problems created by mental defectives, that it fosters immorality, and that it concedes to the state a dangerous control over man. But, even if none of these criticisms were true, eugenic sterilization could not be permitted. It involves a deliberate mutilation of a human being, since an organ is impaired in its vital functions. It is an unnecessary mutilation, since the conservation of the whole body of the defective person is not dependent upon the sacrifice of this part. It is an immoral act, because it is a deliberate and serious invasion of the supreme rights of the Creator over one of His creatures. For these reasons, it must be said that eugenic sterilization could never be permitted, even if it were capable of achieving its stated objectives.

(c) Sterilization of all mental defectives would not lead to a marked decrease in the number of children born mentally defective.

A certain percentage of mental deficiency, probably between twenty and forty per cent, is due to environmental factors.

Before the birth of the child, there are numerous causes which can so affect the expectant mother that injury will be done to the child. Some of these factors are certainly capable of causing mental deficiency by the harm they may do to the brain of the unborn child. Other influences may possibly produce this effect. The more outstanding causes of this type are: dietary deficiency, bacterial poisons (such as syphilis), excessive alcoholism, glandular deficiencies, and abortifacients.

At the birth of the child, there are very often injuries inflicted which produce mental deficiency. Extreme pressure on the delicate brain and the harmful use of instruments are the main causes. Some authorities on mental deficiency believe that seventeen per cent of our mental deficiency is due to brain injuries at birth.

After the birth of the child, there are several important factors which produce mental deficiency. The principal conditions of this type are those infectious diseases which cause an inflammation of the brain and its delicate coverings (meningitis).

Sleeping sickness likewise produces an acute inflammation of the brain and is frequently followed, especially in children, by progressive mental deterioration.

Epilepsy beginning in early life may also arrest mental development. Frequently, however, it is difficult to know whether the epilepsy is the cause of the mental deficiency or the effect of some underlying condition which has also had a deteriorating influence on the mind.

A very high percentage of our mental deficiency is, however, admittedly due to hereditary influences. As previously mentioned, a great deal of research in recent years has been devoted to the study of the application of the Mendelian laws of hered-

ity to the transmission of physical and mental diseases. The
results have been much less fruitful than is ordinarily supposed. Man presents poor material for observation as compared
with animals and plants: the span of his generations is short, his
families are small, and neither his mating nor his environment
is subject to scientific control. For these reasons, a common
disease or physical deficiency may occur several times in succes-
sive generations of a family and be due, not to heredity, but
to ordinary causes.

Excellent studies have shown that certain physical diseases,
such as hemophilia, a few eye conditions, and certain varieties
of nervous disease, follow definite and easily demonstrated
Mendelian laws. These conditions are, however, comparatively
rare and show no tendency to increase in frequency.

Many other ailments are probably hereditary, but are uncertain and erratic in their mode of transmission or are dependent
on special environmental conditions for their development.

Other diseases, formerly thought to be definitely hereditary,
such as cancer, are not so considered any longer.

In brief, there has been much speculation on the inheritance
of physical and mental diseases, but science has not yet given
much positive information on this field.

At first glance, the estimates given on the percentage of
mental defectives who are in this condition because of hereditary factors, seem impressive. The estimates vary between
twenty-four and eighty per cent. Tredgold, one of the most
outstanding authorities on the subject, is the one who believes
that nearly eighty per cent of our mental deficiency is due to
hereditary factors. Yet it is this same authority who reminds
us that the bulk of defectives are the progeny, not of defective
parents, but of "carriers" of the defect.

Anyone familiar with the Mendelian laws of heredity understands that a person may be a "carrier" of a characteristic and
yet personally give no evidence of that characteristic. So,
although it may be true that almost eighty per cent of our
mental deficiency is caused by hereditary factors, Tredgold
states that no more than ten per cent of our mental defectives
are born of mentally defective parents. He reminds us that the

effect of a sterilization program would therefore merely be to
diminish the number of mental defectives by that relatively
small proportion arising from defective parents. Briefly,
although eighty per cent of our mental deficiency may be
coming into society through channels of heredity, all but ten
per cent of it is being passed on through persons who are
"carriers" of these traits. These "carriers" give no evidence
of mental deficiency and are not able to be detected. A sterilization program, therefore, would not affect seventy-two per
cent of the hereditay mental deficiency, and would have no
influence on mental deficiency which is the product of environmental factors.

It is such facts as these which have led Tredgold to insist
that a program of eugenic sterilization would not produce any
appreciable difference in the total incidence of mental deficiency.

Two other investigators on this subject, Huetkrantz and
Gunnar, state that it would take ten generations before the
percentage of defectives would be reduced one half of one per
cent, and that the subsequent rate of decrease would be still
lower.

It is interesting to note that the eugenicists quote Tredgold
with respect whenever his statements can be made to serve
their purposes; but they will not mention this authority when
his judgments are opposed to their opinions. Thus, in his
volume entitled *The Case for Sterilization*, Whitney emphasizes that Tredgold maintains that eighty per cent of our mental
deficiency is due to hereditary factors; but the same author
neglects to mention that Tredgold states that only ten per
cent of this number comes from defective parents and would
be affected in any way by a program of eugenic sterilization.

Even if one were to assume that sterilization would decrease
mental deficiency much more rapidly than these authorities
believe, the rate of decrease would still be so slow and negligible that it could not be regarded as a method capable of
achieving its stated objectives.

(d) Sterilization of mental defectives would not lessen the
state's financial burden of providing institutional care for the
mentally ill and feebleminded.

Sterilization will not increase a person's appreciation of social responsibility, and the mental defective who was not safe to be at large before sterilization will be no safer because of it. Sterilization does not make the feebleminded less feebleminded, the criminal less criminal, nor the insane less insane.

The eugenicist places strong emphasis on the fact that sterilization makes living in society practical for high-grade defectives once the possibility of children is removed.

It is true that sex plays a major rôle in human life, but it would be very narrow not to perceive the many other aspects of man's life in society.

Danger to society lies in the fact that once sterilization is accomplished, the temptation is to release the individual from institutional care without special training or fitness for community life. Thus, in California, where sterilization is most practiced, it is acknowledged that two-thirds of the boys and four-fifths of the girls who are sterilized are operated on within a year from the date of their commitment and almost always leave the institution within the next year.

High school and college teachers realize how difficult it is to train those of normal intelligence for community living. It borders on the ridiculous to conceive of taking a mentally defective person, imposing sterilization, and returning the individual into society within two years.

Modern life is so complex, education and at least normal intelligence so necessary, that the mental defective can never hope to cope with it. Under the abnormal manpower shortage created by war, some of these persons might find employment. In normal times, however, not to speak of depression periods, the dark economic outlook for a mental defective is quite obvious.

Sterilization, moreover, will not eradicate from the defective tendencies toward crime and immorality. These tendencies are in all persons, but in a person of normal intelligence they can be controlled by a proper exercise of reason. To release a person whose nature is imbued with inclinations toward evil, and who has no adequate intelligence to guide him, is to invite social problems of the first magnitude.

In particular, sterilization would not solve the many social problems which would confront the mentally defective person who entered marriage. It is true that many domestic problems revolve around children; but it is rash to believe that, once the possibility of children is removed, the mental defective is capable of intelligently solving the remaining domestic problems. Such an attitude shows little knowledge of the serious problems which confront a husband and wife who try to earn a living, maintain a home, and fulfill countless social obligations.

The mental defective will be happier in an institution, be more properly cared for, and, under a program of skilled instruction, he need not always be a burden on the state.

There are many fine institutions in which the patients, under skilled supervision, do most of the work. They care for extensive farms, dairies, and herds. They keep the buildings in good order and the grounds attractive. They produce articles of handicraft and manual arts which are admirable. They are contented and happy with the considerate care they receive and the recreational facilities made available to them.

Outside society is cruel to the handicapped person, especially to the mentally defective person. It shuns the unfortunate, and the patient's family is in a constant state of embarrassment.

The advocate of sterilization remarks that we are spending millions of dollars on the care of mental defectives. Our answer is that the millions of dollars are well spent. The federal and state governments spend millions, and even billions, of dollars on projects which range from parks to battleships, from scientific research work to superhighways. These material necessities and luxuries of life are appreciated. But anyone who believes in the spiritual nature of man and the inherent dignity of a human being will not begrudge the comparatively little that is spent to care for these unfortunate children of God.

(e) Eugenic sterilization would result in an increase in immorality and social diseases. The best authorities on mental deficiency, such as Tredgold, agree that the release of mental defectives into society would cause an increase in sex offenses and social diseases.

The advocates of sterilization, of course, strenuously oppose this statement. They labor the point that scientific studies show that, physically and psychologically, mental defectives are no more prone to sex irregularities after sterilization than they were before the operation. They insist that the removal of the possibility of conception does not entice them into a freer attitude toward matters of sex.

The foregoing statements of the eugenicist may be true, but they are not to the point. The increase in immorality will result from these poor unfortunates being victimized by ruthless and unscrupulous members of society. Unfortunately, there are many persons in society who would unhesitatingly take advantage of a feebleminded girl whom they knew to be sterile.

As a matter of fact, the advocates of sterilization admit that these feebleminded girls will be victimized, but they simply shrug their shoulders and say "What does it matter? No baby will be born." This blunt, materialistic attitude is expressed on two occasions in Whitney's work on *The Case for Sterilization.*

Apparently, for the proponent of eugenic sterilization, the sole criterion of immorality is whether or not an act creates an embarrassing social problem. When the eugenicist insists that sterilization will not result in increased immorality, he means only that it will not increase social problems. For those who do not have a materialistic concept of life, these thoughts are far from being the same. For those who have an appreciation of moral law and conscience, the intrinsic character of morality, and the dignity of a human being, no further comment is needed.

The spread of social diseases would also be a natural consequence of promiscuity by mental defectives. These unfortunates have no realization of the dangers of exposure to certain diseases, no appreciation of the gravity of the condition once it is contracted, and no interest in seeking badly needed medical care.

(f) Eugenic sterilization would lead to abuses of state power over the citizen. No conceivable method could be devised for preventing so-called "voluntary" sterilization from becoming compulsory on the poor. State agencies could adopt countless pressure tactics, such as the refusal of social services, to those

who would not consent. Authorities could make discharge from
a mental institution conditionate upon consent to sterilization.
This is not a mere possibility. It is the actual practice in many
states in this country.

The trend on the part of the states is, moreover, to break
away from all restricting influences. Thus, in 1945, Alabama
endeavored to liberalize its law on eugenic sterilization to the
extent of placing full power to inflict sterilization in the hands
of the director of the state's hospitals for the mentally ill, acting
in conjunction with a committee of doctors. The proposal did
pass the state house of representatives but failed to make further
progress. Strenuous efforts to secure such legislation are still
being made in Alabama, and the laws of some other states are
already equally liberal.

Legislation which permits the sterilization of mental defectives at the discretion of state officials provides a clear-cut
example of governmental encroachment on the rights of the
individual citizen and, as such, is an approach to totali-
tarianism.

One of the first legislative steps of the Nazi regime in Germany was to set up a body of sterilization laws, passed on July
14, 1933. These laws determined the classes of persons who
could or should be sterilized and the procedure that was to be
followed. As is well known, these laws later enabled the Nazis
to perpetrate deeds of incredible cruelty against great masses
of their people, even against entire racial groups, such as the
Jews. (On January 15, 1935, for example, the *Volkische Beo-
bachter* stated that there were 410,600 persons in Germany who
should be sterilized.)

The Nazi sterilization laws, as enacted, were carefully qualified and restricted; but, within a few years, they resulted in
conditions which were so horrible that they surpass imagination.

The principle underlying our sterilization laws is essentially
the same as that which guided the Nazi regime—the principle
that there are no inalienable personal rights on the part of the
individual citizen; hence, civil authorities may treat their subjects in any way which will lighten the burdens and responsibilities of the state.

The eugenicist will sometimes answer that our sterilizations are usually voluntary on the part of the patient. It is an inter-esting contradiction to hear that a mentally defective person gives a *voluntary* consent, especially when his release from an institution is conditionate upon this consent.

At other times, the eugenicist will say that parents or guard-ians give the required consent. Factually, many of these pa-tients have no parents or guardians (recall that those steril-ized in California are usually between twenty-seven and thirty years of age). Moreover, it is well known that innumerable parents and guardians are only too glad to have anything done to the patient which will decrease their care, responsibility, and problems.

Finally, once the state is authorized to sterilize patients upon the consent of specified parties, the law can readily be amended to permit the state to sterilize without the patient's, parent's, or guardian's consent. Such an amendment would simply authorize the state to impose sterilization whenever a refusal by those concerned was deemed unreasonable. As a matter of fact, the trend in the United States today is to take the matter out of the hands of patients and their families, and to allow the decision to rest with a director or committee of the state mental institution.

Once it is conceded that a state may sterilize a person at the discretion of civil authorities, it can logically be maintained that persons could be put to death by the state if their physical or mental condition rendered them helpless burdens upon society. Many of the reasons that are adduced in favor of the sterilization of the mentally ill and feebleminded could surely be used to extend the power of the state to the infliction of death on such persons as would be regarded as a burden to themselves and to the community.

Conclusion

We must accept mental deficiency as a fact in our social structure. We may deplore its existence; but, regardless of what we may do, it will remain with us for generations to come. The problems created by mental deficiency must be solved by methods in accordance with natural law. Society will never benefit by any attempt to solve its problems by immoral practices. Some of the important measures which would aid greatly are: slum clearance, public health work against tuberculosis and venereal diseases, proper prenatal care of prospective mothers, education on the evils of excessive alcoholism, and specialized training schools for the care and instruction of mentally-handicapped children.

The eugenicist may retort that social conditions have been steadily improving for some years, but mental deficiency continues to increase. In answer, one might say that we are not sure that mental deficiency is on the increase. The increase may be only apparent. We may be more conscious of mental deficiency and better able to detect it than ever before in our history. Again, the problem is given more attention today than in previous years, and new methods for detecting the condition have been devised. Furthermore, many mentally defective children are physically weak and diseased. A high percentage of these children died in early life in former years, whereas our increased knowledge and care of the handicapped conserves life for these persons.

If mental deficiency is actually on the increase, it may be due to the nature of modern life. In contrast to the leisurely pace of other ages, science, industry, and our high level of education place excessive demands upon the mentally weak. These strains unquestionably result in breakdowns which sometimes disturb mental balance; and, secondly, science and education have become so vital a part of our society that those who lack them are very apt to be regarded as mentally defective.

After all, our best test of mental deficiency is the inability to cope adequately with the problems of life. It is for this reason that mental deficiency has been defined as "a condition of incomplete development of mind of such a degree or kind as to render the individual incapable of adjusting himself to his social environment in a reasonably efficient manner, and to necessitate his care, supervision, and control by responsible people."

If this be so, the mere fact that more people today are classified as mental defectives than ever before does not necessarily imply that there has been an increase in mental deterioration. It would mean only that there are more people who cannot meet the exacting demands of our type of society than the number who could not cope with the more simple society of earlier years.

The more thorough, sympathetic, and enlightened is our treatment of defectives, the better will be the return which the state will get for the money it spends on this work. A proper system of institutional training, such as that followed in the "colony" method, usually results in high-grade defectives being self-supporting and personally bettered.

The early years of the mental defective should probably be spent at home. After the age of six, the child makes best progress under skilled care in an institution. After a long period of special training, usually extending over adolescence, it is sometimes feasible for the high-grade defective to return to the guardianship of interested parents in a healthy family environment. Such release depends a great deal upon the degree of self-control the patient has developed, whether or not the patient can earn his living by a trade learned in the institution, and upon the quality of the home environment.

It must not be thought that we advocate a policy of permitting those who are mentally defective to exercise sexual activity indiscriminately. Those who lack the requisite mental ability to contract marriage and to fulfill its obligations, should not be allowed opportunities which might furnish them with the occasion to employ their reproductive powers. But supervision, segregation, and protective custody are the remedies against such abuses, not a physical mutilation that degrades the dignity of human nature and places man in the same class as a diseased animal which is not to be allowed to propagate its kind.

Our opposition to eugenic sterilization is, therefore, not based merely on the teaching of the Church. It is a moral truth, arising out of the Natural Law itself, that every human being possesses an inalienable right to bodily integrity, because he is made to the image and likeness of God and belongs totally to his Creator. For this reason, it is a grave injustice to subject an

innocent person to serious bodily mutilation merely for the
sake of expediency or for the attaining of objectives which can
be procured just as effectively in a humane, decent, and moral
manner.

Punitive Sterilization

Little need be said about the morality of *punitive* sterilization. There is no doubt that, where crime has been committed,
the State possesses a power over man's life and over less than
life, namely, man's freedom and integrity of body. The State,
however, possesses only a qualified power; that is, it may not
use its power as it pleases. It may not use man as it would
use a piece of material property. Its control of man is sub-
servient to the prior rights of man. These rights arise out of
the very nature which God has bestowed upon man and are
not derived from the state. Neither are these rights forfeited
by man simply because he lives with other men in society in
order that the state may protect him and aid him directly and
indirectly in attaining the temporal and spiritual objectives
of human existence.

It is true that the State exists, by Divine Plan, to procure
the temporal welfare of the community. To perform this task,
the state must make laws and impose an adequate penalty or
sanction on their violation. For this reason, the state can
deprive man of his liberty, the integrity of his body, and even
his life, for serious crimes against society. *But any penalty
imposed for crime must conform to certain moral principles.*

Punishment must be in proportion to the offense; it must
be reasonable. To be a "reasonable" act on the part of the
state, it must serve a purpose, and there are only four conceivable purposes which punishment can serve.

(a) A punishment is *retributive* when it inflicts a loss on
a person for the injury which has been done to the victim.
This is the Old Testament idea of "an eye for an eye, a tooth
for a tooth."

To be truly retributive, the "loss" must not be merely objective but also subjective; that is, the culprit must really suffer
or feel the privation.

Sterilization of the sex criminal is not a retributive punish-

ment. In fact, instead of regarding sterilization as a loss, criminals of this type regard it as something desirable. It makes the commission of sex crimes easier, by removing the possibility of conception. The fear of conception and the consequent social complications constitute one of the major deterrents from sex offenses for those who are attracted to immorality. So true is this fact that approximately seven hundred criminals in San Quentin Prison, California, have been sterilized by the state upon their wholly voluntary request.

(b) A punishment is *medicinal, corrective,* or *reformatory* when it tends to eradicate from the character of the culprit the trait which led him into the crime. As has been just explained, sterilization of sex criminals will make them worse by removing a major barrier to the commission of that type of crime. *Sterilization of the sex criminal is, therefore, not a medicinal punishment.*

(c) A punishment is *exemplary* when it serves as a warning and deterrent to others who might be inclined to commit the same offense. But the threat of sterilization would not deter those interested in the commission of sex crimes. Sterilization holds no fears for them. In fact, it is regarded as something desirable. *Sterilization is, therefore, not an exemplary punishment.*

(d) A punishment is *amendatory* when it restores to the victim a value equivalent to the loss which has been suffered. Quite obviously, the innocent victim of a sex crime has suffered a loss which sterilization of the offender can never restore. *Sterilization is, therefore, not an amendatory punishment.*

It is for these reasons that moralists agree that, in practice, sterilization is immoral when imposed by the state as a punishment for sex crime. It serves no purpose, whereas there are countless real punishments which the state can inflict for grave crimes of the above type.

Problems for Discussion

1. What would you think of the morality of using irradiation to produce a *temporary* sterility in patients having tuberculosis? The objective is to render the patient sterile until the tuber-

cular lesions have healed (due to the danger created by pregnancy while the lesions are still present). If the dosage is not excessive and the age of the patient is favorable, medical science feels that only a temporary sterility will be produced in most cases by irradiation of the ovaries. (Reference: *Acta Apostolicae Sedis,* Feb., 1940, XXXII-73.)

2. Why is it that you hold *therapeutic* sterilization to be sometimes morally permissible, while never permitting *therepeutic* abortion? Is not the same moral principle—the supreme dominion of the Creator over a creature—involved in both sterilization and abortion? If you permit therapeutic sterilization when this step is necessary to save the patient's life would it not appear that you should logically permit therapeutic abortion when the cessation of the pregnancy is required to preserve a patient's life?

3. If the State can call upon a citizen to sacrifice his life for his country in time of war, would it not seem reasonable to say that the State could call upon mental defectives to sacrifice their reproductive powers in the interests of the social welfare of the nation?

4. In Beck's *Obstetrical Practice* (Baltimore, 1935, pp. 473-475), the author treats the subject of ovarian tumors during pregnancy. In this passage he states that "whenever cesarean section is performed on potentially infected women, the uterus should also be removed." Is this a morally permissible sterilization or not?

5. Read the section on "Sterilization" in the Encyclical on *Christian Marriage.* Do you think it more or less leaves open the morality of punitive sterilization? Do you think that there could be a case in which sterilization would be a cruel but nevertheless *retributive* punishment?

6. The State subjects its citizens to vaccinations in the interests of avoiding social problems. These vaccinations may produce fevers, temporary illness and permanent scars. Why, then, is it wrong for the State to perform sterilization on defective citizens to avoid the social consequences of their propagating their kind?

7. Does the Church's condemnation of eugenic sterilization imply its approval of marriages between the mentally unfit, as well as their having children?

8. Is it permissible to remove the tubes in the case of a patient who is having a kidney removed?

9. Does the *Encyclical on Christian Marriage* forbid attempts to dissuade mentally defective persons from marrying?

10. Does segregation of certain mentally defective persons meet with the Church's approval? If so, is it not just as wrong to deprive them of personal freedom as it is to deprive them of integrity of body (as is done in eugenic sterilization)?

11. If only the fallopian tubes need be removed in a specific case to restore the health of a woman, is it morally permissible to remove the uterus also? Over and above the rôle in pregnancy which this uterus can no longer serve, are there any other purposes helpful to the body which its presence will achieve? If it were removed, what would be the effect on menstruation and on the ovaries?

References for Reading

BONNAR, A.: *The Catholic Doctor* (2nd ed.), pp. 83; 97-119, N. Y., 1939.

BONZELET, H.: "Irradiation of Ovaries," *American Ecclesiastical Review*, pp. 125-127, August, 1943.

————: "Irradiation or Ligature of Vasa Deferentia in Cases of Enlarged Prostate," *American Ecclesiastical Review*, p. 127, August, 1943.

BRUEHL, C.: *Birth Control and Eugenics*, N. Y., 1928.

CAMMACK, J.: *Moral Problems of Mental Defect*, N. Y., 1939.

CONNELL, F.: "The Caesarean Operation," *American Ecclesiastical Review*, pp. 470-471, Dec., 1944.

————: "The Catholic Doctor," *American Ecclesiastical Review*, pp. 439-448, Dec., 1944.

————: "The Removal of a Healthy Appendix," *American Ecclesiastical Review*, June, 1947, pp. 469-470.

————: "Sterilization in Cases of Uterine Prolapse with Systocele and Rectocele," *American Ecclesiastical Review*, Sept., 1947, pp. 222-223.

————: "The Morality of Autopsy," *American Ecclesiastical Review*, Jan., 1948, pp. 63-64.

————: "How Soon May Embalming Begin," *American Ecclesiastical Review*, March, 1948, p. 230.

—————: "The Disposal of Blood in Embalming," *American Ecclesiastical Review*, April, 1948, pp. 309-310.

—————: "Sterilization after Cesarean Section," *American Ecclesiastical Review*, July, 1948, pp. 65-66.

CUNNINGHAM, B.: *The Morality of Organic Transplantation*, Catholic University, Washington, D. C., 1944.
(This is the most complete work in English on mutilation and it contains an extensive bibliography on both the scientific and moral aspects of the topic.)

DAVIS, H.: *State Sterilization of the Unfit*, London, 1931.

—————: *Eugenics: Its Aims and Methods*, N. Y., 1930.

—————: *Moral and Pastoral Theology* (4th ed.), Vol. 2, pp. 156-166, London, 1945.

DONOVAN, J.: "A Case of Sterilization," *Homiletic and Pastoral Review*, Aug., 1947, pp. 927-928.

FINNEY, P.: *Moral Problems in Hospital Practice*, pp. 145-166, St. Louis, 1930.

KELLY, G.: "Organic Transplantation," *Theological Studies*, March, 1947, pp. 97-101.

—————: "Suppression of Ovarian Function to Prevent Metastasis," *Hospital Progress*, April, 1948.

—————: "Problems Concerning Excessive Uterine Bleeding," *Hospital Progress*, June, 1948.

—————: "Orchidectomy," *Hospital Progress*, Aug., 1948.

—————: "Lobotomy," *Hospital Progress*, Dec., 1948.

—————: " Disposal of Amputated Members," *Hospital Progress*, May, 1948.

KREMER, P.: "Irradiation of the Ovaries," *American Ecclesiastical Review*, pp. 271-273, April, 1943.

MAZER-SPITZ: "Irradiation of the Ovaries," *American Journal of Obstetrics and Gynecology*, p. 214, August, 1935.

McCARTHY, J.: "The Morality of Organic Transplantation." *Irish Ecclesiastical Record*, March, 1946, pp. 192-198.

MONTAVON, W.: *Eugenic Sterilization in the Laws of the States* (pamphet), N. C. W. C., Washington, D. C., 1930.

MOORE, T.: "Irradiation of Reproductive Organs in Removal of Cancerous Prostate," *American Ecclesiastical Review*, pp. 444-446, June, 1942.

MUENCH, A.: "Sterilization by Law," *Graduate Nurses*, pp. 45-92, N. Y., 1938.

O'BRIEN, P.: "Prefrontal Lobotomy," *American Ecclesiastical Review*, Sept., 1948, pp. 196-201.

O'NEILL, P.: "The Voronoff Operation," *Irish Ecclesiastical Record*, Vol. 53, pp. 415-417.

ROCHELLE-FINK: *Handbook of Medical Ethics*, pp. 131-163, Westminster, Md., 1943.

RYAN, J.: *The Moral Aspects of Sterilization* (pamphlet), N. C. W. C., Washington, D. C., 1936.

————: *Human Sterilization* (pamphlet), N. C. W. C., Washington, D. C., 1930.

TENNESSAN, M.: "Catholic Care of the Psychiatric Patient," *Hospital Progress*, Aug., 1948.

"May the State Sterilize the Insane?" *American Ecclesiastical Review*, p. 589, Dec., 1937.

"May a Catholic Doctor Employed by the State Perform Eugenic Sterilizations?" *American Ecclesiastical Review*, p. 634, Dec., 1930; p. 589, Dec., 1937; p. 285, Sept., 1938; p. 147, Feb., 1944.

"Sterilization Law in Germany," *American Ecclesiastical Review*, pp. 50-68, July, 1936.

"Is Sterilization Ever Permissible? *American Ecclesiastical Review*, pp. 292-293, March, 1938.

"The Marriage Rights of a Sterilized Person," *American Ecclesiastical Review*, p. 563, Dec., 1938.

"Sterilization to Avoid Dangerous Pregnancy," *American Ecclesiastical Review*, p. 631, June, 1933.

"Sterilization After Caesarean Section," *Homiletic and Pastoral Review*, p. 758, May, 1942.

"Contraceptive Sterilization," *Homiletic and Pastoral Review*, p. 609, May, 1944.

"A Sterilization Operation," *Homiletic and Pastoral Review*, p. 216, Dec., 1943.

CHAPTER 13

Assistance at Immoral Operations

The title of this chapter is more restrictive than its contents. For here we present those moral principles which govern, not only assistance at immoral operations, but also coöperation in any type of immoral action.

The importance of these moral principles can hardly be over-emphasized. Every doctor and nurse realizes only too well how frequently the application of these principles is required in the medical field. And medico-moral problems of this type are often difficult to solve.

At the outset, it is to be acknowledged that the aid given by an assistant surgeon to a principal surgeon, or by nurses to doctors, in the commission of immoral acts is often rendered unwillingly.

Difficult situations of this type frequently arise because of neglect on the part of those who hold positions of authority in the hospital. When hospital authorities rigidly forbid all immoral operations and place a strict sanction on their prohibition, few embarrassing situations will occur. If hospital authorities deliberately close their eyes to these matters, moral problems will constantly arise for the assistant surgeons and nurses on the staff.

In many cases, of course, the moral problems do not arise as the result of a malicious determination on the part of hospital surgeons to perform operations which they know to be immoral. Frequently, the problem has a deeper and more serious basis, namely, the attitude on the part of hospital

330

authorities that certain truly immoral operations are not immoral at all. When the ethical code of a hospital and the superior members of its staff is deficient, the doctors and nurses in the institution who possess true moral ideals can expect no end to their problems.

This situation is unfortunately not at all rare. For instance, therapeutic abortion, and sterilization to make impossible future pregnancy which would endanger health, are regarded as wholly justifiable by many secular hospital authorities. No doctor or nurse is morally free to accept such a view and their employment in institutions which hold such opinions is fraught with grave moral difficulties.

Situations which are difficult to handle will probably fall to the lot of the nurse more often than to the doctor. Throughout her professional training, the nurse is taught to obey authority without question. She is trained to carry out the commands of doctors and surgeons quickly, and without comment. The thought of taking exception to the moral character of an operative procedure of a surgeon is, for many nurses, a thought too fantastic to imagine.

The nurse remains, however, a person in her own right. She has her own spiritual nature with all of the moral obligations which are proper to it. The fact that she is a nurse does not mean that she may indiscriminately aid others in the commission of sin. She must be guided in such difficulties by the same moral principles which direct any member of society in problems of a similar type.

In order to determine accurately the moral principles which govern assistance at immoral operations, it is necessary to distinguish between several kinds of such assistance.

The Nature of Coöperation

In a broad sense, any influence which is exerted upon the will of another, in an effort to have that other person commit sin, can be construed as coöperation. This influence would be *direct and positive* whenever it took the form of command, counsel, enticement, or pleas to commit the act. It would be *indirect and negative* if one neglected to warn and impede a person contemplating sin when there was both the opportunity and obligation to do so.

In a strict sense, however, *coöperation is any real or physical help given to another person in the commission of a sinful act.* It is in this strict sense that we shall use the term "coöperation" in the present chapter.

Coöperation is classified as *immediate* when the one coöperating intimately participates, under the direction of the principal agent, in the immoral act itself. Thus, an assistant surgeon who performs one or more parts of an immoral operation, by way of aiding the principal surgeon, is rendering *immediate* coöperation.

Coöperation is classified as *mediate* when the one coöperating supplies the means which make it possible for the principal agent to carry out his sinful act.

Mediate coöperation is called *proximate* or *remote,* according as it is more or less intimately connected with the act of the principal agent. Thus, a nurse who would stand beside a surgeon who was performing an immoral operation and hand him all of the required instruments and materials would be rendering *proximate assistance.* In contrast, a nurse who would prepare the patient in a hospital room for the forthcoming immoral operation, or the nurse who would sterilize and set out the instruments for the operation, would be rendering *remote assistance.*

Thus far, our analysis of coöperation has been solely from the objective standpoint; that is, we have considered only the physical nature of the aid given and its degree of proximity to the immoral act itself. A moral act, however, always involves knowledge and freedom. For this reason, it is necessary to distinguish between *formal* and *material* coöperation.

Formal coöperation is said to be present when the one who is aiding the principal agent freely agrees with the latter's sinful intentions and freely chooses to help in the performance of the immoral act.

Material coöperation is unwilling aid given to another in the commission of an immoral act; that is, the one coöperating neither agrees with the sinful intentions of the principal agent nor desires the sinful effect to take place, but does actually render some aid because of some personal benefit that will be derived or because of some loss which will thereby be averted.

The Morality of Coöperation

Formal coöperation proceeds from a bad intention and involves approval of an immoral act. For this reason, *it is never morally permissible,* and it is a sin of the same nature as the immoral act of the principal agent.

Material coöperation, however, is not the result of a malicious will or desire to achieve an immoral objective. It is, instead, the fruit of a reluctant decision to help in the commission of an immoral act simply because, by so doing, a loss or inconvenience to oneself will thereby be averted or a personal gain be procured.

Material coöperation which is *immediate* cannot, however, be permitted. It involves partial execution of the immoral act itself and is, therefore, intrinsically evil. Even though one is not interested in seeking the immoral objective and is motivated by purely extrinsic factors, *no reason, however grave, would ever allow a person to participate actively, as a partial efficient cause, in the immoral act itself.* For example, an assistant surgeon could never render *immediate* coöperation in a purely eugenic sterilization.

It is not often that a nurse will be called upon to give *immediate* coöperation. Usually, she stands outside the act itself and is simply called upon to hand over or prepare the required materials and instruments for the use of those who are performing the operation.

It is not unheard of, however, for nurses to be confronted with a request for immediate coöperation. Nurses working in the offices of doctors who do not hesitate to perform private therapeutic, and even criminal, abortions are sometimes called upon to render what is certainly immediate coöperation. *Such assistance is intrinsically evil, and no reason whatever would allow the nurse to participate so intimately in an immoral act.*

Material coöperation which is *mediate* involves an action which is *in itself* morally indifferent. It is an action which one would ordinarily have a right to do, such as sterilizing instruments or handing them to a surgeon. It is an action whose moral character here and now becomes questionable only *because it is being made to serve an immoral end.*

Both doctor and nurse must recall the all-important two-fold effect principle. Actions which are morally indifferent in their own nature may be performed, *under due conditions,* even though they are productive of an evil effect, as well as a good effect. It is this principle which is involved in the morality of mediate coöperation.

The first condition of the twofold effect principle requires that the act which is productive of the good and bad effect be a morally indifferent act. This first condition is verified in all cases of mediate material coöperation.

The second condition demands that the good effect proceed directly from the indifferent act, not through the medium of the evil effect. This condition will probably be fulfilled in almost all cases of mediate material coöperation.

The third condition insists that the motive prompting the act must be a desire for the good effect and in no way a result of attraction toward the evil effect. This condition is presumably verified in most cases of mediate material coöperation.

The fourth condition states that the good effect must be at least equivalent in value to the evil which results. *It is this condition which will necessitate deep analysis in problems of this type.*

The evil effect in these cases is the violation of moral law and the loss which will result from the violation (such as the injury to bodily integrity in eugenic sterilization or the destruction of innocent life in therapeutic abortion). The good effect in these cases is the benefit which will be derived by the one coöperating as the result of rendering the aid, or the loss which that person will thereby avert.

With this background, we may now ask: *May a doctor or nurse ever give proximate or remote material assistance to one who is performing an immoral operation?*

The answer is that such assistance may be given *provided there is a sufficient reason for so doing.* The gravity of the reason must be in proportion to the proximity of the act to that of the principal agent. The closer and the more necessary such aid is, the more grave will the reason have to be to justify it.

A doctor or nurse must have *a very grave cause* before it is morally permissible to render *the closer and more necessary forms of proximate material assistance.* Hence it would be morally permissible to give *close proximate and necessary* assistance in an immoral operation only if a refusal to assist would inflict *a very grave loss* on oneself or on some other person. Thus, one might render such assistance if refusal would involve a risk to one's own life, grave personal harm, notable injury to one's reputation, serious financial setback, possible loss of life to the patient, or the loss of one's profession. Reasons of lesser weight would justify the rendering of such assistance if it is close *but not necessary aid* for the one performing the evil act (for example, if he could go on and perform the act alone or if someone else would immediately step in to help him as soon as we refused).

A doctor or nurse must have *a grave cause* before it is morally permissible to render the more distant forms of proximate material assistance to one who is performing an immoral operation. A notable and permanent reduction in salary, a demotion in official position, or a long suspension would ordinarily constitute a grave loss. Only if refusal to render this aid would result in the above or similar losses would one be justified in granting such assistance. As mentioned above, however, not only the proximity of the assistance to the act of the principal agent should be taken into consideration but also his degree of dependence on it.

A doctor or nurse must have a *normally serious cause* before he or she is morally justified in rendering *remote material assistance* to one who is performing a sinful operation. If refusal to render such aid would result in suspension for a week, with consequent loss of salary, or some equivalent loss, one would usually be morally justified in giving this aid.

It cannot be emphasized too strongly that it is a most difficult matter to evaluate the causes which justify rendering the various types of material assistance. Each individual case, with all of its circumstances, must be given specific consideration. What would be a normally serious loss for one person might well be a grave loss for a second person, and a negligible loss for someone else.

For instance, the loss of a week's salary through suspension would usually be *a normally serious loss*. But if a nurse were, for example, the sole support of herself and her aged parents, the loss of this salary might often be *a grave loss*. On the other hand, another nurse might have plenty of money and would welcome such a suspension as a splendid opportunity for a pleasant vacation.

The conscientious doctor and nurse must give full consideration to the details of each difficulty which they encounter. They will have to consider carefully the type of assistance which is demanded of them. They will have to weigh conscientiously the gravity of the loss which will come to them as the result of a refusal to render the material assistance. Then, and then only, will they be able to decide whether they are morally justified in doing what is asked of them, or whether they are morally obliged to refuse such aid in the particular case.

In summary, no one may *ever* render either *formal* or *immediate* material coöperation. Doctors and nurses must have *a very grave reason* before they may give close proximate material aid. They must have *a grave cause* to justify the rendering of the *somewhat more remote forms of proximate coöperation*. *A normally serious reason* must be present before they may give truly *remote* material assistance to an immoral operation.

The rendering of aid to one who is acting immorally is more difficult to justify if it is foreseen that the demand will be habitual. If the demand is not likely to recur, it is much more easy to permit the giving of the aid in a single case for an apparently proportionate reason.

The giving of aid to one who is acting immorally is likewise more difficult to allow when a refusal will mean that the principal agent will be unable to perform the action. On the other hand, if many persons are willing and capable of rendering the requested assistance, it is much more easy to justify the giving of such aid when there is present an apparently proportionate reason.

The rendering of aid to one who is acting immorally is more difficult to justify in proportion to the gravity of the contemplated evil. Thus, a "mercy killing" or an abortion would be a graver evil than an immoral sterilization.

The following observations should provide matter for serious reflection for many doctors:

> "It has come to our attention in enough cases to warrant mention here that Catholic physicians, sometimes in good faith because of ignorance or thoughtlessness, refer patients to other physicians for such things as therapeutic abortion, sterilization, advice about contraceptive devices and measurement for them, and the like. Their opinion seems to be that as Catholics they cannot do these things themselves, but that they can send their patients to others or call others into consultation for the purpose. This attitude is also found in non-Catholic physicians who do not feel that they can do these things ethically. In referring patients in this way, the physician gives scandal to a serious degree both to the patient and to the physician to whom he refers the patient, since he gives other persons the opportunity to do the wrong which he knows in conscience he cannot do himself. This is true regardless of whether either the physician or the patient is a Catholic, since the Natural-Divine-Moral Law is binding on all."
> (Good-Kelly, *Marriage, Morals and Medical Ethics,* p. 26)
> We might also add that a physician who acts in such a manner becomes a cooperator in the sins of the other physician and in the sins of the patients referred to him.

Analysis of several typical cases will serve to illustrate the application of the moral principles presented in this chapter.

(1) A nurse engaged in social service work is ordered by her Superior to give instruction in the use of contraceptives. She hesitates and is told that if she does not give the instruction she will be dismissed from her position. May she give this instruction?

The answer is "No." To give such instruction is *formal coöperation* in the sin of the patient. To instruct a patient in a method of committing sin is in itself a morally evil act. Hence the nurse's rôle cannot possibly be regarded as one of material assistance. It is formal coöperation rendered to another in the commission of sin. Such assistance is always immoral, and never permissible.

> (2) A nurse, employed in a non-sectarian hospital, is told to assist the surgeon in what she knows is to be an immoral operation. It would be her duty to work by the side of the surgeon, handing him the instruments and materials which he would require. When she hesitates to comply with the order she is told that refusal will mean dismissal from the hospital. May she render the aid demanded of her?

The answer to this question must be determined by a further analysis of the case. At the outset it is clear that the nurse is confronted with giving *material* but not *formal* assistance. The material aid demanded from her is, however, of a most serious type, namely, very close proximate coöperation. Only *a very grave cause* will justify her in giving aid which is so intimately connected with the sinful action itself.

The circumstances of the case must be studied before one can decide whether or not dismissal from her present position would be *a very grave loss*. In some cases, it appears that the loss of a position would constitute a very grave loss. For instance, in a period of severe economic depression, when there would be no reasonable expectation of getting another position, a nurse who was the sole support of aged parents might reasonably regard the loss of her present job as a very grave loss. If these or comparably severe circumstances are implied in the above case, the nurse may render the demanded assistance.

Secondly, let us assume that the nurse involved in the above case is a student nurse. Let us presume that her refusal would involve dismissal from the Nursing School and also make it impossible for her to gain entrance to another school. In such an instance, refusal would really deprive the girl of her life's profession. This might constitute a very grave loss. One is reluctant, however, to acknowledge that refusal to assist at an immoral operation would make it impossible to gain entrance to more ethically-minded institutions.

Thirdly, if we are to assume that the loss of her present position would be only a serious or grave matter, she may not render the aid demanded of her. This is the more likely possibility in the usual cases of this type.

The nurse is reminded that when the evil resulting from an immoral operation is the destruction of an innocent life, as in criminal or therapeutic abortion, a much graver cause is needed to justify the rendering of assistance than when the immoral operation produces some lesser evil, such as the destruction of healthy vital organs in eugenic sterilization.

(3) A nurse enters upon an operation posted as an appendectomy. She is giving close proximate assistance to the surgeon. After the removal of the appendix, the surgeon goes on to an immoral operative procedure. Must the nurse leave the operation or may she continue to assist at it?

It must be said that the nurse is morally justified in continuing to assist at the operation. To leave the operation might well risk the life of the patient. Hence there is present *a very grave cause* which justifies the aid which she gives. If she believes that it would prevent either scandal or a recurrence of the problem, she should tell the surgeon and supervisor that she would not have entered on the operation had she previously known its character.

(4) A nurse is told to act as an anesthetist at an immoral operation. Refusal will bring dismissal from the hospital. She knows that economic conditions are such that it will be very hard to obtain another position. May she give the anesthetic at the operation?

The first point which must be decided is the nature of the assistance demanded of the nurse. Is the giving of an anesthetic during an immoral operation immediate or proximate assistance? Obviously, it is closer to the immoral act than the sterilizing and setting out of the instruments. It does appear to be somewhat comparable to the rôle of the nurse who hands the surgeon the instruments and materials in the course of the operation.

The present writer has questioned many nurses of all types on their opinion on this matter. In practically all instances, the personal conscience of the nurse tells her that the giving of an anesthetic is close proximate material assistance.

In his *Moral and Pastoral Theology*, Father Davis holds the opinion that the rôle of the anesthetist is not one of immediate coöperation. He regards her position as on a par with the nurse who sets out the instruments for the operation. This reasonable opinion would classify her rôle as *close proximate* material assistance. In the light of this view, the threatened loss of a position, when another would be very hard to obtain, would justify the nurse in giving the anesthetic in the above case.

(5) A nurse is assigned to a patient and told to prepare her for an operation. The nurse knows that the operation is immoral in character. It is to be her duty to give the patient medicines which will prepare her for the operation. May she render such assistance?

The giving of these drugs for the above purpose is *remote* material assistance in the forthcoming immoral operation. The nurse may not give such aid if refusal would bring simply displeasure or a reprimand from her superior. If, however, refusal would result in a normally serious loss, the nurse would be morally justified in giving the medicine.

Before going on the next phase of our topic, a few unrelated thoughts should be mentioned:

First, both doctors and nurses who work in an institution wherein they are periodically asked to assist at immoral operations should look for another position. They may continue temporarily to hold their present position and even assist proximately and remotely at immoral operations provided they have a proportionately grave cause each time to justify the type of assistance requested of them. But they should remain constantly on the lookout for a position in a more respectable institution.

Second, doctors or nurses may find themselves holding superior positions in nonsectarian institutions with the burden of selecting personnel for operations falling on their shoulders. They may know only too well that some of these operations are immoral. It would appear that, by virtue of their office, they are giving *mediate* material coöperation in these operations. It is true, of course, that the assigned personnel need not be guilty of formal coöperation and are not often asked to render immediate material coöperation. Their rôles usually involve proximate and remote types of assistance, and in many cases they will have reasons which will justify them in giving such aid. It would appear to be a sound moral principle that one may legitimately designate persons to do that which it is morally permissible for them to do. Since their office demands it, the doctor or nurse holding such a position could assign medical personnel to these operations. They should endeavor, however, to assign only those who, to the best of their knowledge, have sufficient reasons to justify the type of assistance which they render. If, through continuance in their office, they can achieve some worthwhile good for religion and morality, *without any danger of scandal being given,* they should retain their post. If this is not the case, they should remain constantly on the lookout for a comparable position in a more respectable institution.

Third, if a doctor or nurse is in doubt about the morality of an operation, he or she may render any form of material assistance. But they should have the matter cleared up as soon as possible for their future guidance.

Occasionally, one hears the remark that nurses are incapable of deciding on the moral character of an operation. Such a decision frequently depends upon medical judgment which is beyond the capacity of a nurse. For instance, the excision of diseased vital organs is morally justifiable, while the excision of healthy vital organs is almost always immoral. But, we are told, only a skilled surgeon is capable of deciding whether or not an organ is diseased.

As frequently happens, there is just sufficient truth in the above argument to make it quite attractive. The fact of the matter is that many operations, such as therapeutic abortions, are known by nurses to be immoral. As a matter of fact, surgeons frequently state that they are doing a purely therapeutic abortion or eugenic sterilization.

In the comparatively few cases wherein a surgeon professes that he is removing an organ because it is diseased and the nurse doubts the sincerity of his statement, she may render whatever assistance is requested of her. In these few cases, she is truly incapable of knowing that the operation is immoral. She may then give the surgeon the benefit of the doubt.

The present chapter has probably made it very clear that conscientious doctors and nurses should seek employment in a hospital which respects the moral precepts of the Natural Law. *The best solution in these difficult moral problems is to avoid working in an environment which creates them.*

When a doctor or nurse, who is employed in a secular institution, is told to assist at an immoral operation they should act in a prudent manner. There is no need to insult the surgeon or hospital authorities. They should state respectfully that assistance at this type of operation is contrary to their moral ideals and that they would appreciate being excused. When approached tactfully, most hospital authorities will be found sufficiently considerate.

If, in exceptional cases, someone in authority insists on participation in an immoral operation, there is no alternative left but to apply the moral principles explained in the present chapter. If there is a sufficiently grave reason to justify the type of assistance demanded, such aid may be given. If there is lacking a sufficiently grave cause, one must refuse to participate in the operation.

Civil Law and Illegal Operations

In concluding the chapter on *Assistance at Immoral Operations,* it is fitting to recall the attitude of civil law on these matters. In general, immoral operations are also illegal operations. This is exactly as it should be. Civil law should certainly prohibit immoral operations and severely prosecute all offenders. Unfortunately, there are a number of immoral operations which, under certain circumstances, are not banned by civil law. Therapeutic abortion and eugenic sterilization, for instance, are not always opposed to civil law.

The deficiencies of civil law in these matters are very regrettable and productive of grave evils. On one hand, civil law does not classify all immoral operations as illegal. On the other hand, civil law is frequently very lax in enforcing the laws which do exist.

It is essential, however, for both doctors and nurses to understand the attitude of civil law on those operations which it regards as illegal.

Civil law reminds the nurse that when a doctor's negligence results in the death of a patient, any nurse who assisted him is regarded as equally guilty if, in the light of her training, she could and should have foreseen that the doctor's act was going to harm the patient. This is true even though criminal intent never entered her mind. The nurse must stamp indelibly on her mind the resolution that she will never assist any doctor in any action which she feels certain will result in harm for the patient.

When civil law holds a nurse legally responsible for assistance given to a doctor in the commission of a criminal act, it is proceeding on sound moral principles. The graduate nurse has had a definite professional training which implies the acquisition of certain knowledge. Society recognizes her as one possessing that professional knowledge. Those who directly or indirectly engage her services are fully justified in expecting her to exercise the professional knowledge and skill which she claims to possess. If she assists in an act which endangers the life of her patient, there are only two possible explanations: either she does not possess the knowledge and skill which she is obliged to have, or she has deliberately failed to use this knowledge and skill in a situation which requires it. In either case, the nurse is obviously at fault. She has committed a sin and has also made herself liable to criminal prosecution.

An excellent illustration of the attitude of civil law toward a nurse who assists a doctor in an act of negligence is furnished by the well-known Somera case.

In the Somera case, a surgeon who was preparing to do a tonsillectomy on a thirteen-year-old girl gave an order to the head nurse in the operating room for ten per cent cocaine with adrenalin for injection. The surgeon apparently intended to say "novocaine," not "cocaine."

However, Miss Somera, the head nurse, without further question, gave the surgeon ten per cent cocaine with adrenalin, and watched him give two injections. After the second injection, the patient became pale and dizzy. Silently, Miss Somera watched the surgeon give a third injection. A few moments later the patient showed signs of convulsions. Two injections of adrenalin were given but the patient showed further signs of convulsions and died in a few minutes.

The surgeon asked Miss Somera if the "novocaine" was fresh. She replied that he had asked for "cocaine" and she had given it to him.

In the extended civil proceedings which followed this death, the surgeon and assistant surgeon were exonerated and Miss Somera was sentenced to one year imprisonment and forced to indemnify the family of the deceased girl.

It is evident that the courts felt that a graduate nurse should have known the effects of cocaine injections. In the eyes of the law, Miss Somera either lacked knowledge which she was morally and legally obliged to possess or she knowingly furnished the doctor with solutions which she knew would harm the patient and then silently stood by while he repeatedly endangered the life of the patient by the injections. In either case, she was guilty of grave negligence in the light of both moral and civil law.

It should be clear to the nurse that any assistance given by her to the principal perpetrator of a criminal act makes her guilty of an immoral act and subject to criminal prosecution. The nurse must remember, moreover, that civil courts have held that anyone who is present at the commission of a criminal act and aids the principal in any way is legally regarded as a principal in the second degree to the commission of the crime. Thus, a nurse who would assist a doctor in any way in a criminal abortion would be subject to prosecution by civil law.

In the performance of an immoral and illegal operation, there are usually several parties to the commission of the act. Normally, the surgeon who actually performs the operation is held by civil law as the principal agent, the others being regarded as assistants. Under certain circumstances, however, some other party may be regarded as the principal agent of the crime. Thus, when a crime is committed by a person under duress or coercion, the author of the duress is legally regarded as the real perpetrator of the crime. If a hospital authority should force a member of the staff to perform an immoral operation under threat of dismissal for refusal, the hospital official would be liable to criminal prosecution.

It is quite to the point to remark that a nurse may face criminal prosecution without even being present at the illegal operation. For instance, a nurse who would tell an expectant mother where she could procure a criminal abortion would immediately become liable to civil prosecution. Even though the nurse were not present when the offense was committed, even though the woman never had the abortion performed, the mere advice of the nurse is all that civil law requires in order to hold her as an accessory before the fact in an attempt to procure a criminal abortion.

Similarly, a nurse might be aware of the fact that a certain doctor had performed a criminal abortion which had resulted in the death of the patient. The nurse may neither have assisted the doctor in any way in this act nor advised the woman to seek this operation. Actually, she may have had nothing whatsoever to do with the matter beyond the fact that she has accidentally learned about it. Yet, if the nurse withholds her knowledge before a civil court investigating the case, she immediately becomes subject to criminal prosecution. Civil law regards her as an accessory to the crime. The courts have held that all that is necessary to render a person an accessory to the crime is the knowledge of the crime and the use (or non-use) of that knowledge in any way that obstructs justice.

The nurse should fully realize that a plea that coercion or threat forced her to assist in an illegal operation will rarely save her from criminal prosecution. Before such a defense will be accepted by a court, the nurse will have to present clear and convincing evidence that she was forced to assist in the operation. Even though such compulsion was exerted on the nurse, she will usually find it a very difficult matter to prove convincingly that she was the victim of coercion. When she does fail to prove that she was forced to assist in the illegal operation, she must expect to receive the penalities of civil law for the imprudent assistance she gave.

The present chapter should stamp one thought indelibly on the minds of both doctors and nurses. In the eyes of both moral law and civil law, each one is a person in his or her own right with very definite personal obligations. They must have the moral courage to resist any attempt by anyone to force them into participation in any immoral or illegal action.

Problems for Discussion

1. What kind of coöperation is rendered by an X-ray technician who reluctantly operates an X-ray machine, under the direction and at the command of a superior, to effect an immoral sterilization?

2. A nurse works in the office of a doctor who frequently recommends contraception to his patients. The task of measuring women patients for certain contraceptives and giving these contraceptives to them, is assigned to the nurse. Discuss the type of coöperation she is rendering. May she continue in such a position?

3. A woman has attempted abortion and has not succeeded, but her efforts have destroyed the life of the unborn fetus. She is brought to the hospital in a serious condition. Would it be permissible to accept her and to cleanse out the uterus?

4. Is it permissible to allow a Jewish rabbi to perform a circumcision in a Catholic hospital?

5. A Catholic woman is married in the Church to a Jewish man. The Catholic mother tells the Catholic hospital authorities that a Jewish rabbi is coming to perform a circumcision on her baby. She states that she is doing this simply to please her husband and that, as far as she is concerned, it is only a physical operation and not a religious rite. What do you think should be done in this case?

6. A senior nurse orders a junior to chart temperatures, pulses, and respirations of convalescent patients, although these had never been taken. The junior nurse answers that she will not record a lie. The senior nurse insists that she has the right to give orders and that she will assume full responsibility in the matter. What do you think of the situation?

7. A doctor ordered a dose of medicine for a patient. The nurse is temporarily alone on the floor. She feels certain that she has been taught in her classes that this dose would be fatal. She calls the attention of the doctor to the quantity of the dose, and he rebukes her severely. He states that she is there to carry out orders and not to question them. What do you think the nurse should do? Actually, she secretly administered a dose smaller than the one the doctor ordered. What do you think of her action?

8. Suppose you discovered that a nurse on a case with you was giving the patient drugs which were neither ordered or charted. Would it be permissible for you to take the attitude that her actions were 'none of your business'?

9. Suppose you were caring for a patient who has been the victim of an auto accident. You discover quite accidentally that he is a drug addict and that his family, wishing to keep the matter secret, gives the drugs to him without the knowledge of the doctor. They tell the nurse that she is there to care for the patient as an accident victim, that she has no responsibility with reference to the drugs, and that she must not tell the doctor. What do you think of the case?

10. A patient disobeys the doctor's orders and asks you not to report it to the doctor. Probably no harm has resulted. What would you do?

11. What would you do if you had just nursed a scarlet fever case and a doctor asked you to assist at a delivery? He states that he will assume full responsibility.

12. Is it right for a nurse to watch a doctor making a mistake which may cause the death of a patient? Would it not be better to question him, or report him, rather than be 'ethical' and remain silent?

13. Suppose you felt certain that your patient had broken bones which the doctor had not discovered. After hinting at it to no avail, would you tell the doctor and suggest an X-ray?

14. If a doctor insisted on a treatment which you believed to be harmful, would you simply omit the treatment and leave him under the impression that his orders had been carried out?

15. What would you do if a doctor asked you to assist him in the pelvic examination of a patient and refused to wait until sufficient precautions were taken to avoid infection?

16. What would you do if a doctor, whom you must assist frequently while making physical examinations of male patients, unnecessarily and habitually exposes the patients in your presence?

17. When visiting her own family and friends, a nurse is frequently asked for advice on the care of various illnesses and diseases. What do you think she should do in this situation?

18. A nurse has secured a position in a General Hospital. In order to obtain the post, it was necessary for her to sign a contract for a certain period of time. The contract does not specify that she is to work in any particular department during the contract period. Shortly after entering the hospital, she was transferred to a clinic within the hospital where abortions were habitually performed. The hospital authorities insist upon their right to assign her to this clinic. The position means a great deal to the nurse, since her younger sisters and brothers are being supported by her. Would it be possible for her to hold this position if she had the firm intention of getting a different one as soon as her present contract expired?

References for Reading

BONNAR, A.: *The Catholic Doctor,* pp. 39-40, N. Y., 1939.

BURKE, E.: *Acute Cases in Moral Medicine,* p. 60, N. Y., 1929.

CONNELL, F.: "The Sale of Contraceptive Devices in the Army," *American Ecclesiastical Review,* pp. 440-441, Dec., 1942.

CONNELL, F.: "May Circumcision by a Jewish Rabbi Be Done in a Catholic Hospital?" *American Ecclesiastical Review,* pp. 223-224, March, 1944.

————: "Attendance of Catholic Doctors at Public Meetings in Favor of Planned Parenthood," *American Ecclesiastical Review,* July, 1948, p. 63.

————————: "The Morality of a Doctor Advising a Woman Not to Have Any More Children," *American Ecclesiastical Review,* Dec., 1947, p. 468.

DONOVAN, J.: "May a Catholic Nurse Summon a Non-Catholic Minister?" *Homiletic and Pastoral Review,* pp. 942-943, June, 1941.

KELLY, G.: "The Attendance of Nursing Sisters at Obstetrical Cases," *Hospital Progress,* Feb., 1948.

O'MALLEY, J.: "The Morality of Selling Contraceptives," *Homiletic and Pastoral Review,* pp. 1247-1248, August, 1940.

————————: "Assistance of Nurses at Illicit Operations," *Homiletic and Pastoral Review,* pp. 47-52, Oct., 1942.

McCARTHY, J.: "The Obligation of a Medical Doctor to Correct the False Conscience of His Patient," *Irish Ecclesiastical Record,* Nov., 1947, pp. 1002-1004.

ROCHELLE-FINK: *Handbook of Medical Ethics,* pp. 279-284, Westminster, Md., 1943.

WOYWOD, S.: "The Sale of Contraceptives," *Homiletic and Pastoral Review,* pp. 1188-1189, August, 1935.

————————: "The Catholic Nurse Who Works for a Doctor Who Performs Operations and Gives Advice Contrary to Moral Law," *Homiletic and Pastoral Review,* pp. 1197-1199, August, 1937.

"Giving Instruction in the Use of Contraceptives," *American Ecclesiastical Review,* pp. 417-418, Oct., 1935.

"Nurses in Training Assisting in Abortion," *American Ecclesiastical Review,* pp. 639-642, Dec., 1931.

"Cooperation by a Nurse in Direct Abortion," *American Ecclesiastical Review,* pp. 58-59, Jan., 1944.

"The Sale of Contraceptives," *Homiletic and Pastoral Review,* p. 282, Dec., 1939.

American Ecclesiastical Review, pp. 275-276, Sept., 1939; p. 70, July, 1942.

"The Druggist and a Prescription for Abortion," *Homiletic and Pastoral Review,* p. 136, Nov., 1943.

CHAPTER 14

Property Rights

God, as a generous Creator, has placed a bountiful Nature at the service of the human race. Man, as the creature of God, therefore, has a strict moral obligation to use this creation to maintain his health and life and to secure for himself the necessities of his temporal existence. For the same reason, he has the right to acquire lawfully and to retain personally as much of nature's resources as is necessary for his own maintenance and that of his family. Once it is understood that man possesses a true title to private property, it logically follows that he is justified in demanding that fellowmen respect this right.

The sound basis of the right of private ownership and of the immorality of theft and unjust damage has just been briefly presented. It may be reasonably presumed that doctors and nurses have had a general religious and moral education on these matters. For this reason the current chapter will be concerned primarily with those aspects of private ownership which undoubtedly require further explanation.

Private Ownership

Private ownership may be defined as the exclusive right of a person to the full and free use and disposition of a thing. It, therefore, implies the moral power to make use of, profit by, exchange, sell, or even destroy a certain object. It implies also the moral power to exercise a permanent control over an object in one's own interest, provided such use in no way infringes upon the rights of our fellowman nor injures the general welfare of society.

Ownership, as explained above, has an important twofold aspect: first, the *right* to claim a given object as one's own; and, secondly, the *use* of that object, along with the benefits to be derived from such use. This distinction between "right" and "use" must always be kept in mind. A person may have the *right* of ownership over many things, but the *use* of these things is always subject to very definite and rigid limitations. The source of these limitations is, of course, the established rights of fellowman and society. In certain instances we shall even discover that the *right* of ownership may belong to one person while another person may be entitled to at least the temporary *use* of the property.

Private persons, as individuals, enjoy the right of ownership; but a number of individuals may enter into an agreement with each other to hold certain goods in common. In this latter manner, families, institutions, and the State, as corporate units, legitimately retain, use, and dispose of property. *The hospital is a typical corporate unit of this type.*

Theft

Theft is the most common way in which the right of private ownership is violated. It may be defined as "secretly taking something that belongs to another with the intention of keeping it, at least for a time, against the reasonable will of the owner."

Along with the taking of another person's rightful property with the intention of permanently keeping it, the following acts violate our neighbor's property rights: first, borrowing the property of another without at least the reasonably presumed consent of that person (such an act is equivalent to stealing the temporary use of that property, and "use" is frequently the most desired and beneficial aspect of ownership); second, securing a loan of property, with the consent of the owner, and then neglecting or refusing to restore it; third, deliberately contracting debts that we foresee we will not be able to repay; and lastly, spending so much money on luxuries that it becomes impossible to pay debts that have been contracted.

THE SINFULNESS OF THEFT. To determine the precise degree

of sinfulness of a particular act of theft three factors must be considered: (a) the value of the stolen property, (b) the nature of the person against whom the theft was committed, and (c) the span of time over which the theft took place.

(a) The value of the stolen property may be *absolutely grave, relatively grave,* or *slight.*

A theft is said to be *absolutely grave* when the amount is so great that it would constitute a *mortal sin regardless of the person from whom it is taken.* In order to protect the common welfare and safeguard property in general, the theft of a notable amount of property must always constitute a grave sin. In cases of this type we are not primarily interested in the precise degree of hardship to which the victim is subjected because of the theft. Rather the chief concern here is the fact that stealing an absolutely grave amount from anyone constitutes a serious violation of public order. If the sinfulness of such thefts were measured solely in terms of the inconvenience which they inflict upon the victim, and were therefore classified as only venially sinful, intolerable consequences would follow: peace and order in society would be impossible; disregard for all property rights would prevail; and most people would lack any incentive to accumulate needed property by honest means.

It is extremely difficult to specify the amount that must be considered an absolutely grave sum. Obviously, the amount will vary with the ever-changing value of money. In general, capable moralists regard as absolutely grave an amount which is equivalent to the average weekly wage of the *average* (middle class) worker. On this basis, the sum of fifty dollars is suggested as a fairly accurate estimate under present day (1953) conditions.

A theft is said to be *relatively grave* when the amount is so great that its theft would constitute a serious loss to the person from whom it is taken. In cases of this type, the precise degree of sinfulness of the theft is measured in terms of the inconvenience or hardship which it inflicts upon the victim. Whenever the theft involves a serious loss for the rightful owner of the property a mortal sin has been committed. Obviously the theft of amounts which are *below the absolute standard will frequently inflict a notable loss* on a particular victim and, therefore, be a mortal sin. By way of offering some guide on this matter, moralists frequently state that the loss of an amount equivalent to the victim's average daily wage, or the amount needed by the victim to support himself and his family for a day, would be a mortal sin of theft.

A theft is said to be *slight* when the amount taken is so small that it would violate neither the absolute nor the relative standard, that is, it would not constitute a serious threat to social order nor would it inflict a notable loss upon the person from whom it was stolen.

(b) The second factor which must be considered in evaluating the sinfulness of a theft is the nature of the person whose property has been stolen. The victim may be *a wealthy person, a corporation,* or *a person of average means* (the middle and poorer classes in society). Obviously, thefts against very wealthy persons or corporations must be evaluated in terms of the absolute standard; whereas, thefts against persons of ordinary means are to be measured by an application of the relative standard.

(c) The third factor which must be considered in judging the sinfulness of a theft is the span of time during which the property has been stolen. This matter merits attention because not all thefts involve the taking of a lump sum in excess of the absolute or relative standard *in one single act.* In addition to the cases in which a grave amount is stolen in a single act the following types of theft occur: (1) thefts of small sums taken at short intervals and finally totaling a grave amount; (2) thefts of small sums *begun* with the intention of ultimately reaching a considerable amount, and (3) thefts of small sums that never reach a notable amount.

When small sums are stolen at intervals, the victim does not usually suffer as severe a loss as if the total amount were taken at one time. For this reason, it is said that the amount required to constitute sufficient matter for grave sin is appreciably higher when the amount has been taken, not in a single act of theft, but in small amounts spread over a period of time.

In some instances, a person might form the intention at the outset of stealing a large amount by taking it in small sums at intervals from a particular victim. The reason for spreading the theft over a period of time might be merely a matter of expediency: if a considerable sum were taken at one time, the theft might easily be detected; whereas, it could be extremely difficult for the victim to discover the repeated small thefts. In cases of this type, *all of the small thefts are united by virtue of the original intention to steal a large amount and thus constitute one grave sin of theft.* This principle would apply even though long intervals intervened between the small thefts. Furthermore, no greater amount would be required to constitute sufficient matter for grave sin than if the total sum were taken in a single act of theft.

Finally, small thefts that are repeated at long intervals, and which are not the product of an original intention, as explained immediately above, do *not* unite to constitute a grave sin of theft. These acts remain individual venial sins of theft.

Fortunately, thefts of a serious nature are rarely encountered among doctors or nurses. This is as it should be. It would certainly be a sad commentary on the character of any member of this noble profession who would descend to the level of a common thief.

It is, however, frequently most difficult to make medical personnel understand that they are actually stealing when they help themselves to various small articles around the hospital, such as adhesive tape, bandages, and medicines. When taken to task on this score, they will usually answer that they do not feel that they are stealing when they take such things. The hospital, they say, is like their home and they feel free to make personal use of these articles which are here available in such abundance.

In answer to such an attitude, it must be said that the above articles, as well as others too numerous to mention, belong exclusively to the hospital. In no conceivable sense do they belong to the doctors or nurses. The stamps and stationery in an office belong to the Company, and it is theft when stenographers take them for their own personal use. The equipment in a factory belongs to the industrial firm, and it is theft when the employees take home tools or other materials for their own

personal use. Similarly, upon acceptance of their positions in
a hospital, doctors and nurses become employees of the hospital
and enter into a very definite contract with the hospital: in
return for a certain amount of medical or nursing duty, the
hospital guaranteed them certain benefits, such as board, salary,
training, text books, room, laundry and medical care. When
doctors and nurses have fulfilled their part of the contract by
rendering the specified medical or nursing care they have a
strict right to whatever monetary recompense, if any, the hospital may have agreed to give. During the course of their duty
they have a strict right to those other benefits which the hospital has agreed to give them, such as board, room, and medical
care. *But they do not have the shadow of a right to one thing
more.* The hospital did not agree to allow them to take from
its stock such articles as they desire for their personal use or
for the use of their family and friends. When they help themselves to these articles they are, therefore, taking something
that belongs to the hospital, with the intention of keeping or
consuming it, against the reasonable will of the hospital. *This
is the very essence of theft.*

The hospital, it is true, usually agrees to give needed medical
care to its personnel. But when it makes this agreement it lays
down the very clear stipulation that they are to present themselves for examination and treatment to one or more specified
members of the staff. The drugs or other medical needs of the
sick person are then to be procured through the observance of
an established order. When hospital personnel ignore these
regulations, and help themselves freely to drugs, they are taking something to which their contract with the hospital gives
them absolutely no title.

Since the hospital lays down *as compulsory* the above procedure for procuring medical assistance, it cannot be contended
that a lack of constant complaint on the part of the hospital
amounts to a "silent consent" to such actions on the part of
its personnel.

Unjust Damage

The previous section was concerned with the violation of
property rights through acts of *theft.* This section treats of a

second type of action which also violates the property rights of others. We refer to acts of *unjust damage.*

A person is said to have inflicted *unjust damage* when he has caused harm to the property of another, regardless of whether or not the offender has materially benefited by his act. Thus, a nurse who is simply too lazy to procure proper materials to wipe up spilled drugs and who proceeds to use a good pillow case or tear up a fine linen sheet for the purpose is guilty of *unjust damage.*

A mere listing of *some* of the acts of breakage and waste commonly found in hospitals should provide matter for reflection for all who work in a hospital: glass containers are broken when excessively hot liquids are poured into them; the points of scissors are broken when used to remove corks from bottles; thermometers are broken when placed in the mouths of delirious patients or left with children; hypodermic needles are left without wires and quickly rendered useless; utensil sterilizers are allowed to boil dry; glass barrel syringes are left on window sills or tables, from which they roll off and break; celluloid combs are ruined by steam sterilization; rubber caps are destroyed by ether; clothing and various other cloth materials are injured by olive oil stains; polished woodwork is ruined by hot water, soap, and alcohol; linens are destroyed when used to wipe up tincture of iodine; hot lamps are allowed to remain in contact with, and thereby to burn, bedding, blankets, spreads, sheets, or mattresses; gowns are splashed with harmful solutions; rubber goods are needlessly torn; water faucets are left running; lights are left burning; and clean bed linen is destroyed when it is used in treatments involving extensive wet dressings, as in cases of burns or certain forms of skin disease where remedies of an oily nature are used.

The moral obligation to make restitution for unjust damage is present only if three conditions are verified in the case:

First, *the damage must have actually taken place.* The intention to inflict unjust damage is sinful, but the obligation to make restitution only exists when the intention has been carried out. When the property rights of the other person have not been infringed upon in the concrete order, no restitution is owed. Thus, a nurse might desire and intend to use a good pillow case to wipe up some spilled iodine but be prevented from so doing by the sudden appearance of a hospital authority. This nurse would have committed an internal sin, but she would not be obliged to restitution.

Second, *the offender's act must have been the real efficient cause of the damage.* Thus, a nurse in charge of a specific patient might arrange with another ordinarily reliable nurse to take her place on a certain night. The latter nurse accepts the assignment and proceeds to act in a negligent manner which involves harm to the patient or damage to his property. The regular nurses realizes that this harm would never have occurred if she had remained on duty. The fact remains, however, that *she has not been the cause of the damage and is not morally bound to restitution.* We assume, of course, that there was every reason for her to believe that the substitute nurse was capable and reliable and that no agreement with the patient or hospital prohibited her from making such a substitution. These same reflections would apply to a doctor who would select another doctor to take his calls on a certain evening or during his vacation period.

Third, *the act of damage must have been done sinfully,* that is, it must have been knowingly and willingly committed. This point should not be misunderstood. As explained in the second chapter, there are many ways in which knowledge and freedom can be present in an act. Hence, along with deliberately malicious acts, harmful effects that are the products of habits of laziness and carelessness are unquestionably sinful. In contrast, damage that results from a true and unforeseeable accident does not bind a person to restitution. Thus, a doctor or nurse carrying some medication or expensive instrument might have no way of knowing that some greasy substance had been spilled on a certain spot on the hospital corridor. A serious fall with appreciable damage to property might very well result. The doctor or nurse has no moral obligation to make restitution in this case, unless they have made an agreement with the hospital that they will pay for *all* breakage whether resulting from malice, negligence, or pure accident.

With respect to damage inflicted upon a patient or his property, the principles explained above will determine whether or not there is an obligation to make restitution. It is suggested, however, that it would sometimes seem best for the doctor, nurse (or hospital) to offer to pay for damage to a patient's property when there is no real moral obligation to do so. If this gesture would entail unreasonable sacrifice or impose undue hardship, no one would urge it. But if the damage can be conveniently repaired, it would often seem laudable to do so. Usually the patient, knowing that there was no negligence involved, will refuse the kind offer. In all instances, the goodwill of the patient will be retained and his respect for the nursing and medical profession increased. It is little consolation to know that we are right and the other person wrong if insistence on our right results in the loss of the friendship and good-will of the other person.

The attitude which a hospital should take towards damage done by its employees is always a perplexing problem. Some hospitals make little mention of the matter and do not insist that its personnel pay for breakage and waste. Other hospitals have rigid regulations requiring them to make good, sometimes even for purely accidental breakage.

The former hospitals feel that regulations demanding payment for breakage do more harm than good. They feel that the inevitable queries and investigations about breakage breed ill feeling between the medical personnel and the institution. Such pressing questions also tend to create traits of dishonesty in the character of those who are reluctant to pay for breakage.

Hospitals favoring the second attitude feel that medical personnel, like everyone else, should make restitution when they injure or destroy the property of others. These institutions realize, moreover, that habits of carefulness and economy are necessary qualities in the character of hospital personnel. They know also that few methods are better suited for developing these traits than the realization that they will have to pay for all breakage. When there is no obligation to make restitution for breakage a powerful incentive for carefulness and economy is taken away and persons quickly develop habits of carelessness and wastefulness. The resulting increase in breakage and waste will usually prove a serious financial burden for many institutions.

Our present concern is not to present a comparative evaluation of these two attitudes towards damage. Our purpose is merely to emphasize that in either case the property involved belongs to the hospital. If a hospital wishes to free its personnel from the obligation of making restitution for breakage and waste, it is certainly justified in granting this concession. Hospital personnel in these institutions, however, should always keep in mind the fact that they are being freed from a true obligation. The best evidence of their appreciation would obviously be a sincere effort on their part to exercise a diligent care of all hospital property. Too often, the failure of hospitals to explain these facts results in a complete loss among its employees of a sense of responsibility for hospital property.

When a hospital deems it best to compel payment for breakage resulting from negligence, it is certainly within its rights in pursuing this course of action.

Agreement to pay for *all* breakage, *whether resulting from accident or negligence,* is sometimes demanded as a condition for acceptance or employment in medical or nursing schools. Hospitals are wholly within their rights in making this stipulation and, when students enter a school with this understanding, they are morally obliged to live up to the contract which has been made.

Regardless of the regulations governing breakage in the hospital, those who are sincerely interested in moulding their character on ethical ideals must learn to respect rigidly the property rights of others. There are few who would wilfully waste and break hospital property. But habits of thoughtlessness are easily developed, principally because materials are necessarily available in great abundance in a hospital.

Good judgment is an absolute prerequisite of the economical doctor and nurse. Hospitals want their personnel to give a patient everything needed for his proper care but they do not wish to face the unreasonable expenses brought about by careless breakage and wanton wastefulness. Neither exaggerated economy or undue waste is desirable; the former cripples the efficiency of the hospital by depriving its patients of materials necessary for their welfare; the latter curtails the efficiency of the institution by subjecting it to unnecessary expenses which place a serious drain on its resources and thus prevents it from extending its services, acquiring new equipment, and adding to its personnel. The financial loss to the hospital resulting from needless damage and waste, and the free hospital care which could be rendered to the community for this amount should be a sobering thought for anyone.

It is also well for the doctor and nurse to remember the duty of economy as it pertains to the patient. In the final analysis, it is the patient, or his family, who is paying the bills. Sickness is a serious strain on the financial resources of a family. It is willing to endure any expense, if the expenditure is necessary or helpful; but expense resulting from waste is a trying experience for any family and one they will not be likely to forget. For these reasons, we should be most careful in the use of materials and drugs, always endeavoring to give the patient whatever he needs but always trying to keep the patient's medical expenses as low as proper care will permit.

The Obligation to Make Restitution

The act by virtue of which a person repairs the harm or loss which he has inflicted upon another is known as "making restitution." This obligation arises whenever commutative justice has been violated. Hence acts of theft or unjust damage to the property of another give rise to the duty of making restitution to the victim. In general, we might state that whenever a mortal sin of theft or unjust damage has been committed, the obligation to make restitution binds under pain of grave sin; and whenever a venial sin of theft or unjust damage has been committed, the obligation to make restitution binds under pain of slight sin. A detailed presentation of the complex moral principles governing the making of restitution need not be offered here. The precise amount that must be restored to the victim, the course of action to be followed in making restoration in the particular case, and the permissibility of delaying the fulfillment of the obligation are matters that exceed the moral training of a doctor or nurse. Moral problems of this type should be submitted to the sound judgment of an experienced confessor.

Civil Law and Property Rights

In the preceding treatment on the moral aspects of ownership, a clear-cut distinction was made between the *right* and the *use* of private property. The *right* of private ownership is *personal*, while the *use* of the property is a *social activity* and thus subject to limitations imposed by outside factors. Secondly, the *right* of private ownership may belong to one person, while the *use* of the property may be shared with another person or even belong exclusively for the time being to another person. Thus, when an owner leases a house to a second person, the former retains the *right* of ownership over the property but the *use* of the house belongs temporarily to the second person. This moral distinction between the *right* and the *use* of property is accepted by civil law and becomes of paramount importance in many matters which directly concern the nurse.

OWNERSHIP OF X-RAY FILMS. Civil law expressly states that the *right* of ownership of x-ray films belongs exclusively to the physician or the hospital that has made them. These films do not belong to the patient, even though they may have been made at his expense.

By the "maker" of the x-ray film we do *not* mean the firm that has produced the mere photographic material (such as the Eastman Kodak Company). By the "maker" of the x-ray film we mean the doctor, hospital, or laboratory that has taken the x-ray picture for the patient.

Besides the right of ownership, there are, however, numerous other important aspects to the property interests vested in x-ray films. In endeavoring to understand these complex property interests, it is helpful to regard the maker of the x-ray film as the *trustee* of the films. (A trustee usually retains property which he is obliged to use primarily for the benefit of another person who is known as the *beneficiary* of the trust.) The ownership and possession of x-ray films does belong exclusively to the doctor or hospital that has made them; but the *use* of these films must be directed primarily to the benefit of the patient for whom they were made. For this reason, we might say that the physician or hospital making the x-ray films has a relative, not an absolute, right of ownership. This is true for the simple reason that the x-ray films were made primarily as an aid to diagnosis, prognosis, and treatment of the patient. Hence, the films may never be used by the owning physician or hospital in any manner that would be harmful to the patient. For this reason, the doctor or hospital may be regarded as a trustee who both owns and retains the x-ray films but who has a strict obligation to use them primarily for the benefit of the patient.

An exception to the general rule would appear to be present in any case in which the x-ray films are produced by one of the so-called x-ray laboratories. These laboratories do not interpret the x-ray plates, diagnose the patient's condition, nor suggest a treatment. Laboratories of this type are more correctly regarded as commercial organizations than as medical institutions. They agree to make the x-ray plates for a specified amount of money and, when they have done their work and received their compensation, the contract is completed and the laboratory has no further interest in the matter. In these cases, the x-ray plates are apparently purchased by the patient and become his lawful possession.

There is one other exception to the general ownership of x-ray films. If a patient were to make a special contract with the doctor or hospital to the effect that the completed film would become his property, the finished x-ray film would then lawfully belong to him.

The fact that the owning physician or hospital retains the x-ray films primarily for the patient's benefit results in a strict obligation to safeguard such films. All reasonable efforts must be made to preserve the films. Extreme care must be exercised so that no one shall be allowed to consult them who would use the acquired knowledge to the detriment of the patient. The owning doctor or hospital must grant a courteous coöperation to the patient or his legal respresentatives whenever they wish to consult the films. The doctor or hospital, however, may lawfully demand that this consultation take place while it retains possession of the films and witnesses the examination of them.

OWNERSHIP OF CHARTS AND CASE HISTORIES. The principles governing the ownership of x-ray films are practically identical with those which refer to the ownership of clinical charts, case histories, and pathological specimens. One important distinction, however, must be kept in mind: *the above principles apply only to those charts and records which were made primarily for the patient's benefit.* Such charts and records are those which were made and retained as an aid to diagnosis, prognosis, and treatment of disease or injury. It must be kept in mind that certain institutional records are made *primarily* for the purpose of aiding science, promoting public health, securing needed vital statistics, and maintaining accurate data on matters demanded by local, state, and federal legislation (for instance, complete records on narcotics that have been dispensed to patients).

The ownership of all clinical charts, case histories, and pathological specimens obtained primarily as an aid to diagnosis, prognosis, and treatment of the patient belongs, as a general rule, to the doctor, nurse, or hospital that has made them. The *use* of these charts, case histories, and pathological specimens, however, must be directed *primarily* to the benefit of the patient.

When any employee of a hospital (nurse, doctor, or laboratory technician) makes a clinical chart or case history, such a person acts merely as an agent of the hospital. The ownership of these charts and records belongs therefore to the institution itself. The patient or his legal representative, of course, has the undisputed right to inspect, copy, or photograph these charts or records while they remain in the possession and presence of their legal owner. *This statement is true even when it is evident that such inspection will incriminate the hospital in some way or other* (for example, in a malpractice suit).

A private duty nurse who takes care of a patient in a hospital is legally regarded as an agent of the hospital when she makes charts and case histories of the patient. The hospital is therefore regarded as the legal owner of this property. The private duty nurse must respect these charts and records as belonging to the hospital and must not allow anyone to consult them who is not a legal representative of the patient.

Despite the undisputed right of the patient and his legal representative to inspect, copy, or photograph clinical charts and records, many hospitals permit such inspection only under court order and give their employees definite orders to observe this regulation. This procedure would at first appear to work a hardship on the patient and constitute an infringement on his rights. Further consideration, however, should make it clear that this is a wise precaution. Among other benefits, it serves to establish beyond question the fact that those who desire to consult the records are truly legal representatives of the patient and that they desire to use them for the benefit of the patient.

The wise nurse should learn a valuable lesson from the procedure outlined in the above paragraph. She will always be on her guard and never hand over charts or records on her own authority, even to those who appear to be legal representatives of the patient. Whenever approached on these matters, the prudent nurse will refer the investigator to the superintendent of the hospital and thus free herself from a source of possible difficulty.

A nurse who is on private duty work *outside an institution* must exercise even greater caution in handling charts and records. She is not in a position to place the responsibility on the shoulders of a Superintendent, as a wise institutional nurse will do. She becomes the legal owner of whatever charts she may make and becomes, as it were, the trustee of these records, with the obligation to use them primarily for the benefit of her patient. She has absolutely no right to give, lend, or show these records to anyone who is not a legal representative of her patient. In short, these charts and records must be made available only to the attending doctor, to other nurses on the case, and to authorized agents of her patient. The nurse must never forget that any negligence in handling these records may create serious legal difficulties for her. She should, therefore, make certain that the object of any inspection of these records is in the best interests of the patient and not to his detriment.

Whenever a patient changes his doctor or nurse, the new doctor or nurse has the right to inspect and copy the charts made by those who formerly attended the patient. The records, of course, belong to those who made them, and they are fully justified in retaining possession of them. The patient is, of course, entitled to have his new doctor or nurse, or his legal representative, consult, copy, or photograph the records. The legal owner of the charts is justified in insisting that the inspection be made under his supervision and while he retains actual possession of them. If the case records are of no particular value to the doctor or nurse who made them, courtesy would dictate that they be given over to those who are presently caring for the patient.

Throughout the present chapter there has been a constant emphasis on the point that the maker of x-rays and records is their legal owner but that their use is to be directed primarily to the benefit of the patient. At this point it is well to recognize that, just as the *maker's right of ownership* is not absolute but relative, the *patient's right of use* is also not absolute but relative. In other words, in addition to the benefit which the patient may derive from the charts, there may be important goods which others can also obtain from them. These benefits must, of course, be realized without infringing on the patient's right of professional secrecy, without violating the patient's primary beneficial interest in the records, and without injuring the patient in any other way. Thus, the publishing of a clinical chart or case history in a scientific journal may foster the progress of medical science and benefit mankind. The name of the patient should, of course, be omitted from all such published case histories. The publication of charts and records in this manner brings great good to medical science and to mankind, while the patient is in no way injured by the procedure. Both moral law and civil law uphold the right of the doctor to publish case histories in the above manner, and the patient who would object to this action would be "unreasonably unwilling."

In order to clear up any misunderstanding on the matter, doctors and nurses should remember that when they fill out blank forms supplied by insurance companies, governmental departments, or similar agencies, neither they nor the patient acquires any rights whatsoever to the ownership of such forms. The primary purpose of these forms is to confer a benefit on the agency which submits them. When the doctor or nurse fills in these forms, they momentarily become, in the eyes of civil law, an agent or employee of the agency submitting the blank. They are, therefore, obliged, as faithful employees, to fill in the forms in an accurate and truthful manner.

Both doctors and nurses should realize that they may get themselves into very serious difficulties through an unsanctioned filling-in of the above forms for outside organizations. There is the constant danger of violating professional secrecy, as well as the possibility of giving out information which may be used to the detriment of the patient. The hospital nurse should ordinarily refuse to take it upon herself to fill in these forms for outside organizations. The easiest and safest procedure is for the nurse to refer the request to the superintendent of the hospital. If proper hospital authorities then sanction the filling-in of the blanks, the responsibility has been lifted from the shoulders of the nurse.

The nurse on private duty outside the hospital must, as mentioned previously, exercise even greater caution. She must remember that her knowledge of the patient has been derived from professional contact and falls under the obligations of professional secrecy. In States wherein professional secrecy is regarded as binding the nurse, her actions might readily be regarded as illegal. Regardless of the State law on professional secrecy, the nurse may easily violate moral law and also become immeshed in a civil court case if the data she places on the blank are later used to the detriment of her patient. The safest course for the private duty nurse would be to secure the written permission of her patient to give out the information requested in the blank forms. (Whenever the requested information could possibly be used to the detriment of the patient, and the latter lacks the education or present capacity to realize this fact, the nurse should protect her patient by informing him of the possible implications of the knowledge being sought from him.) The only instance in which doctors or nurses may feel *legally* free to fill out the forms in question is when they are required to do so by local, State, or Federal law. (Whether or not they are *morally* free in *all* of these cases would have to be evaluated in the light of the principles treated in the chapter on *Truthfulness and Professional Secrecy*.) In all other cases they will do well to remember that a moment of caution in these matters may prevent years of regret.

Problems for Discussion

1. Nurses readily develop the habit of "borrowing." Small amounts of money, wearing apparel, and countless other items are constantly "borrowed" by nurses from each other. What do you think of this widespread practice?

2. A nurse is on private duty with a patient. The latter has received many gifts of candy and fruit from friends. Without the knowledge of the patient, the nurse takes a box of candy and gives it to a friend. Her attitude is that the patient has received so much candy that he will never miss this box and, furthermore, that he is not well enough to eat it. What do you think of her act?

3. A graduate nurse is engaged to be married within a year or so to a young man who is now an intern in the hospital in which she works. She realizes that it will take a lot of money for her future husband to outfit his office when he enters private practice. She resolves to help him by taking small items during the coming months and storing them up until the young doctor opens his office. Some of the items she takes are: drugs, bandages, adhesive tape, thermometers, scissors, hypodermic needles, syringes, small instruments, and countless other articles which will be of value. Evaluate the morality of her act.

4. A nurse who is on private duty in a patient's home charts certain items of importance at the request of the doctor. The latter desires this information for his own further study and for adding to other records concerning the patient in his office files. Who is the legal owner of this chart?

5. Over and above the use of charts and records for the diagnosis and treatment of a patient while in the hospital, to what other use can they be put?

6. A nurse places her tray containing a thermometer and some
   costly drugs on a table in the hospital corridor while she
   attends to a patient in one of the rooms. She returns to find
   that the tray has been accidentally knocked to the floor by
   someone who has left the scene of the accident. Is the nurse
   obliged to make restitution in this case?

References for Reading

AIKENS, C. A.: *Studies in Ethics for Nurses,* pp. 178-188, Phila., 1938.

GARESCHE, E. F.: *Ethics and the Art of Conduct for Nurses,* pp. 134-
139, Phila., 1929.

HARRISON, G.: *The Nurse and the Law,* pp. 120-131, Phila., 1945.

HEALY, E. F.: *Moral Guidance,* pp. 214-240, Chicago, 1943.

KENNY, J. P.: *Principles of Medical Ethics,* Westminster, 1952, pp.
29-32.

MCALLISTER, J. B.: *Ethics,* pp. 301-307, Phila., 1947.

MOORE, T. V.: *Principles of Ethics,* pp. 112-152, Phila., 1937.

SCHEFFEL, C.: *Jurisprudence for Nurses,* pp. 153-160, N. Y., 1938.

CHAPTER 15

Truthfulness and Professional Secrecy

The virtue of truthfulness is possessed by any really worth-while person. For members of the medical profession, however, it is not merely a quality which should adorn their character. It is a quality which they *must* possess if they are to do effective work in their profession.

Moderation is a characteristic of most virtues. For this reason it is said that one may offend against virtues *by excess,* that is, by going beyond the standard of moderation; or *by defect,* that is, by not coming up to the required standard of moderation.

Truthfulness demands moderation in the use of the great gift of speech. This virtue is possessed only by one who habitually speaks the whole truth when truth should be spoken; who does not offend *by excess* through the telling of truth when it should not be told (as in a violation of professional secrecy); who does not offend *by defect* through the telling of partial truths (as in the writing up of incomplete and, therefore, inaccurate charts).

The virtue of truthfulness is, of course, completely shattered by the telling of an outright lie. Lying is so universally regarded as a degrading and detestable habit that there should be no need to remind doctors and nurses that it should have no part in their lives.

A lie is the deliberate use of an external expression which is contrary to one's interior conviction.

The intrinsic immorality of a lie resides in the abuse of a God-given faculty. Man was created by God with a nature that is *social,* as well as individual. By nature man was created to

369

live in society. God endowed this nature with the perfection
of speech in order that man, living in society, would possess an
apt means of communicating his thoughts to fellowman. A
lie is, therefore, a deliberate misuse of an endowment of our
nature. In a lie, instead of using speech to manifest his internal
thought, man makes speech serve the opposite purpose to that
which the Creator intended. It is a perversion of the law of
nature and an act destructive of the divinely-established purpose of speech. Such is the rational basis for the *intrinsic*
immorality of lying.

The *extrinsic* basis for the immorality of lying resides in the
fact that truthfulness is a *social* virtue, as well as an individual
one. The harmonious and effective operation of society depends
upon the ability of man to have faith and confidence in the
word of fellowman. For this reason, a lie is not only a personal
immoral act; it is a socially disruptive act.

By nature, man is a social being. No one can be a law unto
himself. An attitude toward life based on ruthless individual-
ism reduces man to the level of the beast. On that level, survival of the strong is the law of nature. *In contrast, man gives
evidence of the spiritual nature within him almost in proportion to his desire to help the weak.* A truly spiritual person
sees Christ in his fellowman. A really intelligent person never
forgets that all men are creatures of God; that all are equally
precious to the Creator; that all live in society, not by individual choice, but by Divine Plan; that all must strive together
in harmony to work out their eternal destiny. *Ruthless indi-
vidualism is as unnatural as it is immoral.*

Doctors and nurses are integral parts of a thoroughly social-
minded profession. Their walk of life is motivated in all its
acts by the desire to love and serve fellowman. For them, in
particular, any socially injurious habit, such as lying, is a glar-
ing contradiction in their life to the ideals of the profession in
which they serve.

Over and above the twofold rational basis for the immorality
of lying, they have been taught from childhood the Divine
Commandment: "Thou shalt not bear false witness."

There should certainly be no further need for comment on

the attitude which all medical personnel should have toward lying. The sincere determination should be to live up to the ideals of the virtue of truthfulness in every aspect of their medical career.

Reports to superiors and the records on charts should be a clear, concise, sufficiently detailed and accurate presentation of ascertained facts. Useful charts require critical observation, careful judgment, and much practice. Accurate charts do not contain the products of anyone's imagination or guesswork.

Mental Reservation

It should certainly be possible for the doctor and nurse to live in accordance with the ideals of the virtue of truthfulness. They will, however, frequently encounter instances wherein this will be most difficult.

Occurrences will arise in which they cannot tell the truth, because the revealing of actual facts would constitute a violation of professional secrecy.

They will never be able to solve their problem by telling a lie, because a lie is an intrinsic moral evil and can never be permitted.

Often they will find it impossible to maintain silence. In the first place, silence would frequently be taken as consent to a suggestive statement made about a patient. Secondly, many insistent questioners demand an answer and it is often difficult to handle such people without creating a disturbing scene.

Doctors and nurses are rightfully determined to be virtuous. Their position is not enviable when they can neither prudently nor tactfully remain silent, and yet are morally obliged neither to reveal the truth nor to tell a lie. *The careful use of a mental reservation will provide the solution to such difficulties.*

Mental reservation is the use of an expression which has two meanings; one meaning is the more obvious and usual interpretation of the words; the other meaning is the less obvious and less frequently used meaning of the words; the more obvious interpretation of the words is the one which the speaker believes the hearer will place upon the response; the less obvious

*interpretation of the words is the meaning which the speaker
actually intends.*

An illustration will serve to clarify this concept of mental
reservation. Let us assume that a patient is afflicted with some
physical condition which has produced a temperature of one
hundred and two degrees. The patient asks: "What is my
temperature?" The doctor and nurse feel certain that the patient will identify the expression "normal temperature" with
98.6 degrees, the temperature of an average healthy person.
They realize also that the temperature of one hundred and
two degrees is the "normal," the usual and expected temperature for the precise physical condition with which the patient
is afflicted. Since they are not permitted to tell the patient his
temperature nor to tell a lie, they answer casually, "Your temperature is normal today."

In the above illustration, the doctor or nurse has not told
a lie. A lie is an abuse of speech consisting in the deliberate
use of an expression which is contrary to one's internal thought
or conviction. In this instance, an expression has been used
which has two meanings, and the meaning which is intended
is certainly represented by the answer which has been given:
The patient's temperature is normal for his physical condition.

The criterion which one must keep in mind in the use of
mental reservation is this: *Is the expression which is being
used actually representative of the thought in the mind of the
speaker?* Could an intelligent person carefully analyzing the
expression detect the less obvious meaning of the response? If
so, the speaker certainly has not told a lie; rather, an expression
has been used which does represent the thought in the mind.

Under due conditions, it might well be that even the answer
"I do not know" could be a proper mental reservation. Intelligent people understand that professional secrecy binds doctors
and nurses. A request for confidential medical information by
one who has no right to the knowledge could be met with the
above answer. It would be a mental reservation, and not a lie,
because that expression, used under the above conditions,
could surely mean that the doctor or nurse has no knowledge
which he or she may communicate.

In the permissible mental reservation, the speaker does not deceive the questioner. Rather, the questioner places a hasty interpretation on the words he hears and thus misleads himself.

Even though a mental reservation is not a lie, one can readily perceive that it may frequently produce the same effects as a lie. For this reason, *the indiscriminate use of mental reservations is not morally permissible.*

First, *one may never use mental reservations in answering the questions of a person who has a right to the information which he seeks.* Such persons have a title to a clear and complete presentation of the knowledge which is due them. Hence, a nurse could not use a mental reservation in answering the questions of a doctor about the physical condition of his patient.

Second, *one must always have a proportionate reason for having recourse to mental reservation.* Greater good must result from the use of the mental reservation than the harm or inconvenience to which it may subject the unsuspecting questioner. (The morally justifiable use of a mental reservation actually involves a successful application of the twofold effect principle.)

The illustration given above of a mental reservation is a simple one of everyday occurrence. Both doctors and nurses, however, will often be faced with questions having a much more serious import. They should learn to profit from each of these experiences. The first time they find themselves in one of these predicaments, they may not handle the situation very tactfully or successfully. It would be helpful if they would think back each time to the answers they might have given. The next time the same type of question confronts them, they will then be prepared for it.

Finally, a mental reservation should not be regarded as a deceitful use of speech. When the proper conditions for its use are not present, it is truly immoral and not permitted. When the required conditions are present, it is a priceless asset in maintaining one's own moral standards, and it is often the best aid at hand for preserving inviolate the reputation of a patient from a prying questioner.

The Nature of a Secret

Preliminary to the study of professional secrecy, it is necessary to establish the precise nature of a "secret" and to analyze the three basic types of secrets.

> A secret is some hidden knowledge belonging to a person by strict right, which hidden knowledge another may not lawfully seek to possess contrary to the reasonable will of the owner; and which, if already possessed by another (whether in accordance with or contrary to the reasonable will of the owner), may not lawfully be used or divulged contrary to the reasonable will of the owner.

Briefly, then, a secret is some hidden knowledge, pertaining to a person by strict right, which another may not lawfully seek to possess, use, or reveal, contrary to the reasonable will of the owner.

Moralists usually distinguish three types of secrets: the *natural* secret, the *promised* secret, and the *entrusted* or *committed* secret.

The *natural* secret is so called because it imposes an obligation of secrecy based upon natural law. All men are bound in justice and charity to refrain from revealing any secret which would injure fellowman in any of his natural rights. For this reason, no contract, either expressed or implied, is required to make the natural secret a binding force. The owner of the secret need not even know that information private to himself has come into the possession of another person. All that is required is that someone come into the possession of knowledge which he realizes is not commonly known and which would injure the one to whom it refers if it were publicized.

Briefly, *the violation of the natural secret is a grave sin whenever serious harm is intended or foreseen as the result of the revelation. The violation is a slight sin whenever only slight harm is intended and actually results from the revelation.*

The *promised* secret is so called because the obligation to maintain secrecy results from a promise freely given and accepted. The distinguishing mark of the promised secret is that the promise *follows* the acquisition of the knowledge.

It happens frequently that the promised and natural secrets overlap. Thus, one might accidentally learn something about a person which would injure him if it were revealed; the person whom the secret concerned might then ask for and receive the discoverer's promise that nothing would be said about the matter. In such a case, both the natural and promised secrets are present.

The promised secret which is not also a natural secret has its binding force in fidelity to one's word. The confidential knowledge involved in this type of secret is such that its revelation could do no harm to the owner of the secret. *The violation of the pure promised secret is, therefore, a slight sin against the virtue of truthfulness.*

The *entrusted* or *committed* secret is one whose obligation arises from an agreement entered into *previous* to the disclosure of the information. This antecedent agreement is to the effect that secrecy will be maintained rigorously by the one to whom the disclosure is made. For this reason, moralists hold that the entrusted secret is based on an onerous contract or a quasi-contract.

The antecedent agreement which is an indispensable condition for the arising of an entrusted secret may be either explicit or implicit. It is *explicit* when the agreement to secrecy is formally requested and given. It is *implicit* or *tacit* when no agreement to secrecy is requested or given, but the office or function of the person to whom the secret is communicated makes it clear that the confidence will be faithfully and rigidly observed.

The violation of the ordinary entrusted secret (exclusive of the official secret) is an offense against commutative justice. *Whenever such violation is intended to inflict a serious loss on the owner of the secret, or if it is foreseen that it will do so, grave sin is committed. Otherwise, the violation of the ordinary entrusted secret is a venial sin.*

The *implicit entrusted secret* is known to moralists as the official secret because the confidence is imparted, and the obligation to maintain silence arises, precisely in view of the *office* or function which the recipient exercises. More commonly, it is known as the *professional secret*. *It is the professional secret which merits the intensive consideration of both the doctor and the nurse.*

Professional Secrecy

The first step necessary in the study of the professional secret is to arrive at a proper concept of a "profession." Admittedly, the term "profession" is today frequently used in a broad sense. In reliable dictionaries, one will find a profession defined as "an occupation that properly involves a liberal education or its equivalent, and mental rather than manual labor."

A much stricter concept of a "profession" must be used in referring to those fields of endeavor which are bound by "professional secrecy." The opening lines of the *Principles of Medical Ethics of the American Medical Association* furnish us with a satisfactory concept of "profession." It states that "a profession has for its prime object the service it can render to humanity; reward or financial gain should be a subordinate consideration."

The practice of medicine is certainly a profession. But the question immediately arises: *Just what persons may be said to be bound by the medical secret?* In earlier days, this question was readily answered. Today the matter is quite different. The medical field has expanded and become extremely specialized. A division of medical labor among many grades and types of persons is the inevitable result of this expansion and specialization. To recall only a few such persons, one might mention the family doctor, the specialist, the pharmacist, the laboratory technician, the hospital with its staff of doctors, surgeons, and nurses.

The solution to this problem apparently rests in the application of the principle that "all those who belong to the medical profession and perform one or other of the various duties which pertain to the medical profession are bound by the obligations of professional secrecy."

The answer to two questions will help determine whether or not a person belongs to the medical profession:

First, *does the person in question render a service that one would rightly call a medical service?*

Second, *does this person acquire the confidential information about the patient, not by accident, but as knowledge necessarily acquired in the exercise of a medical office?*

Whenever the answer to both of these questions is definitely in the affirmative, the obligation of *professional secrecy* may be said to exist. Quite clearly, therefore, family doctors, specialists, surgeons, nurses, pharmacists, and laboratory technicians would fall under professional secrecy. This list of persons is not meant to be exhaustive. The decision on any other class of person will depend upon the application of the above principle.

The Oath of Hippocrates

The tradition of observing secrecy has characterized the medical profession from the earliest days. This tradition finds expression in the very ancient oath of Hippocrates, a Greek physician of the period 460 to 349 b. c. The Oath is regarded, at least substantially, as the work of Hippocrates. It is known, however, that it underwent some accidental changes after the birth of Christianity. The Oath contains the following pertinent passage:

> And whatsoever I shall see or hear in the course of my profession, as well as outside my profession in my intercourse with man, if it be what should not be published abroad, I will never divulge, holding such things to be holy secrets.

American Medical Association

The tradition of observing professional secrecy which characterized the medical profession throughout the ages is emphasized in the *Principle of Ethics of the Americal Medical Association.* In this Code of Ethics, we read:

> Patience and delicacy should characterize all the acts of a physician. The confidences concerning individual or domestic life entrusted by a patient to a physician and the defects of disposition or flaws of character observed in patients during medical attendance should be held as a trust and should never be revealed except when imperatively required by the laws of the state.

Civil Law

While the obligation to maintain professional secrecy is insisted upon by moral law and universally accepted by the medical profession, Civil Law does not always make such an acknowledgment. A brief survey of existing Civil Law on this topic will clarify its attitude.

The laws of continental Europe, in general, make the violation of professional secrecy an act punishable by law. With the exception of France, these laws make due provision for the lawful revelation of secrets under certain definite conditions. Most of these countries also recognize the right of medical personnel to withhold in civil court such confidential information as is acquired through professional contact with a patient.

The Common Law of England, in contrast, does not make the violation of professional secrecy an act punishable by law. An injured party may undoubtedly seek a remedy in tort or contract or in tort arising out of contract. The medical profession would also undoubtedly rebuke with severity any of its members who might violate this sacred obligation.

The Common Law of England, moreover, does not recognize as "privileged" any knowledge that a member of the medical profession may have obtained while attending a patient. In consequence, the law does not grant medical personnel the privilege of exemption from testifying in court on confidences obtained in professional practice.

Since the Common Law of England is used as the basis of jurisprudence in the United States, the legal status of any member of the medical profession is the same in this country as in England—except in those states where the Common Law has been changed by statute.

It is not to be thought that the absence of any protective statute necessarily implies that a civil court will always demand the revelation of professional knowledge. It merely indicates that the court does not recognize any legal right on the part of the professional person to withhold such information. Absolutely speaking, the court could demand the information and could regard the professional person as obstructing justice should there be a refusal to testify. In practice, however, a fitting restraint is usually shown by civil courts whenever it is clear that its queries are touching upon professional secrecy.

In many states, however, a statute law has bestowed the privilege of exemption from testifying in court on matters falling within the scope of professional secrecy.

New York State led the way in this field by its statute law of 1828 on privileged communications. This statute served as the model for many similar enactments by other states throughout the country.

Missouri adopted the law in 1835, and it was quickly followed by Wisconsin, Michigan, Ohio, Indiana, Minnesota, and Iowa. At present, all of the states west of the Mississippi, except Texas, have enacted similar statutes. East of the Mississippi, such statute law exists only in Indiana, Kentucky, Michigan, Mississippi, North Carolina, New York, Ohio, Pennsylvania, West Virginia, and the District of Columbia. Statutes of this type have also been adopted by Alaska, Hawaii, the Philippine Islands, Puerto Rico, and the Virgin Islands.

In some instances, the above states have placed definite limitations upon the privilege. Thus, the North Carolina statute entitles the presiding judge of a superior court to compel a disclosure of professional information whenever the same is necessary for a proper administration of justice. The Pennsylvania statute limits the privilege of withholding of information in court to such knowledge as would injure the good name of the patient.

Since the statute of New York State served as the model for most of the other states, it is worthy of being quoted:

> A person duly authorized to practice physic or surgery, or a professional or registered nurse, shall not be allowed to disclose any information which he acquired in attending a patient in a professional capacity, and which was necessary to enable him to act in that capacity; unless where the patient is a child under the age of sixteen, the information so acquired indicates that the patient had been the victim or subject of a crime, in which case the physician or nurse may be required to testify fully in relation thereto upon any examination, trial, or other pro-

ceeding, in which the commission of such crimes is the
subject of inquiry.

The position of the nurse before Civil Law is somewhat
more vague than that of the doctor. The New York statute,
which has served as the model for most other states, explicity
concedes the privilege to the nurse. The statute of Arkansas
makes a similar explicit mention of the nurse.

The outstanding authority on *Evidence* is J. H. Wigmore.
His ten-volume work on *Evidence* is entitled *A Treatise on the
Anglo-American System of Eidence in Trials at Common Law.*
In this work, it appears that this authority holds that, even
though nurses are not *explicitly* mentioned in most of the
statutes, they are *implicity* included under these laws when-
ever they act as an *assistant* or *agent* of a regular practitioner.
In most cases a nurse acts as an assistant or agent of a doctor.
Hence it appears that most states implicitly extend the privilege to the nurse. In the words of Wigmore:

> The person consulted must be a *professional physician,*
> in the usual sense of the word. This does not include a
> veterinary surgeon, nor a pharmacist. It does not include
> a *nurse,* or other skilled therapeutic practitioner, except
> when acting as assistant or agent to a regular practitioner.

In many instances wherein no statute law exists, the court
will not press the nurse for information which it is clear was
obtained in her professional capacity. Should the court insist
upon such revelation, the nurse is confronted with a moral
problem which will be discussed later in this chapter.

The statutory laws which have been adopted by the various
states are sufficiently similar that their general nature can be
summarized:

(a) The privilege is granted by law to the patient for his
protection, not out of deference to the dignity of the doctor or
medical profession. Hence, the member of the medical profession is not free to reveal confidential matter about the
patient. The privilege may be waived only by the patient.
Permission to waive the right of a deceased patient will not
be granted readily by civil court. Such a waiver will usually

be granted only when the information to be revealed will in no way bring disgrace upon the name of the deceased.

(b) Like all privileges granted by law, the statute should be given a liberal interpretation, always keeping in mind, however, the purpose for which the privilege has been established.

(c) The privilege survives the patient, that is, even after the death of the patient, the medical profession must continue to observe secrecy about the deceased in any court cases that might later arise and involve the deceased patient.

(d) A definite relationship must have existed between the patient and the member of the medical profession. It is not necessary that the relationship have resulted from the patient's employing the member of the medical profession. In fact, the privilege exists even though the patient was treated without his consent, or as a charity case, or even though he was treated against his will and expressed objections.

(e) The privilege pertains only to confidential information, not to any knowledge that is public and notorious and which the member of the medical profession simply happens to learn while attending the patient.

(f) The patient is entitled to this privilege even though there has been no payment of a fee or salary to the member of the medical profession. Hence, both patients who have been accepted as charity patients and those who are remiss in fulfilling their financial obligations still enjoy this privilege.

(g) The privilege embraces all confidential information obtained through oral communication, examination, and observation, as well as from the statements of those persons who may surround the patient.

(h) Confidential communications made by a patient in furtherance of criminal objectives do not fall under this privilege.

(i) Whenever a patient brings a malpractice suit against a member of the medical profession, he is regarded as having waived his right to secrecy. The right to defend oneself entitles the member of the medical profession to speak out about the patient's case and condition under such circumstances.

(j) Only the *content* of the confidential communication is

covered by the privilege. The *fact* that such communication has been made, the *date* thereof, *the number of consultations or treatments,* and the *place* and *duration* of treatment do not fall within the privilege.

Even in those states where statute law exists, the protection given to the patient by the statute is of a negative type. The member of the medical profession will not be compelled by a civil court into revealing professional communications nor is it permissible for him to do so. *But the statute does not provide any positive protection for the patient by making the violation an act punishable by law.*

A patient who has been the victim of a violation of professional secrecy may, of course, bring suit against the offender. The action must lie either in tort or in contract, or in tort arising out of contract. In all likelihood, the patient would have to prove that personal loss has ensued before the offense would be objectionable. The mere fact the professional secrecy has been violated, without any damage resulting, would hardly constitute a hopeful court case for the patient.

A second sanction protecting the patient is the action which the medical profession itself would take against one of its members who would violate professional secrecy. Upon conviction, the Medical Association would punish the offender, even to the extent of enforcing expulsion from the profession.

The *Principles of Ethics of the American Medical Association* urges physicians to expose corrupt and dishonest practices before proper medical and legal tribunals:

> Physicians should expose without fear or favor, before the proper medical or legal tribunals, corrupt or dishonest conduct of members of the profession. All questions affecting the professional reputation or standing of a member or members of the medical profession should be considered only before medical tribunals in executive sessions or by special or duly appointed committees on ethical relations. Every physician should aid in safeguarding the profession against the admission to its ranks of those who are unfit or unqualified because deficient either in moral character or education.

The Owner of the Secret

Ordinarily, the patient is the *sole* owner of his medical secrets. The possession, use, and disposal of such secrets is a strict right of the patient. A member of the medical profession would ordinarily have no more right to publicize such confidential information than he or she would have to ruin a neighbor's reputation or steal his private property. (There are unusual cases wherein the revelation of secrets is compulsory; these cases will be discussed under the "Revelation of Secrets"; at the moment, reference is being made only to ordinary situations.)

In the case of *infants,* the parents or, in the absence of parents, lawful guardians are acknowledged as the owners of the confidential information. They are also the rightful owners of such knowledge as pertains to the insane and others who never progress beyond the mental level of an infant.

In the case of the *insane* or *low-grade mental defective,* the parents or guardians are *not* entitled to *all* secrets but only to those which they must possess in order to care adequately for the person. The insane or low-grade mental defective is reasonably presumed to be willing that they have such knowledge. The same principles would apply to *aged persons* who have become dependent upon others.

The case of *minors* who have reached the age of reason, and *majors* who are still living with their parents, present a somewhat more difficult problem.

Parents are morally obliged to supervise the mental, moral, and physical upbringing of their children. To achieve this objective it is often necessary to place the children under the care of the medical profession. Moralists hold that members of the medical profession may and must submit to parents, or guardians, a report of what is learned through the *examination* of the child. Should the minor child *volunteer personal admissions,* moralists hold that, unless there be a proportionately grave reason necessitating revelation, medical personnel should respect such confidence as secrets of trust or as natural secrets.

Parents do *not* have the same obligations of responsibility over *major* children. But they do have definite obligations toward the safety of their home. Hence, whenever parents find it necessary in the interests of the family unit to place a major child under the care of the medical profession, they have a right to request and to receive a report on the physical condition of the child.

In certain cases, a doctor who examines a patient acts in the interests of a corporation. Thus, a physical examination might be required by an Insurance Company before it would issue a policy, by a Nursing School or Religious Community before it would accept an applicant. In such cases, the applicant freely submits to the demand of the Corporation, School, or Religious Community that they have assurance of health before granting acceptance. In these instances, the doctor acts as an agent of the Corporation, School, or Religious Community, and there is either implicit understanding or explicit agreement with the applicant that the report is to be issued to the interested Corporation, School, or Religious Community.

A word of caution should be added here. If a doctor is compelled to reject an applicant, he should issue the rejection *in the most general terms possible*. Rather than issue a report which would seriously discredit a person, a doctor should urge the applicant to withdraw the request for admission.

A somewhat similar case is present in the action of the government in subjecting prospective military personnel to physical examinations. The State has the moral right to demand the military service of its citizens in time of war, and physical examinations are a necessary means to this end.

Needless to say, the State should not seek confidential information that is not required for its purpose, and it should take reasonable steps to keep secret the medical records of those it has examined.

A final word of warning should be given to both patients and members of the medical profession. Even though the patient is the owner of a secret, there are times that the revelation of a secret might injure his family, friends, or a corporation to which he belongs. Unless there be a sufficiently grave reason present, the patient has no right to reveal such secrets nor may he legitimately give a member of the medical profession permission to do so.

Subject Matter of Secrecy

It is important to explain just what matters fall under the seal of professional secrecy.

Earlier in this chapter, the *natural* secret was distinguished from the *professional* secret. Certainly the doctor and nurse learn many things about their patients that must be classified as *natural* secrets, rather than as professional secrets.

First, the doctor and nurse have received a specialized medical training and it may sometimes happen that this training will result in their perceiving certain facts, not commonly known, about persons whom they meet in the ordinary contacts of social life. When such knowledge is not possessed by the community in general and when the revelation of it could do any possible harm to the one to whom it pertains, the doctor or nurse is bound to silence by the *natural* secret.

Second, while attending a patient, a doctor or nurse will frequently come into the possession of knowledge which does not fall under the professional secret. Thus, while attending a patient, a doctor or nurse may incidentally acquire much intimate knowledge about the patient's household and its various members. These confidences, however, are obtained on the *occasion* of the exercise of the medical profession, rather than in actual exercise of the medical office itself. It might be stated, then, as a principle that any secrets which a doctor or nurse learns upon the *occasion* of the exercise of their office fall under the *natural* secret.

In order that confidential information fall under the professional secret, certain definite requirements must be fulfilled:

First, knowledge must be truly secret before it can become matter for the professional secret. If it were commonly known in the community that a person had epilepsy, pneumonia, tuberculosis, or any other disease or condition, such knowledge could not possibly fall under the professional secret.

Second, it must be valid matter for a secret. Thus, there are certain instances in which secrets *must* be revealed. These instances are discussed later in this chapter under "the Revelation of Secrets." For the moment, one example will suffice: persons who have been found by examination to have certain serious contagious diseases cannot expect such knowledge to be kept secret. The welfare of the community demands that this knowledge be revealed to public health authorities who will take adequate steps to protect innocent citizens from infection by the diseased persons.

Third, the confidential information must not only be received by a member of the medical profession *but must be given to such a person in his or her professional capacity.* It is only when a patient establishes a professional relationship with the doctor or nurse by seeking medical services which they are trained to give that there is the required basis for the professional secret.

Any confidential information given to a doctor or nurse simply as a friend, counsellor, or in any other capacity, will fall under the *natural,* the *promised,* or the ordinary *entrusted* secret. The precise nature of the confidential information and the type of agreement to secrecy would determine which of the above secrets is involved.

Finally, *all confidential information about a patient obtained by a doctor or nurse in the exercise of their medical capacity falls under the professional secret.* Not only must medical personnel keep secret confidential information which would slightly or gravely injure the patient if it were revealed *but all confidential information whatsoever must be kept secret.*

A secret is something that is private. It belongs more intimately to a person than any material article he may own. The giving of a secret to others is a right that belongs to its owner. Regardless of what the practice may be, a doctor or nurse may not indiscriminately reveal the secrets of their patients simply because such revelations will not injure the patient. For example, a respectable married woman who is under the care of a doctor and his assistant nurse in the early months of pregnancy has a strict right to have her secret respected by the medical profession, even though the revelation of her condition would do her no harm in the community.

An added fact is that the doctor or nurse does not know all of the complex sides of his patient's social life. For this reason, it would frequently happen that matters which they believed could do no harm by being revealed would actually inflict some injury upon the patient.

The patient could, of course, give the doctor or nurse explicit permission to reveal non-injurious confidential information to others. There would also be times when the doctor or nurse could act upon the "reasonably presumed consent" of the patient. Thus, one might reasonably presume that a patient would not object to a doctor or nurse revealing some non-injurious fact about his condition or progress in order to alleviate the worry of a close friend or relative. Great care, however, should be taken that no abuse is allowed to arise. Frequent and unnecessary presumptions upon the consent of the patient are violations of his right to secrecy.

Confidential information about a patient may be obtained by oral communication, writing, signs of any type, observation, or physical examination. Needless to say, the professional secret binds rigidly regardless of the manner in which it is acquired.

The Violation of Professional Secrecy

All members of the medical profession have a sacred and grave obligation to preserve inviolate the secrets of their papatients. The duty of medical secrecy is owed to the patient in commutative justice and to society in legal justice.

It is a sound moral principle that whenever one is bound to an end, he is bound to adopt all reasonable means to achieve the end. Since the professional person is obliged to rigid secrecy, all reasonable steps to fulfill this obligation must be taken. Included under this heading would be *privacy arranged for interviewing and treating patients, privacy assured for all case records, and other documents pertaining to patients,* and *assurance of trustworthiness in all assistants who necessarily share the confidential information.*

Needless to say, the professional secret is able to be violated not only by words but by a nod of the head, a smile, a shrug of the shoulders, a gesture of the hand, or by any other equally significant acts of omission or commission.

A special word of warning should be directed to the nurse, warning her never to give out confidential information about a patient to Insurance Companies, Beneficial Societies, and similar agencies. Even if the patient were to give his express consent, the nurse should refer the matter to the doctor. Usually, the patient would lack the medical and legal background to appreciate the implications of the information he was about to give to the interested group. Proper medical and legal advice should be received by the patient before any such statements are made.

Theoretically, the violation of professional secrecy is a sin, grave or slight, depending on the nature of the fact revealed and the degree of harm that follows.

Factually, the deliberate violation of professional secrecy is so apt to produce serious harm that grave sin will usually be committed. *The welfare of the patient is often at stake. The reputation of the medical profession and the confidence of society in that profession are also seriously endangered.*

Society truly needs the medical profession and it will use that profession only if it possesses a perfect confidence in its pledge of secrecy. Should the patient suffer a grave loss as the result of the violation, should the reputation of the medical profession in the community suffer serious taint, should the confidence of any members of society be so shaken that they fear to utilize the medical profession, grave sin has been committed.

Narcotherapy

In recent years the constantly increasing practice of narcotherapy has given rise to a moral problem.

Narcotherapy could be briefly described as the use of a drug, usually sodium pentothal, as a treatment for the cure of certain mental illnesses. The purpose of the drug is to enable the patient to talk freely of his troubles. Actually, the use of such a technic in handling mental cases has been attempted before in psychiatric practice. Hypnotism and, more recently, sodium amytal was used for this purpose. But it is said that sodium pentothal has definite advantages over either of the former methods: it not only aids the physician in the diagnosis of the patient's illness but also helps the patient to adjust and rehabilitate himself.

A short description of the use of sodium pentothal on a patient suffering with a neurotic condition may add some clarity to this discussion: a feeling of confidence is built up in the patient by a series of interviews with the psychiatrist. The latter endeavors to discover the repressed emotional situations which have brought on the present neurotic condition. When no further progress along these lines can be made by ordinary methods the psychiatrist may feel that further results depend upon the use of sodium pentothal. While the drug is being administered intravenously, the patient is told to begin counting backwards from one hundred. When the counting becomes confused the injection of the drug is discontinued. While under the influence of the drug, the patient usually talks freely about himself; emotional conflicts which are at the root of his present condition frequently come to light; at times the trend of the patient's thought and speech can be skillfully directed by the psychiatrist into the most helpful channels; and in some cases the patient may dramatically relive, in both word and emotion, some unfortunate experience which underlies all his mental troubles. As the effect of the drug wears off the patient returns to rational consciousness, often with a good insight into the source of his difficulties and with a readiness to take the steps most necessary for his own mental welfare.

The four conditions required for the legitimate use of narcotherapy are clearly set forth by Father Gerald Kelly, S.J., in his article on this subject (*Hospital Progress*, March, 1948):

First, if the patient has the use of reason, the treatment should not ordinarily be used without his explicit consent. If the patient lacks the use of reason, the consent of his natural guardian or guardians should be obtained. As Father Connell pointed out in the *Ecclesiastical Review* (Dec., 1945), a patient possessing the use of reason may not be forced to take this treatment against his will, while its use on a patient lacking the use of reason must be sanctioned by the person who is his natural guardian (wife, husband, father, mother, etc.). Any forced or surreptitious use of this treatment against the will of his natural guardian (if the patient is not rational) is an act of injustice, even though it is done by a public official, such as an army doctor.

In the ordinary interview with a psychiatrist, a rational

patient is in the full control of his faculties and is free to refuse
to answer any question which he may be asked. It may be perfectly true that a patient's refusal to answer such questions may
make it impossible for the doctor to help him. But it is still
the natural right of the patient to refuse to make these disclos-
ures. Under the influence of sodium pentothal, however, the
patient loses his rightful freedom. Hence, the induction of
this state without his consent is a form of violence and an
invasion of his natural rights.

Father Gerald Kelly has stressed the point that "ordinarily"
such a patient's consent must be *explicitly* obtained. He points
out that occasions will sometimes arise in which the psychiatrist
knows that the patient really wishes to do everything necessary
to get well but nevertheless shrinks from narcotherapy because
of some exaggerated and unfounded fear. He states that there
may be some cases of this type in which *the psychiatrist could
legitimately presume the patient's consent* to the treatment.
This is undoubtedly a valid principle and a valuable reflection.
But it lends itself so readily to abuse that one hastens to remark
that it should be used most sparingly. As is so often the case, a
point of this nature emphasizes man's need of scientifically
competent and morally conscientious doctors in the medical
profession.

In reference to patients who lack the use of reason, the consent of the natural guardian, which must ordinarily be
obtained, can also be dispensed with in certain cases. Thus,
Father Connell states that if it is clearly evident that the guardian in question is unreasonable in his refusal, inasmuch as it
might be morally certain that the treatment will notably help
the patient, the guardian's wishes in the matter may be ignored.

*Second, there should be no unjustifiable risk of harm to the
patient.* It does not appear that narcotherapy involves any
risk to the patient, but this principle applies to any use of
drugs or surgery, hence it should be mentioned in discussing
this subject.

*Third, the psychiatrist must take the necessary means of pro-
tecting himself, and particularly the hospital, from harmful
effects.* Narcotherapy could prove to be the source of serious

law suits and damaging gossip, particularly in cases involving *presumed* consent of a rational patient to the treatment, in instances in which the treatment is given to an irrational patient against the wishes of the natural guardian, and in countless cases involving a woman patient. No psychiatrist, acting as an agent of a hospital, would be justified in performing such acts without the knowledge and consent of the hospital authorities. After all, it would be the institution, not the agent doctor, which would be sued in civil court, and the hospital surely has the right to decide what risks it cares to take in these matters. In all cases, whether in private or hospital practice, adequate steps should be taken to prevent any unpleasant aftermath to these treatments. Written consent of the patient or guardian, confirmation by another competent psychiatrist on the probable value of the treatment for the patient, and possibly, with the patient's consent, a witness to the treatment might not be too much to suggest in some cases.

Fourth, professional secrecy must be rigidly observed concerning the information acquired in the course of the treatment.

This condition applies, of course, to all knowledge acquired by a doctor in his professional capacity. But it needs special emphasis here because of the condition of the patient. Under the influence of the drug he may often reveal matters that he would never otherwise reveal. His revelations are therefore particularly inviolable. In this reference, it must be stated that there can be no justification for giving this treatment to a patient in the presence of a group, unless the patient fully understands the effects of the treatment and consents to such a procedure. Too many cases are encountered in which unscrupulous doctors use the mentally ill and the poverty-stricken people who must frequent our clinics as demonstration material for medical classes without any fitting regard for the inviolability and dignity of the human person.

Finally, it is not morally permissible to use narcotherapy to force a confession from a person suspected of crime. First of all, it is not certain that what the man asserts under the influence of the drug is an accurate picture of his rôle in the crime (he may be portraying only an imaginary deed which he describes as his own). Secondly, even if the man's words were an accurate account of his acts, the use of the drug would still be illicit, because it is never morally permissible to use violence to secure a confession of crime.

The Revelation of Professional Secrets

Throughout the current chapter, several references have been made to the fact that there are certain instances wherein the member of the medical profession *must* reveal a secret. These cases are reducible to four basic types:

(a) Cases in which society would be gravely harmed unless the secret were revealed.

(b) Cases in which the owner of the secret would himself suffer grave harm if his secret were not revealed.

(c) Cases in which an innocent third party would be gravely harmed unless the secret were revealed.

(d) Cases in which the member of the medical profession who possesses the secret would suffer grave harm unless the patient's secret were revealed.

(a) *A professional secret must be revealed whenever its retention would result in grave harm coming to society.* Under such circumstances, the member of the medical profession has both the legal right and moral obligation to make such a revelation.

A first type of case falling under this principle would be an instance in which a patient had a disease of a highly infectious and contagious nature. The doctor has the obligation to take whatever steps may be required, such as quarantine, to protect the other members of society.

Similarly, if a dangerous criminal came to a doctor seeking treatment for gunshot wounds, the doctor would be obliged to report the man to proper civil authorities. The basis for this conclusion is not the fact that the culprit is a fugitive from justice nor that he has committed serious crimes. The real basis for our conclusion is that a dangerous criminal constitutes a serious, present and future threat to society. The welfare of society, therefore, demands the revelation of the secret of the dangerous criminal. (Theoretically, if the criminal were giving up his life of crime and the doctor could be *certain* of it, there would be no moral obligation to report the criminal. In practice, however, the doctor could rarely have any certain assurance on this matter.)

A final example of a case falling under the first principle of exemption would be that of a patient whose physical condition created a hazard to the lives of many members of society. It might well be that the patient would be in some position, such as railroad engineer, in which the lives of many people would depend upon him. Examination might reveal to the doctor that the patient was affected by some condition characterized by sudden fits or seizures which might wholly or partially incapacitate the person. Should the patient refuse to make known his condition to his employer or to leave his present position, the doctor would be obliged to make the fact known to proper authorities.

(b) *A professional secret must be revealed whenever its retention would result in grave harm coming to the owner of the secret.* The harm involved might be either a physical or moral loss. Thus, a patient with an incurable disease might tell a doctor or nurse that he intended to commit suicide upon his release from the hospital.

All moralists agree that whenever the secret involved is the *natural* or *promised* secret, there is the obligation to reveal it.

Moralists differ in their opinion on this matter when the *professional* secret is involved. Some moralists hold that the common good achieved by maintaining professional secrecy takes precedence over the private good of the owner of the secret. The more prevalent opinion, however, holds that charity demands that a patient be safeguarded from serious harm, even if it be necessary to reveal his professional secret in order to achieve this objective. Even if the patient expresses his unwillingness to have the revelation take place, he is regarded as "unreasonably unwilling." No one can be reasonably unwilling to be protected from grave harm.

In view of the difference of opinion on this matter, the

doctor or nurse may feel free, though not morally obliged, to reveal a professional secret in order to safeguard the patient from himself.

(c) *A professional secret must be revealed whenever its retention would result in grave harm coming to an innocent third party.* Reference is here made to instances in which the patient is not merely the *occasion* of harm to another but is, or is soon to be, the actual *cause* of harm to the innocent person.

For example, there is the case of the patient whom the doctor discovers to be suffering from a serious disease in a highly infectious state (such as syphilis) and contemplates marriage with an unsuspecting, innocent person.

The general principle which must be used in the solution of such cases might be stated in this way: *the professional person is obliged to maintain the secret just as long as the patient retains the right to his secret.* The same principle might also be stated in another form: *the professional person should reveal the secret whenever the owner of the secret would himself be committing sin by not revealing it.*

The obligation imposed by Natural Law on the member of the medical profession in the above mentioned case of syphilis is to protect the innocent person.

The *Principles of Ethics* professed by the American Medical Association upholds this conclusion:

> Patience and delicacy should characterize all the acts of a physician. The confidences concerning individual or domestic life entrusted by a patient to a physician and the defects of disposition or flaws of character observed in patients during medical attendance should be held as a trust and should never be revealed except when imperatively required by the laws of the state. *There are occasions, however, when a physician must determine whether or not his duty to society requires him to take definite action to protect a healthy individual from becoming infected, because the physician has knowledge, obtained through the confidences entrusted to him as a physician, of a communicable disease to which the healthy individual is about to be exposed. In such a case, the physician*

should act as he would desire another to act toward one of his own family under like circumstances. Before he determines his course, the physician should know the civil law of his commonwealth concerning privileged communications. (Italics ours)

Needless to say, revelation of the secret should be a last alternative. The patient should be urged to delay marriage until his physical condition is satisfactory or be given the chance to tell the prospective partner. Only when the patient refuses to confess his condition to his future spouse, or at least to delay the marriage, is the innocent party to be told. In practice, it seems that the member of the medical profession would rarely have to reveal the secret. The culprit would have little choice if he were told by the doctor to choose between delaying the marriage, informing the unsuspecting party, or having the information conveyed by the doctor himself.

In such cases as the above, a girl might be too young or too immature to appreciate the gravity of the situation into which she is entering. As a last resort, the father, mother, or guardian of the girl could be told.

As of July 1, 1952, the following States are the only ones which do *not* require premarital blood tests: Arizona, Arkansas, Maryland, Minnesota, Mississippi, Nevada, New Mexico, South Carolina, and the District of Columbia. (A certificate of examination is required for the groom in Louisiana. An affidavit as to the state of being free from communicable disease is necessary in the State of Washington.)

Prenatal blood tests of the mother to detect syphilis are required in forty-two states at the present time (1953). The States which do *not* have this requirement are: Alabama, Maryland, Minnesota, Mississippi, Tennessee, Wisconsin, and the District of Columbia.

These laws would usually prevent the emergence of the moral problem in the precise form in which it was stated above. But the problem could still arise in a slightly different form. For example, examination of a husband might reveal that the man had contracted syphilis outside marriage. In the light of the above principles, the doctor would be justified in demanding satisfactory proof that the unsuspecting wife has been made aware of her husband's condition.

The problem will still arise in those states lacking the blood test laws. It will sometimes arise even in the other states, due to the contraction of the disease between the time the blood test is taken and the actual time of the marriage. (Many States allow sixty days to elapse between blood test and marriage.)

(d) Finally, *a professional secret must be revealed whenever its retention would result in grave harm coming to the member of the medical profession.*

In certain instances, it is quite possible that a member of the medical profession would not be able to preserve the secrets of his patient without running the risk of suffering grave harm himself.

There is no question about the freedom of a member of the medical profession to suffer personally a grave loss, *if he so chooses,* in order to maintain the professional secret. The question is whether or not the member of the medical profession *must* suffer such harm to preserve the secret.

Whenever the harm threatening the member of the medical profession is wilfully caused by the patient, the problem is relatively simple. The patient then stands in the position of an unjust aggressor, and the intended victim is certainly justified in using the secret of the patient to whatever extent may be necessary to protect himself.

Whenever the harm threatening the member of the medical profession is not wilfully caused by the patient, the problem is much more difficult. Moralists agree that, unless the preservation of the secret is needed for the good of society, the revelation of such secrets is permissible whenever the retention of it would result in the gravest kind of loss for the member of the medical profession (such as loss of life, complete loss of reputation, or the loss of right to practice one's profession).

Whenever the loss threatening the member of the medical profession is *an ordinary grave loss* and is not being caused by the patient, moralists disagree on whether or not the professional secret may be revealed.

Some moralists point out that even Christianity, which is the highest of moral ideals, obliges us only to love our neighbor *as ourself*, not more than ourself. Hence they will not oblige the professional person to suffer a grave loss to protect an innocent patient from a comparable loss.

Other moralists emphasize the point that society expects self-sacrifice from the medical profession. Its members are expected to risk contracting serious diseases in order to serve mankind. Why, they ask, should the medical profession risk less or suffer less when it is the duty of secrecy to the patient that is involved?

In view of the difference of opinion among moralists on this latter matter, it appears that the more lenient opinion could be followed in conscience by those who desire to do so.

Summary

In view of the preceding principles, the following guides to action are recommended:

(a) The failure of civil law to grant adequate protection to the obligation of professional secrecy is not in itself proof that a strict moral obligation to maintain secrecy does not exist.

(b) A professional secret need not, and ordinarily should not, be revealed in response to the command of a lawful superior, even when this superior is inquiring into matters over which he has authority and a proper legal title.

(c) When a just law requires that certain facts received in confidence by professional persons in the course of duty must be revealed to civil authorities, such a law must be observed; and the professional person may reasonably presume that the patient knows the law, and thus may reveal the secret even though such revelation brings harm to the patient.

(d) Whenever civil law *unjustly demands the revelation* of a professional secret, the doctor or nurse is ordinarily obliged to refuse to make it; if, however, the refusal to make such revelation would result in *grave harm* coming to the doctor or nurse, he or she is morally justified in revealing the secret except in those cases where the preservation of the secret would be gravely necessary for the common welfare.

(e) Whenever civil law *unjustly demands the maintenance*

of a professional secret (which moral law clearly indicates should be revealed), the doctor or nurse is ordinarily obliged to make the revelation. They would, however, be permitted to observe the unjust law and refrain from making the revelation in order to protect themselves from proportionately grave harm, unless the revelation is necessary for the common welfare.

(f) Finally, whenever it is morally permissible or obligatory to reveal a professional secret, the following norms should be observed: (1) the secret should be revealed only to the extent necessary to meet the situation effectively; (2) the secret may be revealed only to the person or persons who have a strict right to the information; (3) those to whom the secret is revealed must be placed under the obligation of an entrusted secret concerning the information that is given to them.

Problems for Discussion

1. A hopelessly incurable patient asks if he is going to get better. What answer should be given?

2. A nurse has a very low opinion of the ability of a certain doctor. A patient asks the nurse for her opinion of this doctor. What should she say?

3. What would you say if one doctor asked you about the condition of another doctor's patient, as well as the type of treatment which was being given?

4. If a patient began to ask a doctor a personal question while you were still in the room, would you leave or remain?

5. What would you do if a young doctor confronted with an emergency case asked you what treatment a more experienced doctor used in handling a recent case of this type?

6. Suppose your patient is not improving as rapidly as was expected and his family asks you if you think it would be advisable to change physicians. If you honestly believed that a much more capable doctor could be had, what answer would you make to such a query?

7. A married woman has a child by a man who is not her husband. This fact is common knowledge. The State Law insists that the husband's name be recorded as the *father*. Would it be permissible to write up the birth certificate in

that way when you honestly knew that the husband was not the father of the child?

8. A nurse is certain that a doctor has neglected his patient. The latter seems to realize this fact and asks the nurse if it is not true that the doctor has been neglectful. What answer would you make in such a case?

9. A friend of yours has engaged a costly specialist to deliver her baby. The specialist does not arrive at the hospital in time and the baby is delivered by an interne. Both the woman and her husband have sound suspicions that the specialist did not deliver the baby and they are unwilling to pay a large sum of money for services never received. Since you were assisting in the delivery room at the time, they ask you for the truth of the matter. What would you do in this case?

10. A patient engages a well known surgeon to operate on him. The surgeon allows his younger assistant to perform the operation under his guidance, counsel, and watchful eye. The patient has a suspicion that the first surgeon did not perform the operation and asks you about it. You assisted at the operation and know the facts. What answer would you make?

11. A woman delivers a deformed or still-born child and she is personally in a very serious condition. She fears that her baby is deformed or dead and begs you to tell her the truth. What answer would you make?

12. A nurse has worked exceptionally hard throughout the night. ✓ She sits down for a moment and falls asleep. When she awakes, she charts certain medications as given (which she never administered) and records temperatures for the patients (which she never took). She feels certain that none of the patients will suffer harm as the result of the omitted medication, and she is equally confident that the temperatures of her patients were about normal, even though she did not check them. What do you think of her actions?

13. Do you think that the knowledge acquired by dentists and undertakers falls under professional secrecy in the strict sense of the term? If knowledge does not fall under *professional secrecy* does that mean that it is exempt from all bonds of secrecy?

14. Comment on this statement: "I cannot see anything wrong in telling a 'white' lie."

15. Through working in the office of a doctor, a nurse learns that a certain man, who intends to marry her best friend, has syphilis. What course of action do you suggest?

16. In the chapter on *Christian Marriage* it was stated that a man who is wholly and permanently incapable of the marital act is barred by Natural Law from entering marriage. Suppose you, as a nurse, had assisted at an operation on a man which had the above effects and you now learn that he is intending 'to marry.' What do you think should be done, if anything, in this case?

17. Through her professional work, a nurse learns that her patient has committed a crime with which an innocent person is charged. The patient has done nothing which has brought about the arrest of the innocent person; the arrest is simply an error on the part of the State. The patient is not a dangerous criminal and does not constitute a future menace to society. Do you think the nurse could or should reveal the matter to State authorities?

18. What do you think of nurses needlessly telling each other the facts and gossip about their respective patients?

19. What do you think of the practice in some Nursing Schools of having student nurses write up actual case histories for presentation to members of the teaching faculty. We refer to instances in which the teachers exercise no direct medical care over the patients; they intend to use these case histories for scholastic evaluation of the nurse. In these case histories, the real name of the patient is sometimes recorded, the data is often such as would injure a reputation, and the teachers frequently live in the same community as the patient.

20. Many states do not recognize the right of a nurse to withhold information in court. What course of action do you think a nurse should follow if she should encounter the unfortunate alternative of revealing a professional secret which would seriously injure her patient or receiving a severe penalty from civil law for obstructing justice by her refusal to testify?

References for Reading

BONNAR, A.: *The Catholic Doctor* (2nd ed.), pp. 164-167, N. Y., 1939.

CONNELL, E.: "Narcotherapy," *American Ecclesiastical Review*, Dec., 1945, p. 448.

DAVIS, H.: *Moral and Pastoral Theology* (4th ed.), Vol. 2, pp. 410-424, London, 1945.

JONES, W.: *The Doctor's Oath*, Cambridge Univ., 1924.

KELLY, G.: "Narcotherapy," *Theological Studies*, March, 1947, p. 104.

————: "Narcotherapy in Catholic Hospitals," *Hospital Progress*, March, 1948.

KENNY, J. P.: *Principles of Medical Ethics*, Westminster, 1952, pp. 33-56.

McCARTHY, J.: "The Obligation of Professional Secrecy," *Irish Ecclesiastical Record*, Nov., 1946, pp. 342-344.

McGUINN, W.: *The Professional Secret in Social Work*, Boston College, Boston, 1938.

MOORE, T.: *Principles of Ethics*, pp. 77-104, Phila., 1935.

REGAN, R.: *Professional Secrecy in the Light of Moral Principles*, Augustinian College, Washington, D. C., 1943.
   (This is the most complete and most scholarly work available on this subject.)

ROCHELLE-FINK: *Handbook of Medical Ethics*, pp. 285-293; 299-304, Westminster, Md., 1943.

SURBLED, G.: *Catholic Moral Teaching in Its Relation to Medicine and Hygiene*, 3 vols., St. Louis, 1930.

WALSH, J.: "The Medical Secret—A Problem in Morals," *Homiletic and Pastoral Review*, Vol. 29, pp. 466-474, 1929.

WHITE, R.: *Confession and the Law*, Catholic University of America, Washington, D. C., 1938.

Principles of Medical Ethics of the American Medical Association, c. 2, sec. 1, Chicago, 1939.

"Professional Secrecy," *Journal of the American Medical Association*, pp. 339-340, Jan. 27, 1940.

"The Revealing of the Professional Secret," *American Ecclesiastical Review*, pp. 147-148, Feb., 1944.

CHAPTER 16

The Last Sacraments

A proper knowledge of the priceless spiritual aids which the Church brings to Her sick and dying children should certainly be possessed by both doctor and nurse.

Ordinarily, we use the expression "Last Sacraments" in referring to the Sacrament of Penance received by a dying person, the Eucharist received as Viaticum, and the Sacrament of Extreme Unction. In this Chapter we shall treat not only of the "Last Sacraments" in the above sense but also of ordinary Confession and Communion of the sick.

The doctor and nurse realize that a sick person is often weakened in his mental powers, as well as in his physical strength. Unoccupied time drags by slowly for the sick person. There is much time for temptation to strike. There is the constant battle to maintain a Christian resignation to suffering. Certainly, the sick person has a difficult spiritual battle to fight. And, in his weakened condition, the need for spiritual aid is indeed great.

The soul approaching death is nearing the most solemn moment of its existence. It needs all possible spiritual aid to combat the final temptations of this life and to maintain itself in the state of grace.

These rich sources of strengthening grace are made available to man by the Church of Christ. No truly Christian doctor or nurse would ever allow a patient, through his or her negligence, to die without all the spiritual help that could be given to him.

The Sacrament of Penance

The knowledge of the value of religion, combined with their own personal experience, will recall to the doctor and nurse the spiritual benefits of the Sacrament of Penance. They will realize that the Sacrament should be received by any Catholic patient who is about to undergo a serious operation, receive general anesthesia, enter upon a difficult delivery, or is in immediate probable danger of death.

Actually, the baptized Christian in danger of death is solemnly bound by both Divine and ecclesiastical law to receive the Eucharist. This obligation is probably fulfilled if the person has received the Sacrament within a week of the danger of death. Needless to say, the obligation is not fulfilled by a sacrilegious Communion. So insistent is the Church on this obligation that *public refusal* to receive the Eucharist in face of danger of death may place the person in the category of a public sinner. As a rule, burial in consecrated ground would be refused to such a person.

Doctors and nurses should certainly do all that they can to insure the spiritual welfare of their patient. At times it may be possible to recommend the Sacrament to the patient. When they choose to make an explicit recommendation, great tact and discretion should be exercised. Many patients will resent suggestions of this nature. Those who have been living up to their religion moderately well may feel that they need no advice on spiritual matters from doctors or nurses. Those who have not been practicing their religion will often resent spiritual advice from anyone.

Ordinarily, medical personnel should not directly interfere in spiritual affairs. But when the above-mentioned grave conditions are present, such as imminent and probable death, they should call upon all of their resources of tact, friendliness, and discretion to get the patient to request the Sacrament.

In the case of the opposite type of patient, doctors and nurses may feel that a confessor is being requested too often or at an unreasonable time. In general, when a patient is in the possession of his faculties, one would advise a doctor or nurse never to refuse the request for a confessor.

When a patient is seriously ill or in danger of death, the request for a confessor should certainly be granted, even though a surgeon be kept waiting who is about to begin an operation on the patient. Not even the physical life of the patient is as important as the salvation of his soul.

After the departure of the priest, much can often be done to make permanent the spiritual good already achieved. A proselytizing doctor or nurse is by no means the ideal. In fact, doctors and nurses who are determined to make spiritual persons out of their patients, whether they will or not, are apt to do more harm than good.

The doctor and nurse should go about their work quietly, winning the confidence of their patient, their conversation and their example mirroring true Christian ideals. At the request of their patient they will always be ready to read appropriate prayers or to pray with him. Whenever there is any reasonable hope that the patient will not resent it, the doctor or nurse may tactfully make positive spiritual recommendations; this is particularly true if the patient is dying and known to be in the state of grave sin. In general, however, they will do their best spiritual work by setting an example of Christian purity and nobility of character in their own lives.

Arrangement of the Sick Room

The professional life of the doctor and nurse revolves around the sick room. It is under their constant care and supervision.

The doctor will expect the nurse to have the patient prepared for his visit; he will expect her to have available any incidentals that she should know ahead of time that he will require.

Similarly, the nurse should have her patient ready for the visit of the priest. And she should see to it, either personally or through someone else, that those things which the priest will require are at hand.

For the guidance of the nurse who must prepare a sick room for the priest's visit, the following essential items are listed.

(a) There should be a small, firm table covered with a clean white cloth. This table should be placed away from the bed, to the side of the bed, and opposite the foot of the bed. This position will enable the priest to move freely around the bed, and it will keep the table within the easy vision of the patient.

(b) A crucifix should be placed between two candles on the table. Immediately before the entrance of the priest, these two candles should be lit.

(c) Holy water—preferably in a holy water bottle adapted for sprinkling.

(d) A small finger bowl.

(e) A small dish on which there are placed six small balls of cotton (required only if Extreme Unction is to be received).

(f) A small dish in which the priest may place the above cotton after each piece is used in the anointing of the sick person (required only if Extreme Unction is to be received).

(g) A small dish on which is placed a little piece of bread (required only if Extreme Unction is to be received).

(h) A small bowl of clean water (required only if Extreme Unction is to be received).

(i) An ordinary glass, preferably a small one, containing about a tablespoonful of water. After the administration of the Eucharist, the priest will use this water to purify the two fingers which have held the Host, and then he will offer it to the patient to swallow. For this reason, the quantity of water should not exceed a tablespoonful or thereabouts; and the glass should not be too deep, as this would prevent the priest's fingers from reaching the water. (This small wine-glass containing the water is required only if the patient is to receive the Eucharist.)

(j) A small spoon, such as a teaspoon, with which the priest can give the patient the above ablution water. (This spoon is required only if the patient is to receive the Eucharist.)

The above items are readily obtainable, and it should be easy for the nurse to familiarize herself with them.

The Administration of Holy Communion

A brief description of the visit of the priest to the sick room will acquaint the nurse with the procedure and indicate to her the ways in which she may be helpful both to priest and patient.

If the patient is to receive Holy Communion or Holy Viaticum, the nurse will see to it that her patient is slightly elevated, that is, raised up by proper supports in a half sitting position. Whenever the disease or condition of the patient contraindicates this procedure, it will obviously have to be omitted.

Upon entering the sick room with the Blessed Sacrament, the priest will say in Latin: "Peace be unto this house and unto all who dwell therin."

The Blessed Sacrament is then placed by the priest upon the prepared table. Those present, including the priest and excepting the sick person, kneel in adoration.

Taking the holy water, the priest will sprinkle those present while saying the prayers proper to the Asperges.

Should the patient desire to go to Confession before receiving the Eucharist, the Confession will be heard by the priest at this point. All present should quietly retire out of the range of hearing but close enough to the sick room that the priest can summon them readily upon the completion of the Confession.

The nurse will now place a clean white napkin under the chin of the patient or stand ready to hold a Communion card should one be available.

The priest will first say the "Confiteor" in Latin. If those present are not sufficiently familiar with Latin it would be fitting for them to say the "Confiteor" in the vernacular.

Following the usual "Misereatur" and "Indulgentiam," the priest will genuflect before the Blessed Sacrament and then prepare to administer Holy Communion to the patient. When the patient is not in danger of death, the priest will use the customary form "Ecce Agnus Dei—Domine non sum dignus." When the patient is in danger of death, the priest will use the form proper to the administration of Holy Viaticum.

After giving the Eucharist to the patient, the priest will cleanse his thumb and forefinger in the small glass containing the tablespoonful of water. A teaspoonful of this water is then given by the priest to the patient, and it will aid the patient considerably if the nurse will gently raise his head while the priest offers the water. Should swallowing the water be very difficult for the patient, it may be omitted.

The priest will next offer the final prayers and then bestow the blessing upon the patient and all those present. If there is no Host remaining in the pyx (the little container in which the priest carries the Blessed Sacrament), the priest will bestow the blessing with his hand. If there is still a Host contained in the pyx, the priest will raise the Eucharist in the sign of the cross over all present.

The latter form of blessing will serve as a cue to the nurse that the priest is still carrying the Blessed Sacrament and should therefore be accompanied with a lighted candle to the door of the home, to the next patient's room, or to the hospital chapel.

When Holy Communion is to be distributed to a number of sick persons in a hospital on the same or different floors, the priest carries the ciborium or large pyx along without purifying his fingers as he passes from floor to floor. *Only in the first room* does he say all of the prayers prescribed in the Ritual for recitation before Holy Communion of the sick. In each of the other rooms he says once only the usual Misereatur tui—Indulgentian—Ecce Agnus Dei—Domine Non sum dignus, etc. Then he says the Accipe, frater (soror), etc., or the Corpus Domini, etc., to each recipient of the sacrament in the room. In the last room to be visited the priest adds the *Dominus vobiscum* and the prayer *Domine sancte* (to be said in the plural form) and gives the blessing with the Blessed Sacrament. On his return to the church or chapel he is to recite the other prayers that are prescribed. (*Am. Ecc. Rev.*, Sept. 1952, pp. 229-230.)

Throughout the entire visit, the nurse should quietly and tactfully guide all present in the proper manner of acting. It is inconvenient and unfitting for the priest to be forced to interrupt his solemn duties to direct the patient and those present in the room. The duty falls upon the nurse to see to it that no one is in the way of the priest and to be ready to lend the priest a helping hand in every possible manner.

When the priest has departed, the nurse should throw any

water remaining in the ablution glass upon a fire, if available, or poured out on some clean spot of earth where it will not be trampled upon by passersby. The candles should be extinguished and the Communion table placed aside.

Finally, the nurse should aid the patient in saying a few fitting post-Communion prayers. When the patient is very ill, he will probably be quite exhausted from the exertion involved in the reception of the Holy Eucharist. In this case, the nurse should restrict the Thanksgiving to several short ejaculatory prayers. Should the patient be somewhat stronger, the prayers may be a bit longer. In general, however, the recommendation is that the prayers be few, that the room be darkened and the patient allowed to sleep. After some rest, the patient will be able to pray longer and more fervently.

The Eucharistic Fast

The following quotations are from the Instruction of the Sacred Congregation of the Holy Office. This Instruction was published in the *Acta Apostolical Sedis* (Acts of the Holy See) of January 10, 1953, and provides an authoritative explanation of the regulations given by Pope Pius XII in the Apostolic Constitution Christus Dominus, which is dated January 6, 1953, and which became effective on January 16, 1953.

First, the new Apostolic Constitution 'Christus Dominus' urges all who are capable of observing the former law of fast from midnight to continue to do so.

> "The Apostolic Constitution 'Christus Dominus', issued by the Sovereign Pontiff Pius XII, happily reigning, grants not a few faculties and permissions concerning the observance of the Eucharistic fast, *but at the same time confirms norms of the code of Canon Law* (Canon 808,858) *for priests and faithful who may be capable of observing said law.*"

Second, the Holy Father states that in the future the drinking of ordinary water will have no bearing whatsoever on the Eucharistic fast. No dispensation or permission from anyone is required to drink water before the reception of Holy Communion. It may be taken at any time, even immediately, before the reception of the Sacrament, and these concessions apply without qualification even to those persons who are wholly capable of observing a total fast from midnight. In a word, ordinary water simply has no bearing whatsoever, for anyone, on the Eucharistic fast.

"Nevertheless, to these also, the benevolent disposition of paragraph I of the Constitution itself is extended, according to which ordinary water (water therefore without addition of any element whatever) does not break the Eucharistic fast."

Third, the new Constitution grants very helpful relaxations *to sick persons.* In the future they are to be permitted to partake of liquids other than water, *alcoholic beverages not included,* before the reception of the Eucharist. Furthermore, they need not be confined to bed to enjoy this privilege.

"Faithful who are sick, even if not confined to bed, may take something in the form of drink, excluding those which are alcoholic, if by reason of their sickness they cannot remain fasting until Holy Communion without real inconvenience."

The Constitution also authorizes the taking of *medicine* in any form, *liquid or solid,* by the sick person—provided it is truly medicinal in nature.

"They may also take something in the form of medicine, either liquid or solid, (excluding alcoholic beverages) as long as it is a question of true medicine, prescribed by a physician or at any rate commonly recognized as such. Let it be remembered that any solid whatsoever which is taken for nourishment cannot be considered true medicine."

Sick persons may use the above-mentioned privilege only if they have obtained permission from an authorized priest either in the Sacrament of Penance or in private consultation outside the Sacrament of Penance. The sick person, however, does *not* need to obtain permission each time he desires to use the privilege; rather, once the permission is obtained, it continues to hold force so long as the same conditions of sickness prevail. Furthermore, once the necessary permission is obtained, there is no time limit preceding Holy Communion prescribed, that is, the permitted liquids or solid medicines may be taken at any time, even immediately, before the reception of the Sacrament.

> "The conditions for being able to take advantage of this dispensation from fast, for which a time-limit preceding Holy Communion is *not* prescribed, must be prudently considered by the confessor; *and without his consent no one may take advantage of them*. The confessor may give his counsel in the internal forum, either sacramental or extra-sacramental, and once and for all so long as the same conditions of sickness obtain. By 'confessor' here is understood a priest who has the faculty to hear the confession of a person who turns to him for advice on this question."

The privilege granted by the Holy Father also extends to the priest who is sick and who desires either to celebrate Mass or simply receive Holy Communion.

> "Sick priests, even if not confined to bed, without question, may avail themselves of the dispensation, whether they intend to celebrate Mass or only receive Holy Communion."

Fourth, the new Apostolic Constitution grants certain privileges to doctors, nurses, hospital personnel, or others, who—through duty or charity—watch or labor throughout the night in the care of the sick. If their task would make it gravely inconvenient for them to fast and still go to Holy Communion in the morning, they may partake of liquids previous to the reception of the Sacrament. Note carefully, however, that they must obtain the permission of an authorized priest; the liquids may never be alcoholic in nature; and, *unlike the privilege of the sick person,* at least an hour must elapse between the taking of these liquids (ordinary water always excepted) and the reception of Holy Communion. Permission need *not* be obtained each time the privilege is used; rather, once it has been obtained, it holds good for the duration of the cause of grave

inconvenience, that is, each time that the person actually
engages in this type of work.

> "It is also granted the faithful who cannot observe the
> Eucharistic fast, not because of sickness but because of
> another grave inconvenience, to approach the Sacred
> Table after having taken something in the form of liquid
> up to an hour before Holy Communion, always excluding
> those drinks which are alcoholic. . . . Here are included
> . . . those who through duty or charity pass the night in
> watching (nurses, hospital personnel, etc.)."

The Apostolic Constitution, of course, extends this privilege
to others than doctors, nurses, and hospital personnel. The
varied applications of the Law to members of the Church in
other conditions of life, however, do not concern us in this
work.

Holy Viaticum to the Dying

> "In danger of death, from whatever cause it may pro-
> ceed, the faithful are bound by precept to receive Holy
> Communion. Though they may have received Holy Com-
> munion the same day, they should be strongly advised to
> receive again if in the course of the day they are in danger
> of death. While the danger of death lasts they may, ac-
> cording to the prudent judgment of the confessor, receive
> Holy Viaticum repeatedly on different days." (Canon
> 864.)

The Church is insistent that the dying person be spiritually
fortified in his last moments by the Eucharist. Even though the
dying person received the Eucharist in the morning as Holy
Communion, the Church urges the second reception of the
Sacrament as Holy Viaticum. It is not rare that persons who
went to Holy Communion in the morning are stricken with a
fatal illness or meet with an accident in the course of the day.
Of course, should the patient be delirious or nauseated, it
would not be fitting to administer the Eucharist.

If a sick person hangs between life and death for some days,
the Church urges the reception of Holy Viaticum each day

while the danger lasts. Needless to say, there is no obligation to fast on the part of such a patient. The Eucharist could not be received as Holy Viaticum twice in the same day, unless there would be a new and completely different danger of death from the one in which Viaticum was first received.

The Eucharist may be received under the form of Holy Viaticum at any hour of the day or night, even on Good Friday, and it is neither necessary nor prudent for the patient to be fasting.

The obligation to notify the priest of the patient's illness will often fall upon either the doctor or the nurse. For this reason, both should understand the precise meaning which is attached to the expression "in danger of death" in the Church's law on Holy Viaticum.

In the nursing and medical profession, we will usually hear the phrase "in danger of death" used as indicating that death is imminent. In contrast, Church law refers to a person as being "in danger of death" whenever there is a reasonable expectation that death may ensue from the patient's condition, even though death is not expected in a matter of hours. Thus, even though death be not imminent, the doctor and nurse must realize that their patient is under obligation to receive Holy Viaticum. So long as the patient is so seriously ill that there is a probable expectation that death will result, he is capable of receiving Holy Viaticum.

Often the nurse will have to relay the opinion of the doctor on the patient's condition to the priest. She should keep in mind the interpretation of "danger of death" in Church Law when she questions the doctor about the precise nature of the patient's condition. Only by so doing will she be able to give the priest the information which he will require to pass judgment on the patient's right to receive Holy Viaticum.

Holy Viaticum for Dying Children

"In case of danger of death, Holy Communion may and must be given to children if they are able to distinguish the Holy Eucharist from ordinary bread and reverently adore it." (Canon 854, No. 2.)

The Church is so desirous of Her members dying in the closest possible union with Christ that She urges that dying children be given their First Communion. Besides the state of grace, the only other requirement imposed is that the child be at least able to distinguish the Holy Eucharist from ordinary bread.

Holy Viaticum for the Mentally Ill and Aged

Certain types of mental defectives may be given the Eucharist, under the form of Holy Communion, periodically, even when there is no danger of death. The principal requirement is that the person be capable at the time of knowing, at least vaguely, that he is receiving the Body of Christ. Needless to say, such persons should be given the Eucharist, under the form of Viaticum, at the time of death—always provided that they are able to distinguish the Eucharist from ordinary bread.

Patients who are delirious or psychotic may be given the Eucharist, either as Holy Communion, or Viaticum, during a conscious and lucid interval. The only requirement is that they formerly possessed the use of reason. Needless to say, the Eucharist could not be given to these patients if there would be danger of either physical or moral profanation. There would be danger of *physical* profanation of the Eucharist if there would be fear that the patient might not be sufficiently rational and might physically mistreat the Host. There would be danger of *moral* profanation of the Eucharist if the patient were formerly an impenitent sinner and gave no indication of any sorrow for past sin during any lucid interval.

Very old people whose minds are not clear should be given the Eucharist at reasonable intervals if they possess at least some idea of what they are doing. It would be fitting for them to receive the Eucharist at Christmas, during the Paschal season, and certainly when in danger of death. One must always safeguard the Eucharist against profanation by one who does not know what he is doing. But one should not minimize the understanding of those in their second childhood. The Eucharist has often been so deep and solemn a part of their whole past life that their failing mind retains a knowledge and respect for the Sacrament long after it has lost a sound grasp on matters of ordinary life.

Finally, those who certainly do not know what they are doing, such as the delirious, those presently psychotic, and the low-grade mental defective, should not be given the Eucharist.

Special Difficulties

Even if a patient has an extremely violent and continuous cough, it will not usually prevent the reception of the Eucharist. Any expectorations which result from the coughing come from the lungs and bronchial tubes, not from the stomach. For this reason there is normally no danger of profanation of the Sacrament.

Should it happen that the coughing is so uninterrupted that there is fear that the Host may not be able to be swallowed, the patient should await a period of relief before receiving the Eucharist.

Whenever a patient is incapable of swallowing, due to some obstruction, Holy Communion may not be given. If, of course, the inability to swallow results merely from dryness of the mucosa, a little water may be given along with the Eucharist and immediately after its reception to facilitate swallowing.

Sick persons who are subject to attacks of vomiting present a special problem. In general, one would say that they should not be given the Eucharist until a reasonable amount of time has elapsed since the last attack and until there is some degree of assurance that they will be able to retain the Host.

The precise amount of time that should be allowed to lapse after an attack of vomiting before giving the Eucharist depends upon the individual case. A short time might suffice in some instances, whereas hours might be required for other patients.

It has been suggested that, in cases where vomiting results from some cause in no way allied to food intake, the patient should be free of the attacks for a notable period of time (all authors require at least several hours, while others suggest as much as five or six hours).

In cases wherein the vomiting is definitely connected with food intake and there is danger of death, the suggestion is to experiment with small quantities of solid or liquid food. If the patient succeeds in retaining this food for half an hour, the Eucharist may be administered.

If, by chance, the Host is expelled by vomiting, the Sacrament will have been received. This point is of importance in determining whether or not a person has fulfilled his obligation to receive the Eucharist during the Easter season or when in danger of death.

Whenever vomiting occurs after the reception of the Eucharist, the problem of preventing profanation is encountered. The following recommendations will be found helpful.

If half an hour has elapsed between the reception of the Eucharist and the actual vomiting, no concern need be shown about the matter. Complete decomposition of the Host will probably have taken place in that space of time.

Whenever the vomiting occurs within half an hour of the reception of the Eucharist, special steps should be taken to prevent profanation.

If the Host is not distinguishable from the rest of that which is expelled, the entire matter should be placed in a linen cloth and conserved in a clean receptacle for the priest. He will burn the linen cloth and its contents, and then place the ashes in the sacrarium.

If the Host is distinguishable from the rest of that which is expelled, the entire matter may be conserved in the previously mentioned manner for the priest. If feasible, however, the Host may be lifted with a spoon and placed in a clean receptacle and kept in a locked place for the priest. Upon complete decomposition of the Host, the priest will deposit the remains in the sacrarium.

The Administration of Extreme Unction

The Sacrament of Extreme Unction involves the anointing of the eyelids, the ears, the nostrils, the hands, and the feet of the patient. The nurse should, therefore, properly bathe her patient before the arrival of the priest and so arrange the bedclothes that they can be turned up easily when the time comes to anoint the feet.

Whenever the sacrament is to be received by a sick person in his home, the nurse should see to it that the family is in the sick room upon the arrival of the priest. Care should be taken that they do not prevent the free access of the priest to the bed and the prepared table.

Upon his entrance into the sickroom, the priest will say "Peace be unto this house and unto all who dwell therein." He will then place the holy oil upon the table, put on a violet stole, and offer the Crucifix to be kissed by the patient.

The Asperges will be given at this point. The priest will sprinkle those present with holy water, while saying the proper prayers. (Whenever Holy Viaticum has immediately preceded Extreme Unction, the Asperges will already have been given and will not be repeated.)

The Confession of the patient will be heard by the priest immediately after the Asperges. Those present should leave the room quietly and remain out of range of hearing, but close enough to be summoned easily by the priest upon the completion of the Confession. (Whenever Holy Viaticum has immediately preceded Extreme Unction, the patient will have made his Confession before receiving the Eucharist.)

The opening versicles, responses, and prayers proper to Extreme Unction are next said by the priest. At their completion, the nurse should lead those present in the recitation of the Confiteor. Immediately afterward, the priest will exhort those present to pray for the patient while he carries out the anointings and offers the beautiful prayers of the sacrament of Extreme Unction.

The Church recommends the recitation of the Seven Penitential Psalms and Litanies by those present. In place of those prayers, the Rosary may be recited. Regardless of what prayers are chosen, they should be said in a low and quiet tone, so as to avoid distracting either priest or patient.

Throughout the anointing, the nurse can be of great assistance to the priest by holding the saucer containing the pieces of cotton which he must use in the anointings and by properly handling the patient. The following suggestions may be of help to the nurse.

After the priest anoints the *eyelids,* he will anoint the *ears.*

The nurse should gently turn the patient's head from right to left to facilitate this anointing.

After the anointing of the *nostrils* and the *lips,* the anointing of the *hands* will follow. The nurse should see to it that the patient's hands are outside the bedcovers and help the patient to present first the palm of the right hand and then the palm of the left hand for the anointing.

The priest will next proceed to the anointing of the *feet.* The nurse should turn up the bedclothes, and each foot will be anointed. In some places, the sole of the foot is anointed; in other places, it is the custom to anoint the instep of the foot.

At the discretion of the priest, the anointing of the feet may be omitted for a reasonable cause without lessening in any way the spiritual value of the sacrament.

Upon the completion of each anointing, the priest cleanses the part anointed with a piece of cotton. The nurse should take these used pieces of cotton from the priest and keep them separate from the clean pieces. For this purpose she may use a separate dish or one side of the dish which she is already holding.

Whenever there is immediate danger of death, the priest may use only a single anointing. It is to be noted that the Church permits the use of the short form of Extreme Unction whenever there is a *real necessity for haste arising from the condition of the patient.* The short form could not be used merely to avoid delaying a doctor or an ambulance.

At the completion of the anointings, the priest will replace the holy oil on the table, cleanse his thumb with the piece of bread, wash and dry his hands.

The nurse should replace on the table the dish containing the used pieces of cotton and then kneel for the concluding prayers. If the nurse is able to answer with the proper responses to these prayers, it is commendable for her to do so.

Having finished the prayers, the priest will replace the holy oil in its proper container and throw the cotton, bread, and ablution water which he used upon the fire. When more convenient, the priest may take these with him to burn at a later time.

After the departure of the priest, the nurse will remove

everything from the table except the Crucifix and the holy
water. She should darken the room, make the patient comfort-
able, and allow him to rest.

The Last Blessing

Immediately after the reception of the sacrament of Extreme
Unction, the Last Blessing is often given. It is a Papal Blessing
which may be given by a priest possessing the proper faculties,
and it carries with it a plenary indulgence effective at the
moment of death. There is, however, no need to wait until
death is imminent to receive this blessing, nor is it advisable to
do so. Whenever a patient is capable of receiving Extreme
Unction, it is lawful to bestow this blessing.

There are three conditions required for the gaining of the
plenary indulgence attached to this blessing:

(a) The patient must be in the state of grace;
(b) The patient must accept death with perfect resigna-
     tion to the will of God;
(c) The patient must invoke once the sacred name of
     Jesus, at least in his heart, if he cannot speak.

If Extreme Unction has just been given, no added preparation will be required for the Last Blessing.

Whenever this Last Blessing is to be received independently
of Extreme Unction, the nurse should make certain that a
Crucifix and holy water are ready for the priest.

Requirements for Receiving Extreme Unction

In order to receive the sacrament of Extreme Unction, three
conditions must be verified:

(a) The patient must be a baptized Catholic;
(b) The patient must have had the use of reason;
(c) The patient must be in danger of death from sickness.
     "Extreme Unction can be given only to a Catholic who,
     after having attained the use of reason, incurs a danger of
     death from sickness." (Canon 940, No. 1.)

A direct objective of Extreme Unction is the remission of
venial sin and the eradication of those spiritual weaknesses

which are the effects of sin. For this reason, only a person who has at least been capable of sin can receive the sacrament of Extreme Unction. Once the capability to sin is present, one may reasonably presume that some venial sins have been committed and that the patient is therefore entitled to the sacrament.

Children who have not yet reached the age of reason (ordinarily regarded as at the completion of the seventh year) and adults who have never possessed the use of reason, are not capable of receiving Extreme Unction.

Children who are capable of making their first Confession and Communion are entitled to this sacrament. This fact is emphasized by Pope Pius X in his decree on First Communion.

Danger of death from accident, sickness, or old age must be present in order that a patient may receive Extreme Unction.

The first question that arises is this: How grave must the danger be in order to justify the administration of Extreme Unction? This question has already been answered earlier in this chapter when an explanation was given the Church's usage of the phrase "danger of death." All that is required is that there be a *probable* danger of death. The probability must, of course, rest on solid grounds but—according to the mind of the Church—a man may be in probable danger of death even though the likelihood of his recovery is more probable, even though death is not expected in a matter of hours. Whenever a patient's condition is so serious that there is a reasonable expectation that it may produce death, he is capable of receiving Extreme Unction.

Danger of death from an *external* cause does *not* justify the administration of Extreme Unction. It is absolutely required that the danger of death arise from the condition of the patient himself. Consequently, criminals about to be executed, soldiers entering battle, travelers about to begin a dangerous journey, those on a sinking ship or in a burning building, are not capable of receiving the sacrament.

On the other hand, anyone in danger of death from an *internal* cause may and should receive Extreme Unction. Hence, not only patients who are gravely ill, but also those who are dangerously wounded, those who have swallowed poison, those seriously injured in accidents, and those rescued from water when almost drowned, are fit subjects for Extreme Unction. In all of these cases, the life of the patient is threatened by an internal cause, that is, by his own bodily condition.

It cannot be overemphasized that this sacrament is not only for those who are certainly about to die, but for all who are so seriously ill that death may probably result from their condition. It is admittedly difficult to evaluate the precise degree of a danger to life. Any condition, however, which may prove fatal to the patient provides sufficient grounds for administering the sacrament. The mind of the Church today is toward a lenient view on the gravity of the condition and the proximity of death required for the valid reception of Extreme Unction.

The very prevalent attitude among many Catholics that a priest should not be called to administer this sacrament until death is imminent should certainly be eradicated.

Similarly, both doctors and nurses should dispel the very common view on the part of patients that the fact that they are being given Extreme Unction is an indication that all hope for their recovery has been abandoned.

Conditional Extreme Unction

"When one doubts whether the sick person has attained the use of reason; whether he is really in danger of death; whether he is dead—Extreme Unction shall be given conditionally." (Canon 941.)

It is presumed that children who have completed their seventh year have attained the use of reason. In the case of children slightly under seven years, the sacrament may be administered *conditionally* whenever there is a reasonable presumption that they have committed venial sin.

Mentally defective persons, who have been so afflicted from infancy, may be given the sacrament conditionally, if it is thought that they have been capable of venial sin at any time in their life.

Whenever there is *doubt as to the probability* of the danger of death, Extreme Unction should be given conditionally. Ordinarily, the priest will be guided by the opinion of the doctor on the condition of the patient. If a doctor is not available for consultation and the priest believes that the patient may be in danger of death, he should administer conditional Extreme Unction.

When there is doubt that the patient is actually dead, conditional Extreme Unction should be given.

The precise time at which death occurs is not known. It is certainly true that actual death does not occur until some time after apparent death. Medical science agrees that there is an indeterminable period of latent life after the patient has apparently died. It also acknowledges that decomposition and true "rigor mortis" are the only certain indications of death.

In the case of sudden death, it is customary to administer conditional Absolution and conditional Extreme Unction at any time within three hours of the apparent death of the patient.

In the case of death from lingering illness, conditional Absolution and conditional Extreme Unction may be given at any time within one hour of the apparent death of the patient.

Repetition of Extreme Unction

"In the same illness the sacrament of Extreme Unction cannot be repeated unless the sick person rallied after the reception of the last anointing and his illness again becomes critical." (Canon 940, No. 2.)

The law of the Church thus clearly states that Extreme Unction may be received *only once* in the same danger of death. The purpose of this sacrament is to give spiritual strength to those who are in danger of death, and the efficacy of the sacrament lasts up to the death or the recovery of the patient.

If a patient has certainly or probably rallied from a grave illness after having received Extreme Unction and again grows so seriously ill that death may result, the sacrament may be administered a second time.

In lingering illness, such as cancer and tuberculosis, the danger of death may truly be present, even though considerable time may lapse before the patient actually dies. Such a patient is entitled to the sacrament of Extreme Unction.

It is admittedly difficult, particularly in lingering illnesses, to know for certain whether one danger of death has passed and a new danger present, or whether one and the same danger still remains. As a guide in doubtful cases, it is suggested that, in protracted diseases, if the patient recovers to such an extent as to feel considerably improved for a period of a month, the sacrament may be administered again.

Whenever it is certain that a patient has rallied from the danger of death after having received Extreme Unction, it is permissible to administer the sacrament again in the same general illness after a short lapse of time (one week), if a new danger should arise.

A typical example is to be found in an asthma patient who is steadily but not always seriously ill with the condition. He may be subject to attacks which are so severe as to be able to result in death but which are relatively short in duration. If it be certain that he has emerged from the danger of death involved in one attack, he should be given the sacrament again when a new attack threatens his life.

Whenever there is genuine doubt that the present danger to life is a new crisis and not simply a continuation of the one in which the patient has already been anointed, the sacrament should be administered conditionally. So long as there is a reasonable basis for believing that a *new* danger may be present, the Church desires the benefit of the doubt to be given to the patient and wishes the sacrament to be repeated.

Extreme Unction in Diseases

It is not uncommon for a patient to be slightly affected by a disease which it is foreseen will subsequently become dangerous. Since Extreme Unction may be administered only in a *present* danger of death, such a patient is not capable of receiving the sacrament.

The mere fact, however, that a patient is suffering very little does not of itself preclude the possibility of a valid and licit reception of Extreme Unction. A person may truly be in danger of death without enduring much bodily pain. The objective condition of the patient, not his feeling, is the point which must be considered. In this regard, many cardiac patients and those extremely weak from old age are fit subjects for Extreme Unction.

Whenever a patient is seriously affected by a disease which is by its very nature capable of producing death, a *conditional* Extreme Unction should be given. Reference is here made to a disease which a skilled doctor believes will eventually take the life of the patient but is presently pursuing its normal course and has not yet placed the life of the patient in proximate danger. Since the patient is suffering intensely from a condition which can produce death, it is justifiable to regard a *probable* danger of death as present and thus to administer the sacrament conditionally.

Instances will be met in which a patient is suffering intense pain from a condition or disease whose precise nature and gravity has not yet been diagnosed. Such a patient may be validly and licitly anointed. It would appear to be in conformity with the spirit of Canon 941 to administer the sacrament under these circumstances.

Whenever the danger of death is certain, but actual death apparently remote, the sacrament can be validly received. Whether or not it is the proper and advisable thing to do depends upon the circumstances of the particular case.

In general, the sacrament should not be given to those who apparently have a long time yet to live. Some cancer patients and many consumptives fall under this category.

In missionary countries, however, it might be foreseen that a priest would not return to a specific locality for a long time. In this latter case, it would be advisable for this type of patient to receive the sacrament.

Specifically, it may be said that the following are some of the conditions which justify the giving of Extreme Unction:

    (a) Thrombosis or embolic heart cases
    (b) Fatty degeneration of the heart

   (c) Some pneumonia cases
   (d) Pre-comatose diabetics
   (e) Those who have just had a 'stroke'
   (f) Any condition associated with hemorrhage
   (g) Severe burns
   (h) Miliary tuberculosis
   (i) Lung abscess

It is not to be thought that the above are the *only* conditions which justify the giving of Extreme Unction. *Neither is it true that the above cases always allow the administration of the sacrament.* As a guide to action, it is suggested that the following question be asked: *Is the present condition of such a nature that it may produce death within a reasonable period of time?* If the answer is in the affirmative, the sacrament should be administered.

Extreme Unction Before Surgical Operations

Patients who are in danger of death may receive Extreme Unction previous to their undergoing an operation whose outcome is uncertain. The patient is truly in danger of death from his own condition, and the mere fact that the operation may restore health does not deprive him of the right to receive the sacrament.

Even though it is practically certain that an operation will restore health to one who is presently in the danger of death, the sacrament may be received.

A typical case of this type would be an operation to remove an obstruction in the windpipe. The victim might well be in danger of death from suffocation, and it could be certain that the operation would immediately restore health.

A patient about to undergo an operation, *who is sick but not presently in danger of death from his own condition, may not be given Extreme Unction. The mere fact that the operation itself is serious and may place him in danger of death does not justify the administration of the sacrament previous to the operation.* Thus, a patient with *chronic* appendicitis should not be given the sacrament before an operation for the removal of the appendix.

Similarly, a patient who is not at all sick nor in any way in danger of death, but who consents to undergo an operation which will place him in danger of death, is not capable of receiving Extreme Unction. Some blood transfusions, some operations to correct physical deformities through plastic surgery, and some operations for the resetting of dislocated parts of the body, would be cases of this type.

It has always been the teaching of the Church that the danger of death required for the administration of Extreme Unction cannot be anticipated. For this reason, moral theologians have always taught that the soldier about to enter mortal combat, and the condemned criminal about to die at the hands of an executioner, are not able to receive Extreme Unction.

It should be clear, therefore, that a patient who is not presently in danger of death, but who is about to undergo an operation which will endanger his life, is not capable of receiving this sacrament. Previous to the operation, he is not in danger of death from his own condition. Any future danger that the surgeon's knife may involve is just as truly extrinsic to him as is the enemy's weapon in the case of the soldier about to enter battle, or the hangman's rope in the case of the condemned criminal.

Likewise, Extreme Unction may not be given simply because a patient is going to receive a general anesthetic. This is true even if the patient already has a physical defect (such as a cardiac condition) which might be aggravated by the administration of a general anesthetic.

After an operation has begun and it is judged that the patient is now in danger of death because of his present condition (even though it is the operation which has produced this condition in the patient), the sacrament may be administered.

If a local anesthetic has been used, it would still be possible for the patient to receive the sacrament in a conscious state. The sacrament obviously would have to be received in an unconscious condition if a general anesthetic has been used.

In the light of the above principles, patients who are being taken to the operating room with the following conditions should usually be given Extreme Unction:

(a) Ruptured or acute appendicitis—suspected or certain
(b) Cholecystectomy
(c) Thyroid removal
(d) Hysterectomy
(e) Intestinal obstruction
(f) Gastropexy
(g) Gastropylorectomy
(h) Gastrotomy
(i) Gastrectomy
(j) Gastroenterostomy
(k) Suspected cancer
(l) Gangrene associated with diabetic condition
(m) Any operation associated with hemorrhage
(n) Brain operation of any sort

It has been stated that the above conditions *usually* justify the giving of Extreme Unction. As a guide to action, it is suggested that the following question be asked: *If an operation were not performed, would the condition produce death within a reasonable period of time?* If the answer is in the affirmative, the sacrament should be administered.

Extreme Unction During Pregnancy

It is frequently foreseen that a woman who is pregnant will have a parturition so difficult that it will threaten her life. The sacrament of Extreme Unction may *not* be given under such circumstances. In her present condition, there is no danger to the woman's life, and future danger does not provide a basis for the administration of this sacrament.

When a woman, who is actually in parturition, is in danger of death from the *usual* pains and difficulties which ordinarily accompany the delivery of a child, she may be given Extreme Unction. It is readily understandable that the condition of the mother's health could be such that the usual hardships of a delivery would present a hazard to her life. When the doctor regards the case as pathological, the sacrament should be given in its absolute form; whenever there is doubt as to the pathological nature of the condition, conditional Extreme Unction should be given.

A woman, who is actually in parturition and in danger of death from extraordinary pains and abnormal conditions accompanying her delivery, should be given Extreme Unction in its absolute form.

Specifically, the following maternity patients should be anointed as soon as possible.

(a) Patients showing evidence of placenta previa accompanied by profuse hemorrhage

(b) Patients suffering from grave uterine hemorrhage

(c) Patients upon whom a caesarean section *must* be performed (in contrast to elective caesarean section)

(d) Patients suffering from eclampsia

Extreme Unction in Old Age

The law of the Church (Canon 1254), which treats of fasting, apparently places old age at the beginning of the sixtieth year. Years alone, however, do not constitute a "sickness" such as is required for the reception of Extreme Unction.

Some authors insist upon a reasonable indication of impending death, in the form of faintings, sinking spells, or alarming weakness, before they will allow the administration of the sacrament.

All authorities, however, agree that there must be a noticeable decline in the physical powers of an old person before he becomes capable of receiving the sacrament.

There is certainly no need to wait until an old person is at the point of death before giving the sacrament to him. In practice, it may be said that Extreme Unction may be validly and licitly given to an old person whenever there is a prudently probable danger of death arising from the weaknesses which affect him.

Extreme Unction to the Unconscious

"Sick persons who while they were conscious asked for the Sacrament of Extreme Unction at least implicitly, or who very likely would have asked for it, may be anointed absolutely though they have lost consciousness or the use of reason." (Canon 943.)

Patients who request the sacrament and lapse into unconsciousness before receiving it, certainly possess the necessary desire for it. Extreme Unction should be administered in the absolute form to such a patient, even though there might be some doubt as to the worthiness of the individual.

Catholics who have been faithful to their religious duties and who have been suddenly overtaken with grave illness and rendered unconscious should be given Extreme Unction in the absolute form. It is a reasonable presumption that such persons would have requested the sacrament if they had realized the approaching danger of death.

Catholics who have neglected their religious duties and who have been suddenly overtaken with grave illness and rendered unconscious should also be given Extreme Unction in the absolute form, not conditionally. Laxity of life does not usually exclude the *desire* for the sacrament. In such cases, Extreme Unction can prove of more value than the Sacrament of Penance. There is always the possibility that such a person conceived sorrow for sin just before lapsing into unconsciousness. There is also the possibility that they possessed the use of their faculties long after apparent unconsciousness overcame them, and were thus able to conceive sorrow for their sins. But even if neither fact were verified, Extreme Unction could still prove of inestimable value, because if up to the very moment of death the person should have even a momentary lucid interval and elicit at least imperfect sorrow for sin, the Sacrament which still remains with him has the power to forgive his sins and restore him to the state of grace. This should indicate to both doctor and nurse the importance of securing this Sacrament for the unconscious patient, even for such as were rendered unconscious in the act of committing grave sin.

If, however, the person has not been merely neglectful of his religious duties but has actually been bitter and antagonistic toward his religion, the Sacrament is generally not to be administered. In a case of this type, there is no basis for a reasonable judgment that the patient would probably have availed himself of an opportunity to request the Sacrament. In such cases, however, the priest should interpret any reasonable doubt in favor of the patient, and administer the Sacrament conditionally.

The sacrament may not, as a rule, be administered, even conditionally, to a patient who has refused it immediately before lapsing into unconsciousness. It would be permissible, however, to give conditional Extreme Unction to such a patient if there were good reasons to believe that his refusal had not been based on a lack of faith in the sacrament, but had originated in a reluctance to believe that he was actually in danger of death.

Problems for Discussion

1. Suppose you were attending a Catholic patient in his home and it is evident that the patient is dying. Hoping for the recovery of the patient, the family refuses to call a priest. Their attitude is that the visit of the priest may cause the patient to feel convinced that death is inevitable and thus deprive him of the will to live. What would you do?

2. Suppose your patient is a fallen-away Catholic and is in danger of death. The family of the patient is not Catholic and is very antagonistic towards the Faith. The patient has not asked for a priest; in fact, he has told you that he is not interested in seeing a priest. You have good reason to believe that his reluctance to see a priest is rather superficial and would probably be broken down by a visit from the priest. Would you summon the priest despite the prohibition of the family and the apparent opposition of the patient?

3. A patient has had a ruptured appendix. He is unable to retain food and constantly expels it. A Levine tube is inserted (with suction apparatus). The patient must drink water at frequent intervals; it serves its cleansing purpose and comes back through the tube. May such a patient receive Communion without fasting? Are such patients in danger of death in the moral sense of the expression? Does not light food return up through the tube? Even if the tube were clamped off for a while after the reception of the Sacrament, is it not true that the profanation of the Eucharist will result from the inability of the patient to retain food? Is it accurate to say that there is danger of profanation of the Sacrament in this case or would it be more correct to say that adminis-

tration of the Sacrament would result in its certain profanation?

4. When a priest enters a small ward to hear a confession, should a nurse leave who is working there?

5. A nurse is tending a patient of a devout Catholic family. The patient is not at the point of dying but is growing steadily worse. The doctor does not want to alarm the patient or the family by having the Last Sacraments administered. The nurse knows that the patient is in danger of death and is therefore capable of receiving the Last Sacraments. What should she do?

6. Is a nurse ever allowed to decide whether or not a patient is sick enough to receive the Eucharist without fasting?

7. May an unconscious dying person who has deliberately attempted suicide be given Extreme Unction?

8. When a priest comes to administer Extreme Unction to a dying person who has a serious communicable disease, certain precautions must be taken in order that the priest will not contract the disease himself or carry it to others. In this regard, discuss the following points: Would you explain the danger to the priest before he encountered the patient? What steps would you take to see to it that the holy oils and whatever else he carries are not contaminated? Would you suggest that he wear a gown over his regular clothes? Would you suggest that he wear a mask? Would you offer him facilities for thoroughly cleansing his hands over and above the usual finger bowl. Would you disinfect the crucifix after the patient has kissed it and before you return it to the priest?

9. In emergency cases, may a priest administer Holy Viaticum, as well as Extreme Unction, outdoors at the scene of an accident or in a factory?

10. What answer would you make to a patient who asks you if he may smoke in the morning before the reception of the Eucharist?

References for Reading

BARRY, D.: "Providing Sacraments for Catholics in Non-Catholic Hospitals," *American Ecclesiastical Review*, pp. 175-179, Feb., 1934.

BECK, SR. BERNICE: *The Nurse: Handmaid of the Divine Physician,* pp. 67-75; 85-89; 109-133; 158-193; 201-216; 222-231, Phila., 1945.

BURKE, E.: *Acute Cases in Moral Medicine,* pp. 101-108, N. Y., 1929.

CONNELL, F.: *Death Can Be Joyous* (pamphlet), Paulist Press, N. Y., 1940.

—————: "The Hospital Chaplain and the Administration of the Holy Eucharist," *American Ecclesiastical Review,* July, 1948, pp. 19-27.

—————: "Viaticum to a Dying Child," *American Ecclesiastical Review,* Sept., 1951, p. 221.

—————: "The Repetition of Extreme Unction," *American Ecclesiastical Review,* Sept., 1949, p. 222.

FLETCHER, J.: *Notes for Catholic Nurses,* pp. 38-165, Catholic Truth Society, London.

FORREST, M.: "Conditional Extreme Unction," *American Ecclesiastical Review,* pp. 455-461, May, 1939.

KILKER, A.: *Extreme Unction,* St. Louis, 1937.

—————: "The Repetition of Extreme Unction," *American Ecclesiastical Review,* pp. 41-54, Jan., 1932.

MAHER, S.: "Enrolling the Dying Person in the Scapular," *American Ecclesiastical Review,* pp. 43-45, July, 1941.

MORRISON, B.: "Blessings in the Sick Room," *Hospital Progress,* Oct., 1948.

OSTLER, D.: *A Nurse's Manual,* pp. 26-57, St. Anthony Guild Press, Paterson, N. J., 1936.

ROCHELLE-FINK: *Handbook of Medical Ethics,* pp. 235-273, Westminster, Md., 1943.

SCHAEFERS, W.: "Catholic Physicians and the Sacrament of Extreme Unction," *American Ecclesiastical Review,* pp. 469-474, Nov., 1934.

SPLAINE, J.: *The Catholic Sick Room* (pamphlet), Paulist Press, N. Y., 1925.

WATSON, M.: *A Good Death* (pamphlet), Mission Church Press, Boston.

WOYWOD, S.: "Using the Bodies of the Dead for Medical Purposes," *Homiletic and Pastoral Review,* pp. 1190-1191, August, 1938.

—————: "Extreme Unction After 'Apparent' Death," *Homiletic and Pastoral Review,* pp. 865-866, May, 1939.

—————: "Absolution and Extreme Unction to Dying Protestants," *Homiletic and Pastoral Review,* pp. 1077-1078, July, 1936.

—————: "The Disposal of Cotton Used in Extreme Unction," *Homiletic and Pastoral Review,* pp. 630-631, March, 1938.

Articles in the *American Ecclesiastical Review:*
    "Communion of the Sick," p. 178, August, 1938.
    "Meaning of 'Danger of Death' in Extreme Unction," p. 311, March, 1934.
    "The Intention Required of a Child to Receive Extreme Unction," pp. 304-307, Sept., 1934.
    "Disposal of Amputated Parts of the Human Body," p. 638, Dec., 1933.
    "Extreme Unction for the Aged," pp. 57-58, Jan., 1933.
    "Apostolic Blessing at Time of Death," p. 409, April, 1931.
    "Communion for the Sick in the Evening," p. 392, May, 1942.
    "The Period Between Real and Apparent Death," pp. 383-384, May, 1942.
    "Conditional Extreme Unction," p. 308, March, 1937; p. 626, June, 1937.
    "Distributing Holy Communion in Hospitals," p. 75, Jan., 1935; p. 588, Dec., 1937; p. 478, May, 1938; p. 551, Dec., 1940; p. 61, Jan., 1944.

Articles in the *Homiletic and Pastoral Review:*

    "Distributing Holy Communion in Hospitals," p. 1037, July, 1941; p. 474, Feb., 1942.
    "Extreme Unction," pp. 865-866, May, 1936.
    "The Burial of Amputated Limbs," p. 1219, August, 1939.
    "The Living and Dead Fetus," p. 1132, August, 1941.
    "Extreme Unction and Electrocution," p. 1060, August, 1942.
    "Difficulties of Extreme Unction," p. 376, Feb., 1944.
    "The Burial of Blood," p. 688, June, 1944.

APPENDIX

The Non-Catholic Patient

It is an astonishing fact that more than half of the patients treated in our Catholic hospitals are non-Catholics.

The presence of the non-Catholic patient in the Catholic hospital rarely presents any sort of difficulty.

In the matter of diet, almost all hospitals offer some type of selective menu. In the Catholic hospitals with which the author is most familiar, some form of meat is always available on the Friday menu for the non-Catholic patient. The selective menu likewise solves the problem which is presented by a patient whose religious faith may sometimes forbid the eating of one specific form of meat.

The request of a non-Catholic patient for a minister of his own religion presents some minor difficulties. The Catholic doctor and nurse realize that there is only one true Church of Christ and they firmly believe that the Roman Catholic Church is that church. They cannot therefore regard any other church either as the Church of Christ or as the true religion in its entirety. For these reasons, they may neither encourage nor formally assist any person in the practice of what they are convinced is a false religion.

The difficulties, however, are easily solved. Whenever the non-Catholic patient makes a request for a minister of his religion, the Catholic doctor or nurse may tactfully request a member of the family, a friend, or a nurse, of the patient's own religious belief, to attend to the matter for him.

If this is not possible or feasible, either because such a person is not available or because such a procedure would offend the patient, circumstances in our country permit Catholic doctors and nurses, without prejudice to their religious beliefs, to inform a minister of the sick person's religious group that one of their patients wishes to see him.

When a non-Catholic minister is visiting his patient, the Catholic doctor or nurse may, in a spirit of courtesy, bring him any materials which he may desire. They must always be courteous and respectful, but they must always avoid actual formal participation in any non-Catholic religious ceremony.

Our special concern in this section on the "Non-Catholic Patient" is to offer some suggestions as to the manner in which the Catholic doctor and nurse may assist such a patient at the approach of death.

The Apostolate to Assist Dying Non-Catholics was founded by Monsignor Raphael Markham of Cincinnati. Monsignor Markham has clearly portrayed the objectives and methods of this plan in a small folder entitled *The Apostolate to Assist Dying Non-Catholics.* With the kind permission of Monsignor Markham, the following matter on the dying non-Catholic patient is taken almost verbatim from his pamphlet.

Is it true that nothing can be done for the dying man, because he is not a Catholic and does not wish to become one? Many seem to be of this opinion; but it does not sound like the voice of our Heavenly Father, Whose mercy is above all His works. It sounds more like the voice of him who is called by St. John "a liar and the father thereof" who is prowling about the world for the destruction of souls, seeking whom he may devour. In furthering his designs, he, no doubt, considers this a very fruitful way—to spread the error among priests, Sisters, doctors, nurses, and all those called upon to care for the dying, that nothing can be done for the poor man, in the way of helping him to prepare for a happy death, because he is not a Catholic and has no intention of becoming one, even though he is in good faith.

The truth about this most important matter is that much can be done for the non-Catholic at the hour of death. It was this consideration that furnished the inspiration for the *Apostolate to Assist Dying Non-Catholics.* The work of the Apostolate is as old as Christianity, and in some ways as old as the human race itself. Only the method is new.

The Apostolate makes an attempt to prepare the non-Catholic for a happy death by placing in his hands, in any way possible, a little ornamented card, which has no appearance of Catholicity, but which contains all the acts necessary and sufficient for his salvation. If the patient is too sick to read, the prayer can be read for him and with him. The *body* of the work is the getting of the little ornamented card into the hands of the non-Catholic with the suggestion that he say the little prayer frequently and as fervently and earnestly as possible. The *soul* of the work, which is by far the more important part, is your earnest prayer to God, that in His mercy He may grant to your patient or friend the efficacious grace of really meaning what he says, when he prays the little prayer.

We all understand that the ordinary means of salvation, according to the will of Christ, is the Catholic Church, and that all who believe Her to be the true Church are under solemn obligation to enter Her fold. But we must remember that the vast majority of Americans have never come in close contact with the Catholic Church or her ministers, and never will, and that they are in good faith about it. While there are many who are practically pagans, the non-Catholic, for the most part, is a well-meaning person. He wants to be saved, especially when he sees death staring him in the face. He hates what he thinks to be the Church, but he wants what the Church alone can give him. The Church that he hates, of course, does not exist. Often he is not even baptized, and never will be. Many know nothing about Baptism; others do not believe in it; others still have neglected it; not a few have been baptized invalidly. Their only salvation lies in making an act of perfect love of God or of perfect contrition, either of which is the Baptism of Desire, and the only Baptism of Desire; a mere desire for Baptism is not sufficient.

The serious question is, and it is a vital one, how to reach this large class of people at this most critical time, when they are about to enter eternity. If anything even suggesting Catholicity be proposed to them, it is rejected on principle, and in many cases considered a positive insult. That the significance and necessity of true repentance for sin are not properly emphasized in the various forms of the Protestant religion constitutes another very serious difficulty. This false idea of

justification leads many into the belief that repentance, in the
Catholic sense, is not at all necessary.

The ornamented card has been prepared in the hope of
solving the question, at least to some extent. There is no mention made of Catholicity, nor does it even suggest it; there is
nothing at all that could possibly offend. In fact, everything
on the card is just as appropriate for well-meaning non-Catholics as for Catholics. Even the "Imprimatur," which has been
properly secured, is omitted by permission of ecclesiastical
authority. The card has been made attractive, so that it will
not be thrown away. The decorations on the hand-tinted card
are classical, not religious; the flower is the acanthus, used
extensively in Greek ornamentation, and the coloring in red is
done by hand. The touch of handpainting is a very valuable
asset. Since good intentions do not supply for essentials, the
act of attrition has been purposely omitted, in order that all
the attention might be centered on the act of perfect contrition, which of itself in most cases must accomplish the work of
the Apostolate without the help of the Sacraments.

It should be very carefully borne in mind that the work of
the Apostolate is not a substitute for conversions. It would be
far better, as is evident, if the person would become a Catholic
and be able to partake of the many blessings of the one true
faith, but this is not the supposition, which should be very
clearly understood. We suppose a well-meaning non-Catholic
seriously sick, or in danger of death, to whom there is no use
speaking about entering the Church, and who is in good faith.

Some might not approve of our plan and say that it savors
of a compromise with heresy, but such is not true. The Acts
on the card are just exactly the Acts which anyone called to
assist a non-Catholic in good faith, in the hour of death, must
in conscience implore the person to make. It is the ordinary
teaching of the Catholic Church that any non-Catholic, whether
or not he is baptized, who sincerely makes the Acts on the
card, will have done all that is necessary for his justification.
It is understood, of course, that if not baptized, he does not
know of the necessity of Baptism, and then this act of perfect
contrition or perfect love of God is for him Baptism of Desire,

which is equally as efficacious as Baptism of Water, as far as justification is concerned.

Anyone can do this work. You can send the card by mail; a little child can deliver it; you can visit your sick friend and leave it. There is no trouble in getting it to him and positively no danger of offense. You may suggest that he say the "little prayer" earnestly several times, and in many cases this will be done. He may not make the Acts the first time he reads the card, as he is prompted principally by curiosity; but he will perhaps say, as he finishes reading it: "These are my sentiments exactly." The next time he will really make the Acts. The plan is simply this: Get the card into the hands of the one in whom you are interested, in any way you choose, with the suggestion that he say fervently and frequently this prayer, entirely suitable for non-Catholics; then pray earnestly to God that he may be given the light and grace to mean what he says.

How strange it is that so much is done for the dying Catholic and so little, and sometimes nothing at all, for the non-Catholic about to enter eternity, even in some of our own Catholic hospitals. Both souls are of equal value in God's sight. Did not Christ shed His Precious Blood on the cross for the salvation of all? After all that has been said by our recent Pontiffs on this question, is it possible that there are still some who do not consider themselves in any way responsible for the spiritual welfare of anyone except the Catholics in the hospitals or institutions in which they labor? Our Divine Lord did not teach any such doctrine either by word or example, nor did St. Paul. Where would we be today if all the priests of the past had confined their labors to Catholics only? We might be falling down in adoration before false gods, as our forefathers did, instead of kneeling in humble worship before the one true God, present in our tabernacles.

We are told by the Fathers of the Church that the most sublime of all works is to act as a minister of God, dispensing the mysteries of Christ, for the salvation of souls. Is it possible that they wish us to understand "Catholic souls" only, or even principally?

A most appalling truth is contained in Ecclesiastes (xi:3),

"If the tree fall to the south, or to the north, in what place soever it shall fall, there shall it be;" and when it is just about to fall, of what vital importance it is that it receive the proper guidance. So it is with the soul. It is about to go into eternity, an eternity of happiness or one of never-ending pain; and just as it falls, so shall it stay! It is still the time of God's mercy; but this time will soon be over, the book will soon be closed, God's mercy will cease, and His justice will reign supreme. The eternal destiny of that soul depends on its last moment of life—*O momentum, unde pendet aeternitas!* "O moment upon which depends eternity!" It is the sincere hope and earnest conviction of the *Apostolate to Assist Dying Non-Catholics* that by the simple means of the ornamented and attractive card, with its fervent Acts of faith, hope, love, and contrition, together with earnest prayer to God for the patient, hundreds of thousands of non-Catholics in their last hours will acknowledge the supreme Dominion of God and the Divinity of Christ, beg pardon for their sins, and implore the Divine Mercy. *The Apostolate to Assist Dying Non-Catholics* is placed under the protection of St. Joseph, the patron of a happy death, for non-Catholics as well as Catholics.

The field is very large and for the most part unexplored. Those belonging to the class that the Apostolate wishes to reach are found in large numbers not only in Catholic and non-sectarian hospitals, but likewise in other institutions, especially the charitable ones, and also in those private homes where either the father or the mother is not a Catholic. From a study made by a committee of the Catholic Hospital Association of the United States and Canada, it was discovered that more than half of all the patients treated in our Catholic hospitals are non-Catholics. This clearly shows the possibilities of the work of the Apostolate in our Catholic hospitals, and its still greater possibilities in nonsectarian hospitals.

Some might disapprove of the method employed. Some were scandalized because our Lord ate and talked with public sinners; some there were who frowned upon the methods used by St. Paul in gaining souls; he became all things to all men that he might save all. Why should anyone question the method or the means, as long as they are legitimate and attain the end, especially when it is one of such supreme importance? The objection should be regarded as just another of the many indirect means used by Satan to further his kingdom on earth. It is the well-founded hope of the *Apostolate to Assist the Dying Non-Catholic* that many souls may be gained for God. Even one soul saved through its efforts would make the work well worth while.

In the use of the card you are not deceiving the patient in any manner whatsoever. It is true, you are paving the way for him to make the Acts, but any doctor or nurse with only a meager amount of zeal and prudence will be continually paving the way in their contact with souls: with the prospective convert, the sick, the sinner, the fallen away—in fact, with every class. You can call it a scheme, if you will; but if we do not use every legitimate means, in opposing the powers of darkness, whose method of warfare is full of schemes, we are, to say the least, very much behind the times. The foundation principle upon which the *Apostolate to Assist Dying Non-Catholics* rests is nothing less than the Mercy of God, Who wills not the death of the sinner, but that he be converted and live.

In the memorable parable of the Good Samaritan, our Lord tells how the priest and the levite, seeing the man wounded and bleeding by the wayside, passed by; but a Samaritan, a stranger, an enemy even, seeing the man, went up to him, bound up his wounds, pouring in oil and wine, and setting him upon his own beast, brought him to an inn and took care of him. *The Apostolate to Assist Dying Non-Catholics* actually tries to do something for the eternal salvation of the poor wounded and bleeding man, who has no one to help him make his peace with God.

It is a well known fact, experienced by all, especially in hospitals, that persons when sick are given to deeper and more serious reflection than at other times. Even those who, when in good health, avoided the Church and everything religious are not the same after a long illness. There is a greater willingness to become the object of spiritual care than one would be inclined to believe. Sickness brings about a new condition in which the person is often more susceptible, in any case, more in need of spiritual care than in days of good health.

Every doctor and nurse comes in contact with many extraordinary occurrences in the care of the sick and dying, especially in our hospitals. They may speak of them as fortunate, wonderful, a coincidence, or perhaps miraculous; but would it not be more in accord with revealed doctrine to consider them merely the exercise of God's ordinary providence over His creatures—God's mercy, which is above all His works? Let us not be unmindful of the many fervent prayers, that are ascending each hour of the day to the throne of God, for those who will die this day or this night. These prayers, offered up either by Religious or lay people, are truly Catholic in character; they are offered for all—for the Catholic and Protestant, for the Pagan and Jew. It is for reasons such as these that we expect great things through the *Apostolate to Assist Dying Non-Catholics.*

It might be asked, what should the doctor or nurse do after the patient actually has made the Acts printed on the card? If it is certain that the patient is a non-Catholic in good faith, to whom there is no use speaking of the Catholic Church and has really made the Acts on the card, this is what should be done: Thank God for His goodness and mercy and ask Him most earnestly to grant the patient the grace of perseverance—that he would not change his mind before he dies. But since his act of sorrow might be only attrition, it would be well to consider what could and should be done about baptizing him, even though he would claim to have been baptized in some Protestant denomination. If he had made the Acts on the card, he would not need Baptism of Water (unless he knew of its necessity) because his act of perfect contrition, or his act of perfect love of God, would be Baptism of Desire. The Acts are, by far, the most important for the patient, before ever thinking about any of the sacraments. The case should be followed up, if possible, for later on the person might see things differently, through God's grace, and seek to be admitted into the body of the Church. Many cases of this kind have already occurred through the efforts of the *Apostolate to Assist Dying Non-Cath-*

olics; it is one of its by-producs. Any priest will know what to do, if the patient wishes to become a Catholic. This would be far better, as is evident, but it is not the special work of the Apostolate, which is to help the non-Catholic who is in good faith and not open to conviction in matters of religion, to attain his eternal salvation.

According to theologians generally, it would be allowed in this case, under certain conditions, for a priest to give the patient conditional absolution secretly. Remember, the person is a non-Catholic in good faith, not open to conviction in regard to the truth of the Catholic Church, in danger of death, and conscious. The priest can sometimes secure from such a patient an implicit request for absolution. He will ask the patient the following questions: (a) "Do you wish me to help you to attain eternal salvation?" and if so: (b) "Do you wish to do everything necessary for that end according to the will of Christ?" If he answers in the affirmative, then the priest should have him elicit the Acts on the card—of faith, hope, love, perfect contrition, etc.—have him declare before God and before him (the priest) that he is a sinner, and that he seeks forgiveness of God for his sins. The priest can then give conditional absolution. (Noldin, Theo. Mor., 1932 edition, Vol. III, No. 297—2,b.) The validity of the absolution in this case would be more certain if the patient could be persuaded to believe that Christ has instituted a means of remitting sins and that the priest has the power to use it. Prudence will sometimes direct him to say nothing at all about this power of remitting sins.

With reference to the administration of the sacraments of Baptism, Penance and Extreme Unction to an *unconscious* dying non-Catholic, Father Connell presents the following explanation:

"The practice . . . is approved by many reliable theologians. It is justified on the score that the general intention of doing God's will and of partaking of whatever helps He has established for the eternal salvation of men (which intention is present in many non-Catholics) implicitly contains the intention of receiving the sacraments beneficial to a dying person. It is generally held that as long as

the non-Catholic is conscious the sacraments should not
be conferred on him, unless he expresses a desire to become a Catholic (Canon 731); though some theologians
teach, with Noldin-Schmitt (Summa theologiae moralis,
III, 297), that sometimes a priest may impart sacramental
absolution to a dying heretic even while he is conscious,
after the sick person has been roused to acts of repentance,
in such wise that he is not aware of the sacramental rite.
Usually, however, the sacraments (Baptism, Penance, and
Extreme Unction) should be given only to one who has
lost consciousness, as far as appearances go, and probably
will not recover it. . . . The sick person may actually be
conscious and internally opposed to the priest's ministrations, in which event the sacraments are not validly
received. But the principle that 'the sacraments were instituted for the benefit of man' will justify the practice, even
in view of this possibility. It is better that the sacraments
be administered invalidly to many rather than that one
who could profit by them be deprived of them at the time
of supreme need, the hour of death." *Am. Ecc. Rev.,*
Sept., 1952, p. 226)

How hopeful we ought to feel in our efforts to save the dying
non-Catholic, when we recall the story of the penitent thief on
the cross. This story is repeated every day and would be repeated far more frequently if all those who are called upon to
care for the dying would use greater effort to obtain for their
patients, from the hands of a merciful God, this greatest of all
graces. Very probably the wounded man, spoken of in the
gospel, did not call for help, but he was very glad to accept it
when offered. So it is with those of whom we are speaking.
They will seldom call on us for help; but when help is offered,
they will generally accept it, and be truly grateful for it. The
zealous doctor and nurse will find many cases of this kind
especially in our hospitals and charitable institutions.

The suggestion was made that a special card be prepared for
Jews and Pagans, with no mention made of the Trinity and
Incarnation. After careful consideration, this idea has been
abandoned as not practical. A card without any mention of
the Trinity or Incarnation would be very misleading, to say
the least, and might do a great amount of harm. Is explicit

belief in these two mysteries necessary for salvation? On this
question, theologians do not agree, but more probably it is.
All agree, however, that in danger of death any means that may
possibly help the person to save his soul can be used. It follows
therefore that, if in danger of death there exists no well-founded
hope that the Jew or Pagan can be brought to a belief in these
two mysteries, nothing should be said about them. In this case
he should be helped as much as possible to make the other Acts,
which all theologians hold to be absolutely necessary for salvation for all by necessity of means. In order to be safe, it would
not be right to leave out all mention of these two mysteries in
dealing with Christians in danger of death. Could they not,
perhaps, be brought to an explicit belief in them, even though
up to that time they had known and believed these mysteries
only in a very obscure and vague way? They would very probably accept it, when told that these are two of the principal
truths of Christianity. Very few are willing to renounce Christianity at the time of death, even though they have been very
poor Christians during life.

Pope Pius XII's message sent to the American Hospital
Association when it met in Toronto is full of encouragement
to the promoters of this Apostolate. "Among the works of
charity enjoined by the Gospel," said the Holy Father, "the
Church has always had most deeply at heart the alleviation of
bodily suffering and the care of all such sufferers, without distinction of race or creed. For She remembers that her Divine
Founder, Jesus Christ, deigned to make His own the cause of
the sick, and identified Himself with them. . . . Following the
example of the Divine Redeemer, Who cured bodily maladies
without forgetting those of the spirit, She is careful not to
separate care of the body from care of the soul. The former,
She holds, must ever be accompanied by spiritual assistance."

The Apostolate is not operated for profit. The only motive
is to help souls in their hour of greatest need. Consequently,
anyone is perfectly free to reproduce the cards. Considering
everything: printing, coloring, postage, etc., it is understood
that the cards cannot be given away, except to those who are
not able to pay; otherwise the Apostolate could not exist.

The content of the card is as follows:

My Daily Prayer

I BELIEVE in one God. I believe that God rewards the good, and punishes the wicked.

I BELIEVE that in God there are three Divine Persons— God the Father, God the Son, and God the Holy Ghost.

I BELIEVE that God the Son became Man, without ceasing to be God. I believe that He is my Lord and my Saviour, the Redeemer of the human race, that He died on the Cross for the salvation of all men, that He died also for me.

I BELIEVE, on God's authority, everything that He has taught and revealed.

O MY GOD, give me strong faith. O my God, help me to believe with lively faith.

O MY GOD, Who art all-good and all-merciful, I sincerely hope to be saved. Help me to do all that is necessary for my salvation.

I HAVE committed many sins in my life, but now I turn away from them, and hate them. I am sorry, truly sorry for all of them, because I have offended Thee, my God, Who art all-good, all-perfect, all-holy, all-merciful and kind, and Who died on the Cross for me.

I LOVE *Thee*, O my God, with all my heart. Please forgive me for having offended Thee.

I PROMISE, O God, that with Thy help I will never offend Thee again.

My God, Have Mercy on Me!

Cards can be furnished in English, French, Italian, Spanish, Portuguese, German, Dutch, Swedish, Norwegian, Polish Slovenian, Slovak, Croatian, Lithuanian, Bohemian, Hungarian, Finnish, Russian, Chinese, Japanese, and Braille (for the blind). Copies of the cards can be obtained from:

(a) Rt. Rev. R. J. Markham, S.T.D., Compton Road, Hartwell, Cincinnati 15, Ohio

(b) Sisters of the Poor of St. Francis, St. Clare Convent, Hartwell, Cincinnati 15, Ohio

(c) Sister Mary Carmelita, R.S.M., Convent of Mercy, 1409 Freeman Avenue, Cincinnati 14, Ohio.

Ethical and Religious Directions
for Catholic Hospitals

These ethical and religious directives have been prepared under the auspices of the Catholic Hospital Association of the United States and Canada for the guidance and benefit of the Catholic hospitals in those dioceses which do not now have official codes of medical and hospital ethics. It is distinctly understood that these directives do not constitute the official code of medical, surgical, or hospital ethics and have no authorative status in any diocese unless and until the Most Reverend Ordinary directs. The following text of this Code is reprinted in the exact form in which it was presented for the first time in the March, 1949 issue of *Hospital Progress*.

INTRODUCTION

Responsibility of Hospital Authorities

Catholic hospitals exist to render medical and spiritual care to the sick. The patient adequately considered, and inclusive of his spiritual status and his claim to the helps of the Catholic religion, is the primary concern of those entrusted with the management of Catholic hospitals. Trustees and administrators of Catholic hospitals understand this responsibility towards each patient whom they accept, to be seriously binding in conscience.

A partial statement of this basic obligation is contained in the present Code of Ethical and Religious Directives. All who associate themselves with a Catholic hospital, and particularly the members of the medical and nursing staffs, must understand the moral and religious obligations binding on those responsible for the management and operation of the hospital, and must realize that they are allowed to perform only such

445

acts and to carry out only such procedures as will enable the owners and administrators to fulfill their obligations.

Vitality of Code

The principles underlying or expressed in this code are not subject to change. But in its applications of principles the code can and should grow and change as theological investigations and the progress of medical science open up new problems or throw new light on old ones.

Extent of Prohibitions

As now promulgated, this code prohibits only those procedures which, according to present knowledge of facts, seem certainly wrong. In questions legitimately debated by theologians, liberty is left to physicians to follow the opinions which seem to them more in conformity with the principles of sound medicine.

Solutions of Doubts

Cases can arise in which the morality of some procedure is doubtful, either because the code does not seem to cover the case or because the application of the code is not clear. In such cases, consultation is obligatory, if possible; and the hospital reserves the right to insist on this and to choose or to approve the consultants. In urgent cases that allow no time for consultation, the physician in charge should do what seems most proper to his own conscience. Having done what he honestly judges best in such an emergency, the physician has not just cause for anxiety of conscience; but he should refer the matter to the hospital authorities to obtain guidance for future emergencies of the same nature.

SECTION ONE

Ethical Directives

These directives concern all patients in this hospital, regardless of religion, and they must be observed by all physicians, nurses, and others who work in the hospital.

General Directives

1. Even the procedures listed in this section as permissible require the consent, at least reasonably presumed, of the patient or his guardians. *This condition is to be understood in all cases.*

2. Everyone has the right and the duty to prepare for the solemn moment of death. Unless it is clear, therefore, that a dying patient is already well prepared for death, as regards both temporal and spiritual affairs, it is the physician's duty to inform, or to have some responsible person inform, him of his critical condition.

3. Adequate consultation is required, not only when there is doubt concerning the morality of some procedure (as stated in the Introduction), but also with regard to all procedures involving serious consequences, even though such procedures are listed in this code as permissible. The hospital reserves the right to insist on such consultation.

4. The physician is required to state definitely to the supervisor of the department concerned the nature of the operation he intends to perform or of the treatment he intends to give in the hospital.

5. All structures or parts of organs removed from patients must be sent at once and in their entirety to the pathologist for his examination and report. If the physician requests it, the specimens will be returned to him after examination.

   (NOTE: In the event of an operation for the removal of a diseased organ containing a living fetus, the fetus should be extracted and baptized before the excised organ is sent to the pathologist.)

Directives Concerning Specific Procedures

The principles given here cover most, if not all, of the ethical problems likely to arise in hospital practice. The lists of practical applications are limited to those cases which seem either specially difficult or of most frequent occurrence.

I. Procedures That Involve Serious Risk To, or Destruction of, Life

A. Principles

1. The *direct* killing of any innocent person, even at his own request, is always morally wrong. (Any procedure whose sole immediate effect is the death of a human being is a *direct* killing.)

2. *Risk* to life and even the *indirect* taking of life are morally justifiable for proportionate reasons. (Life is taken *indirectly* when death is the unavoidable accompaniment or result of a procedure which is immediately directed to the attainment of some other purpose, e.g., the removal of a diseased organ.)

3. Every unborn child must be considered as a human person, with all the rights of a human person, from the moment of conception.

B. Particular Applications

1. *Abortion:*

   a. Direct abortion is a *direct* killing of an unborn child, and it is never permitted, even when the ultimate purpose is to save the life of the mother. Neither *eclampsia,* nor *hyperemesis gravidarum,* nor any other condition of pregnancy constitutes an exception to this prohibition. (Every procedure whose sole immediate effect is the termination of pregnancy before viability is a *direct* abortion.)

   b. Operations, treatments, and medications during pregnancy which have for their immediate purpose the cure of a proportionately serious pathological condition of the mother are permitted, even though they *indirectly* cause an abortion, when they cannot be safely postponed until the fetus is viable.

   c. Regarding the treatment of hemorrhage during pregnancy and before the fetus is viable: No procedure which is primarily designed to empty the uterus is permissible unless the physician is reasonably sure that the fetus is already dead or already detached; procedures which are primarily designed to stop hemorrhage (as distinguished from those designed to empty the uterus) are permitted in so far as they are necessary, even to the extent of risking an abortion. In this case the abortion would be *indirect*.

2. *Cesarean Section* for the removal of viable fetus:
   a. is permitted, even with some risk to the life of the mother, when necessary for successful delivery;
   b. is likewise permitted, even with some risk for the child, when necessary for the safety of the mother.

3. *Cranial* operations for the destruction of fetal life are forbidden. Operations designed to increase the infant's chance to live (e.g., aspiration for hydrocephalus) are permitted even before delivery when such operations are required for successful delivery.

4. *Ectopic Pregnancy:*
   a. Any direct attack on the life of the fetus is morally wrong.
   b. The affected part of an ovary or Fallopian tube may be removed, even though the life of the fetus is thus indirectly terminated, provided the operation cannot be postponed without notably increasing the danger to the mother.

5. *Euthanasia* in all its forms is forbidden.
   a. The failure to supply the *ordinary means* of preserving life is equivalent to euthanasia.
   b. It is not euthanasia to give a dying person sedatives merely for the alleviation of pain, even to the extent of depriving the patient of the use of sense and reason, when this extreme measure is judged necessary. Such sedatives should not be given before the patient is properly prepared for death (in the case of a Catholic, this means the reception of the Last Sacraments);

nor should they be given to patients who are able and willing to endure their sufferings for spiritual motives.

6. *Hysterectomy*, in the presence of pregnancy and even before viability is permitted when directed to the removal of maternal pathology which is distinct from the pregnancy and which is of such a serious nature that the operation cannot be safely postponed till the fetus is viable. (Concerning hysterectomy in the absence of pregnancy, See II, B, 4.)

7. *Post-mortem examinations* must not be begun until real death is morally certain.

8. *Premature delivery:* For a very serious reason labor may be induced immediately after the fetus is viable. In a properly equipped hospital the fetus may sometimes be considered viable after 26 weeks (6 calendar months); otherwise, 28 weeks are required.

9. *Pregnancy Tests:* In all cases in which the presence of pregnancy would render some procedure illicit, the physician must make use of such tests and consultation as may seem necessary.

10. *Radiation therapy* of the mother's reproductive organs is not permitted during pregnancy unless its use at this time is an indispensable means of saving the mother's life by suppressing a threatening pathological condition, and not by attacking the fetus.

II. Procedures Involving Reproductive Organs and Function
A. Principles

1. The unnatural use of the sex faculty (e.g., masturbation) is never permitted, even for a laudable purpose.

2. Continence, either periodic or continuous, is the only form of birth control not in itself morally objectionable.

3. Procedures that induce sterility (partial or total; temporary or permanent) are permitted *only on these conditions:* (a) they must be immediately directed to the cure

or diminution of a serious pathological condition for which a simpler remedy is not reasonably available; and (b) the sterility itself must be an unintended and unavoidable effect.

B. Particular Applications

1. *Artificial insemination* of a woman with semen of a man who is not her husband is morally objectionable. Likewise immoral is insemination even with the husband's semen, when the semen is obtained by means of masturbation or unnatural intercourse. Advising or coöperating in these practices is not allowed in this hospital.

2. *Castration,* surgical or otherwise, is permitted when required for the removal or diminution of a serious pathological condition, even in other organs. Hence:

   a. oöphorectomy or irradiation of the ovaries may be allowed in treating carcinoma of the breast and metastasis therefrom;

   b. orchidectomy is permitted in the treatment of carcinoma of the prostate.

   In all cases the procedure least harmful to the reproductive organs should be used, if equally effective with other procedures.

3. *Contraception.* All operations, treatments, and devices designed to render conception impossible are morally objectionable. Advising, explaining, or otherwise fostering contraceptive practices is not allowed in this hospital.

   (NOTE: Continence is not contraception. A physician is entitled to advise and explain the practice of periodic continence to those who have need of such knowledge.)

4. *Hysterectomy, in the absence of pregnancy:*

   a. Hysterectomy is permitted when it is sincerely judged to be the only effective remedy for prolapse of the uterus, or when it is a necessary means of removing some other serious pathology.

b. Hysterectomy is not permitted as a routine procedure after any definite number of cesarean sections. In these cases the pathology of each patient must be considered individually; and care must be had that hysterectomy is not performed as a merely contraceptive measure.

c. Even after the childbearing function has ceased, hysterectomy is still a mutilation, and it must not be performed unless sound medical reasons call for it. (Concerning hysterectomy during pregnancy, See I, B, 6.)

5. *Sterility Tests* involving the procurement of the male specimen by masturbation or unnatural intercourse are morally objectionable and are not allowed in this hospital.

III. Other Procedures

(i.e., everything not included in I or II)

A. Principle

Any procedure harmful to the patient is morally justified only in so far as it is designed to produce a proportionate good.

Ordinarily the "proportionate good" that justifies a directly mutilating procedure must be the welfare of the patient himself. However, such things as blood transfusions and skin grafts are permitted for the good of others. Whether this principle of "helping the neighbor" can justify organic transplantation is now a matter of discussion. Physicians are asked to present practical cases for solution, if such cases exist.

B. Particular Applications

1. *Appendectomy:* The removal of an apparently healthy appendix while the abdomen is open for some other reason may be allowed at the discretion of the physician.

2. *Lobotomy* is morally justifiable as a last resort in attempting to cure those who suffer from serious mental illness. It is not allowed when less extreme measures are reasonably available or in cases in which the probability of harm outweighs the probability of benefit.

3. *Narcotherapy:* The use of narcosis (or hypnosis) for the cure of mental illness is permissible with the consent at least reasonably presumed of the patient, provided due precautions are taken to protect the patient and the hospital from harmful effects, and provided the patient's right to secrecy is duly safeguarded.

4. *Uterine Malpositions:* Operations devised to correct uterine malpositions (e.g., ligamentary suspensions) without interfering with the normal physiology of the uterus or rendering the patient sterile are permitted. If these procedures induce sterility the principles of Section B (above) must be applied, and consultation is obligatory.

SECTION TWO

The Religious Care of Patients

I. Baptism

1. Except in cases of emergency (i.e., danger of death), all requests for baptism made by adults or for infants should be referred to the chaplain of the hospital, who will see that the prescriptions of canon law are observed.

2. Even cases of emergency should be referred to the chaplain or to some other priest if one is available. If a priest is not available, anyone having the use of reason can and should baptize.

3. When emergency baptism is conferred, the fact should be noted on the patient's chart, and the chaplain should be notified as soon as possible so that he can properly record it.

II. The Other Sacraments

1. It is the mind of the Church that the sick should have the widest possible liberty to receive the sacraments frequently. The generous coöperation of the entire hospital staff and personnel is requested for this purpose.

2. While providing the sick abundant opportunity to receive Holy Communion, there should be no interference with the perfect freedom of the faithful according to the mind of the Church to communicate or not to communicate, and moreover there should be no pressure exerted that might lead to sacrilegious Communions.

3. Regarding the Eucharistic fast, certain privileges are accorded the sick by canon law, and sometimes by special indults. The chaplain should be consulted concerning these privileges.

4. Sufficient privacy should be provided for confession in wards and semi-private rooms, or the patient moved elsewhere for confession, if this is possible.

5. When possible, one who is critically ill should receive Holy Viaticum and Extreme Unction while in full possession of his rational faculties. The chaplain must, therefore, be notified as soon as an illness is diagnosed as critical.

III. Disposal of Amputated Members

1. Major parts of the body should be buried in a cemetery when it is reasonably possible to do so. Moreover, the members of Catholics should, if possible, be buried in blessed ground.

2. When burial is not reasonably possible, the burning of such members is permissible.

IV. *Disposal of Dead Fetus*

1. When there is a sufficient reason for doing so, a fetus may be retained for laboratory study and observation. It may not, however, be preserved in membranes unless so obviously dead that baptism would be of no avail.

2. When sanitation or some similarly *serious* reason demands it, a fetus may be burned.

3. Aside from the cases just indicated, every fetus, regardless of the degree of maturity it has reached, must be suitably buried in a cemetery.

   (NOTE: It is imperative that all who are concerned with the disposal of a fetus should know and observe pertinent prescriptions of civil law. If there seems to be a conflict between the provisions of civil law and the instructions given here the matter should be referred to the hospital authorities for clarification.)

The Ten Commandments

1. I am the Lord Thy God. Thou shalt not have strange gods before Me.

2. Thou shalt not take the Name of the Lord, Thy God, in vain.

3. Remember thou keep holy the Sabbath day.

4. Honor thy father and thy mother.

5. THOU SHALT NOT KILL!

6. Thou shalt not commit adultery.

7. Thou shalt not steal.

8. Thou shalt not bear false witness against thy neighbor.

9. Thou shalt not covet thy neighbor's wife.

10. Thou shalt not covet thy neighbor's goods.

The Oath of Hippocrates

"I swear by Apollo Physician, by Asclepius, by Health, by Panacea, and by all the gods and goddesses, making them my witnesses, that I will carry out, according to my ability and judgment, this oath and this indenture. To hold my teacher in this art equal to my own parents; to make him partner in my livelihood; when he is in need of money to share mine with him; to consider his family as my own brothers, and to teach them this art, if they want to learn it, without fee or indenture.

"To impart precept, oral instruction, and all other instruction to my own sons, the sons of my teacher, and to indentured pupils who have taken the physician's oath, but to nobody else.

"I will use treatment to help the sick according to my ability and judgment, but never with a view to injury and wrongdoing. Neither will I administer a poison to anybody when asked to do so, nor will I suggest such a course. Similarly, I will not give to a woman a pessary to cause abortion. But I will keep pure and holy both my life and my art.

"I will not use the knife, not even, verily, on sufferers from stone, but I will give place to such as are craftsmen therein. Into whatsoever houses I enter, I will enter to help the sick, and I will abstain from all intentional wrongdoing and harm, especially from abusing the bodies of man or woman, bond or free.

"And whatsoever I shall see or hear in the course of my profession, as well as outside my profession in my intercourse with men, if it be what should not be published abroad, I will never divulge, holding such things to be holy secrets.

"Now, if I carry out this oath, and break it not, may I gain forever reputation among all men for my life and for my art; but if I transgress it and forswear myself, may the opposite befall me."

An Excerpt from the New Testament

"Come, ye blessed of my Father, possess you the kingdom prepared for you from the foundation of the world.

"For I was hungry, and you gave me to eat; I was thirsty and you gave me to drink; I was a stranger, and you took me in.

"Naked, and you covered me; sick, and you visited me; I was in prison, and you came to me.

"Then shall the just answer Him, saying: Lord, when did we see thee hungry, and feed thee; thirsty, and gave thee to drink?

"And when did we see thee a stranger, and took thee in? or naked, and covered thee?

"Or when did we see thee sick or in prison, and came to thee?

"And the King, answering, shall say to them: Amen, I say to you, *as long as you did it to one of these, my least brethren, you did it to me.*"

(St. Matthew, xxv. 34-40)

Pledge of Florence Nightingale

I solemnly pledge myself before God and in the presence of this assembly to pass my life in purity and to practice my profession faithfully.

I will abstain from whatever is deleterious or mischievous, and will not take or knowingly administer any harmful drug.

I will do all in my power to elevate the standard of my profession, and will hold in confidence all personal matters committed to my keeping, and all family affairs coming to my knowledge in the practice of my calling.

With loyalty will I endeavor to aid the physician in his work and devote myself to the welfare of those committed to my care.

My Pledge and Creed

In the Name of the Father, and of the Son, and of the Holy Ghost. Amen.

Eternal Father, reverently do I

Name ....

pledge myself to the wholehearted service of those whose care is intrusted to this hospital.

To that end I will ever strive for skill in the fulfillment of my duties, holding secret whatsoever I may learn touching upon the lives of the sick.

Dear Jesus, I acknowledge the dignity of the cure of disease and the safeguarding of health in which no act is menial or inglorious, and of which You, whilst on earth, gave a perfect example, being amongst us as One Who serves.

O Holy Spirit, under Your Divine Inspiration I will walk in upright faithfulness and obedience to those under whose guidance I am to work and I pray for patience, kindliness, and understanding in the holy ministry to broken bodies.

To Our Blessed Lady of Mercy, our Patroness and our Guide, we pledge ourselves to walk always in the path of purity and charity.

In the Name of the Father, and of the Son, and of the Holy Ghost. Amen.

Index